ORDINARY DIFFERENTIAL EQUATIONS

ORDINARY DIFFERENTIAL EQUATIONS

Tyn Myint-U

Department of Mathematics
Manhattan College

NORTH-HOLLAND·NEW YORK

NEW YORK • AMSTERDAM • OXFORD

Elsevier North-Holland, Inc.
52 Vanderbilt Avenue, New York, New York 10017

North-Holland Publishing Company
P.O. Box 211
Amsterdam, The Netherlands

Library of Congress Cataloging in Publication Data
Tyn Myint-U.
    Ordinary differential equations.

    Bibliography: p.
    Includes index.
    1. Differential equations.   I. Title.
QA372.T96   515'.352   77-8639
ISBN 0-444-00233-2

Manufactured in the United States of America

To my wife Aye
and our children:
Thant, Khinlei, A-Thi and Aye Myint Myint-U

Contents

Preface

The theory of ordinary differential equations is one of the areas of mathematics that has long been studied, applied, and developed parallel to the natural sciences. Classical and modern treatments at both elementary and advanced levels have been widely published, yet there are only a few that have presented an introduction covering the essential topics of the theory of ordinary differential equations. The purpose of this text, therefore, is to present a fundamental theory of ordinary differential equations accompanied by an introduction to several important methods and techniques for determining solutions of a diverse class of equations.

The basic concepts and definitions of ordinary differential equations as well as mathematical models in population dynamics and celestial mechanics are presented in the first chapter. First-order equations with an emphasis on Picard's existence theorem are treated in chapter 2. The third chapter is concerned with classical methods for determining solutions of second-order linear equations together with the qualitative behavior of solutions of some types of equations. In chapter 4, equations with analytic coefficients are treated with Legendre and Bessel equations presented as examples of practical importance. Chapter 5 contains an analysis of systems of equations using matrices. Chapters 6 and 7 deal with boundary-value and eigenvalue problems, respectively. Stability of autonomous systems and the method of Lyapunov are the central themes of chapter 8. Chapter 9 describes the Laplace transform and its applications. Numerical solutions and error analyses are the main topics in the final chapter.

Exercises accompany each chapter and are an integral part of the text. They range from solving simple routine types of equations to proving more difficult problems. Some minor topics are added to the exercises for an extended view of related subjects. Selected Solutions to Exercises and a Bibliography appear at the end of the book.

This text is an outgrowth of lectures given at Manhattan College for mathematics and physics majors who normally have advanced calculus and linear algebra in their third year. However, the text is designed for students with a good background in calculus and a knowledge of matrices.

The author wishes to express his sincere appreciation and thanks to the staff of Elsevier for their kind help and cooperation. The author also wishes to thank Miss Constance Engle for her excellent typing.

Chapter 1. Ordinary Differential Equations. Mathematical Models

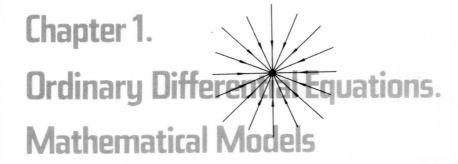

1.1 Basic Concepts and Definitions

Since its inception at the time of Newton and Leibniz the theory of ordinary differential equations has been strongly influenced by its applications in the natural sciences. The applications to physical, behavioral and engineering sciences are numerous and diversified. The theory of ordinary differential equations is one of the leading highly developed fields of mathematics. Its vast theoretical concepts and numerous applications have led to a deeper insight and understanding of some of the more complex problems of world concern.

We shall begin by introducing the basic concepts and definitions pertaining to ordinary differential equations, and then proceed to study the major aspects of its theory, methods of solutions and applications.

DEFINITION 1.1.1 A differential equation that involves an unknown function of one variable and its derivatives is called an *ordinary differential equation*.

1

For example,

$$5\frac{dy}{dx} + 3y = 6, \tag{1.1.1}$$

$$\frac{d^2y}{dx^2} + \sin x \ \frac{dy}{dx} + 2xy = e^x, \tag{1.1.2}$$

$$x\frac{d^3y}{dx^3} + (x^2 - 1)\frac{d^2y}{dx^2} + 4y = 0, \tag{1.1.3}$$

$$\frac{d^4y}{dx^4} + 8\frac{d^2y}{dx^2} + 9y = 0 \tag{1.1.4}$$

are ordinary differential equations. Each equation has a dependent variable y (unknown function) and a single independent variable x. Equations (1.1.1) and (1.1.4) are said to have *constant coefficients*, while Eqs. (1.1.2) and (1.1.3) are said to have *variable coefficients*.

DEFINITION 1.1.2   The *order* of a differential equation is the order of the highest-order derivative appearing in the equation.

For example, Eq. (1.1.1) is of the first order, whereas Eq. (1.1.2) is of the second order.

We shall further classify ordinary differential equations by the appearance of an unknown function and its derivatives. Henceforth we shall denote $y' = dy/dx$, $y'' = d^2y/dx^2$, and so on.

DEFINITION 1.1.3   A differential equation

$$F\left(x, y, y', y'', \ldots, y^{(n)}\right) = 0$$

is said to be *linear* if the function F is a linear function of the variables $y, y', y'', \ldots, y^{(n)}$.

For example, Eqs. (1.1.1)–(1.1.4) are all linear equations.
A differential equation which is not linear is called a *nonlinear equation*.
For example,

$$\frac{d^2y}{dx^2} + xy^2 = 0$$

and

$$\frac{d^2y}{dx^2} + \sin x \left(\frac{dy}{dx}\right)^3 + y = 6$$

are nonlinear equations. So is the equation

$$\frac{d^2y}{dx^2} + y\frac{dy}{dx} + 3y = 0$$

1.2 Mathematical Models

A real event, whether it occurs in physics, social science, economics, or engineering science, cannot be exactly simulated by man. It must therefore be idealized. On the basis of this approximated event, a suitable mathematical model is developed using one or more fundamental laws.

A mathematical model may be represented by differential, integral or functional equations. It may contain relations that are not equations. The best model is the one which yields a solution describing the most realistic picture of the real event under consideration.

1.2.1 POPULATION DYNAMICS

We shall first present the formulation of a simple mathematical model for the growth and decay of a population. The population may comprise people, fish, bacteria, or any other species.

Let us consider a large population. If there is a change of one individual member in the population, the change is very small compared with the given population. Thus we make an assumption that large populations change continuously with time.

Let $y(t)$ denote the population of a given species at time t. Let this population be isolated so that there is no interaction with any other species, and consequently there is no immigration or emigration.

Let a denote the births per individual per unit time (birth rate) and b the deaths per individual per unit time (death rate). If we assume that these rates are constants, then the change in the population Δy during the time Δt is given by

$$\Delta y = (a - b) y \Delta t.$$

Thus if we denote $c = a - b$ and if we let Δt approach zero, we obtain

$$\frac{dy}{dt} = cy, \tag{1.2.1}$$

which is a first order linear differential equation called the *Malthusian Law*.

When the population becomes extremely large, this linear model is no longer satisfactory. The individuals must compete for available food, limited living space, natural resources, and so on. This fact must be taken into account in the formulation of the mathematical model. A reasonable assumption is that the death rate will be proportional to the size of the population. Consequently, we modify Eq. (1.2.1) as follows

$$\frac{dy}{dt} = (a - ky)\, y. \tag{1.2.2}$$

This is a nonlinear equation called the *logistic equation*; it has also been applied to areas such as sociology, psychology and ecology.

1.2.2   CELESTIAL MECHANICS

We shall describe the orbital motion of a planet about a sun under the influence of the gravitational attraction between them. If this is the only force acting on the bodies, the relative motion of the planet about the sun will be in a plane. We shall assume that the sun and the planet are spherical in shape and have homogeneous density, and hence the two bodies are attracted to each other as though their masses were at the centers. Accordingly, we may consider them as particles.

Let the mass of the sun be M and let the mass of the planet be m. Then according to Newton's law of gravitation, the two particles, at a distance r apart, attract one another with equal and opposite forces of magnitude GMm/r^2, where G is the gravitational constant. The attraction of the sun on the planet produces an acceleration GM/r^2 whereas the attraction of the planet on the sun produces an acceleration Gm/r^2. Since the mass M of the sun is much larger than the mass m of the planet, we may neglect the acceleration of the sun assuming it stationary in relation to the acceleration of the planet.

If F_1 and F_2 denote the x and y components of the force, respectively, then according to Newton's second law of motion

$$m\frac{d^2x}{dt^2} = F_1, \qquad m\frac{d^2y}{dt^2} = F_2. \tag{1.2.3}$$

Since the force is acting only in the radial direction, we express the acceleration along the radial and tangential directions. Thus using the polar coordinates

$$x = r\cos\theta,$$

$$y = r\sin\theta,$$

the system of equations (1.2.3) becomes[†]

$$\frac{d^2r}{dt^2} - r\left(\frac{d\theta}{dt}\right)^2 = -\frac{\mu}{r^2},$$

$$2\frac{dr}{dt}\frac{d\theta}{dt} + r\frac{d^2\theta}{dt^2} = 0,$$

(1.2.4)

where $\mu = GM$. The negative sign is introduced because the acceleration of the planet is directed opposite to the radial force.

We will now simplify the system (1.2.4), which is nonlinear. Multiplying the second equation of (1.2.4) by r we obtain

$$2r\frac{dr}{dt}\frac{d\theta}{dt} + r^2\frac{d^2\theta}{dt^2} = 0,$$

which is

$$\frac{d}{dt}\left(r^2\frac{d\theta}{dt}\right) = 0.$$

Thus we have

$$r^2\frac{d\theta}{dt} = h,$$

(1.2.5)

where h is a constant.

If we let

$$u = \frac{1}{r},$$

the first equation of (1.2.4) is transformed into

$$\frac{d^2u}{d\theta^2} + u = \frac{\mu}{h^2}.$$

(1.2.6)

[†]The derivation of Eqs. (1.2.4) and (1.2.6) can be found in F. R. Moulton, *Celestial Mechanics*, Macmillan, 1959.

This is a second-order linear equation which together with Eq. (1.2.5) describes the orbital motion of a planet about a sun.

In this idealized model, we consider the sun and the planet as two particles. Thus the equations governing this motion can be used for other idealized models, such as the motion of an artificial satellite around the earth. For the interested reader, a realistic model for the motion of a low-altitude satellite around the earth is given in Appendix V.

1.3 Properly Posed Mathematical Problems

A mathematical problem consists of finding an unknown function that satisfies an ordinary differential equation and one or more appropriate supplementary conditions. The number of conditions for a differential equation usually depends on its order. These conditions may be initial or boundary conditions. For example

$$y'' + p(x)\, y' + q(x)\, y = f(x),$$

$$y(x_0) = \alpha, \tag{1.3.1}$$

$$y'(x_0) = \beta,$$

is an *initial value problem* which consists of an ordinary differential equation and two initial conditions. The *initial conditions* prescribe the unknown function and its derivative at a point x_0.

When supplementary conditions are imposed at two or more points, these conditions are known as *boundary conditions*. The boundary conditions may take some such simple form as

$$a_1\, y(x_0) + a_2\, y'(x_0) = \alpha,$$

$$b_1\, y(x_1) + b_2\, y'(x_1) = \beta, \tag{1.3.2}$$

or they may appear in more complicated form. The problems which involve boundary conditions are called *boundary-value problems*.

A mathematical problem is said to be *properly posed* if it satisfies the following requirements:

1. *Existence:* there is at least one solution.
2. *Uniqueness:* there is at most one solution.
3. *Continuity:* the solution depends continuously on the data.

The first requirement is an obvious logical condition, but we must keep in mind that we cannot simply state that the mathematical problem has a solution just because the physical problem has a solution. We may well be erroneously developing a mathematical model, say, consisting of an ordinary differential equation whose solution may not exist at all. The same can be said about the uniqueness requirement. In order to really reflect the physical problem that has a unique solution the mathematical problem must have a unique solution.

The last requirement is a useful one. In practice, small errors occur in the process of measurements. Thus for the mathematical problem to represent a physical phenomenon a small variation of the given data should lead to at most a small change in the solution.

EXERCISES

1. Classify the following ordinary differential equations:

   (a) $y'' + 3y' + 4y = 0$.

   (b) $y''' + 2y'' + 5yy' = x$.

   (c) $y^{iv} + y = \sin x$.

   (d) $y'' + (\cos x) y' + x^2 y = 0$.

   (e) $(y'')^2 + y' = e^x$.

   (f) $yy'' + 2xy' + y = 0$.

   (g) $y''' + (y'')^2 y' + y = 5$.

2. State whether each of the following problems is an initial-value or a boundary-value problem:

   (a) $y'' + 3y' + 2y = f(x)$,
   $y(0) = 1,\ y'(0) = 2$.

   (b) $y'' + (\sin x) y = 0$,
   $y(0) = 1,\ y(1) = 0$.

   (c) $y'' + 4y = \cos x$,
   $y(1) = 2,\ y'(1) = 0$.

   (d) $y'' - 2y' + 3y = e^x$,
   $y(0) = 1,\ y'(1) = 2$.

3. Show that

   (a) $\phi(x) = c_1 \cos x + c_2 \sin x$
   for some constants c_1 and c_2 satisfies

   $$y'' + y = 0$$

   (b) $\phi(x) = c_1 e^x + c_2 e^{2x}$
   for some constants c_1 and c_2 satisfies

   $$y'' - 3y' + 2y = 0.$$

4. Show that the first-order equation

   $$|y'| + |y| = -1$$

   has no real solution.

5. Prove that if

   $$y = \frac{ax + b}{cx + d},$$

   then

   $$2y'y''' = 3(y'')^2.$$

   If in addition $a + d = 0$, then

   $$(y - x)y'' = 2y(1 + y').$$

Chapter 2.
First-Order Equations.
Picard's Existence Theorem

2.1 First-Order Equations

A first-order ordinary differential equation, in general, can be written in the form

$$F(x, y, y') = 0, \tag{2.1.1}$$

where F is a function defined on some domain D. The problem is to find all functions $y = \phi(x)$ which satisfy the equation identically on some interval J.

DEFINITION 2.1.1 A function $y = \phi(x)$ is said to be a solution of Eq. (2.1.1) if for all $x \in J$

(i) $\phi(x) \in C^1(J)$,

(ii) $(x, \phi(x)) \in D$, $\tag{2.1.2}$

(iii) $F(x, \phi(x), \phi'(x)) = 0$.

First-order equations are usually expressed in normal form

$$y' = f(x, y). \tag{2.1.3}$$

9

If $f(x,y) = -M(x,y)/N(x,y)$, $N(x,y) \neq 0$, Eq. (2.1.3) can be equivalently written in differential form as

$$M(x,y)\,dx + N(x,y)\,dy = 0. \tag{2.1.4}$$

Example 2.1.1   Consider the differential equation

$$y' = y. \tag{2.1.5}$$

Here the function $f(x,y) = y$ is continuous for all values of y. Thus we can take the domain D as the entire xy plane.

The function $\phi(x) = e^x$, as can be easily verified, satisfies the differential equation (2.1.5) on the interval $(-\infty, \infty)$. Thus ϕ satisfies the conditions (2.1.2) and hence ϕ is a solution of Eq. (2.1.5).

Example 2.1.2   Let us consider another example:

$$y' + xy = 0, \tag{2.1.6}$$

the solutions of which, as can be verified, are

$$\phi(x) = ce^{-x^2/2}.$$

The graphs of these equations, called *solution curves*, form a family of bell-shaped curves as shown in Figure 2.1-1. Each curve represents a solution curve for a value of c. This value of c can be ascertained from a given

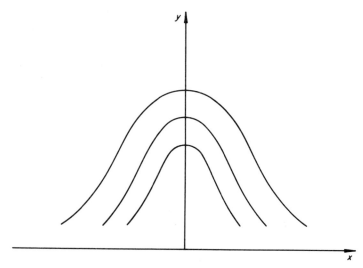

Figure 2.1-1

condition. Thus for instance if we impose the condition $y(0) = 3$, that is, when $x = 0$, y takes on the value 3, we obtain $c = 3$. Consequently

$$\phi(x) = 3e^{-x^2/2},$$

which is a particular solution of Eq. (2.1.5).

The first-order equation in normal form,

$$y' = f(x, y),$$

may be interpreted geometrically. If $f(x, y)$ is defined in D, it is the slope of a tangent line at the point (x, y). Thus a solution of $y' = f(x, y)$ on J is a solution $\phi(x)$ such that $\phi'(x) = f(x, \phi(x))$ whenever the point $(x, \phi(x)) \in D$.

The solution curve tangent at $(x, \phi(x))$ has the slope $\phi'(x)$. Geometrically the problem is then to find solution curves with prescribed directions as tangents. Hence $y' = f(x, y)$ defines a direction field which can be represented graphically by drawing at (x, y) a short line segment with slope $f(x, y)$, as shown in Figure 2.1-2.

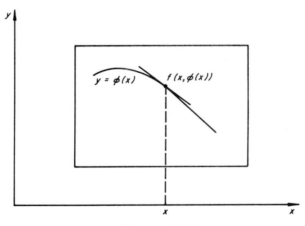

Figure 2.1-2

2.2   Separation of Variables. Homogeneous Functions

One method that is easily applicable to some first-order ordinary differential equations is the method of *separation of variables*.

If $f(x, y) = -g(x)/h(y)$, Eq. (2.1.3) takes the form

$$g(x)\,dx + h(y)\,dy = 0.$$

The variables are separated. Now assuming that g and h are continuous functions in x and y, respectively, we integrate this equation directly by using the chain rule to obtain

$$\int^x g(t)\,dt + \int^x h(y)\frac{dy}{dt}\,dt = c, \tag{2.2.1}$$

where c is a constant of integration.[†] Now by transforming the variable of integration from t to s in the second integral of Eq. (2.2.1) we obtain

$$\int^x g(t)\,dt + \int^y h(s)\,ds = c \tag{2.2.2}$$

This method, though limited in its application, can be applied to all separable equations linear or nonlinear. As an illustration, consider the following example:

Example 2.2.1   Consider the initial value problem

$$\begin{aligned} y' &= -x/y, \\ y(0) &= 1. \end{aligned} \tag{2.2.3}$$

This equation can be easily separated and written in the form

$$x\,dx + y\,dy = 0.$$

Integration yields

$$x^2 + y^2 = C, \tag{2.2.4}$$

where C is a positive constant. Thus solutions are given implicitly in terms of x by Eq. (2.2.4). Explicitly we write

$$y(x) = \pm\sqrt{C - x^2}\,, \tag{2.2.5}$$

if $|x| \leqslant \sqrt{C}$ for all real values of x. The relation (2.2.4) is called the *integral* of the differential equation (2.2.3).

    Between the two solutions of Eq. (2.2.5) that satisfy the differential

---

[†]Henceforth we use the notation $\int^x f(s)\,ds$ to denote an antiderivative of $f(x)$. That is, $\int^x f(s)\,ds$ is to be interpreted as some *particular* function $F(x)$ such that $F'(x) = f(x)$. Functions of this class are contained in $F(x) + c$, where c is an arbitrary constant.

equation (2.2.3) on the entire interval $|x| \leqslant \sqrt{C}$, we must select

$$y(x) = + \sqrt{C - x^2}$$

in order to satisfy the prescribed initial condition $y(0) = 1$.

It should be remarked that frequently an explicit solution $y = \phi(x)$ is not easy or even possible to attain from an implicit relation. If an explicit solution is attainable (by the implicit-function theorem), then at least one function $\phi(x)$ must exist, and it must satisfy the corresponding differential equation.

If, in the relation (2.2.5), $|x| > \sqrt{C}$, then the solution $\phi(x)$ is no longer a real function.

Interesting theoretical aspects of the method of separation of variables can be found in Platt [31].

There is a class of differential equations which can be reduced to separable equations by a change of variable. The condition is that the coefficients $M(x, y)$ and $N(x, y)$ in Eq. (2.1.4) must be homogeneous.

DEFINITION 2.2.1   A continuous function $f(x, y)$ is said to be *homogeneous of degree n* in x and y if for every real number λ,

$$f(\lambda x, \lambda y) = \lambda^n f(x, y). \tag{2.2.6}$$

We see that a polynomial such as $f(x, y) = x^2 + 2xy + y^2$ is of degree 2 in x and y, since

$$f(\lambda x, \lambda y) = (\lambda x)^2 + 2(\lambda x)(\lambda y) + (\lambda y)^2$$

$$= \lambda^2 f(x, y).$$

If we consider the function $f(x, y) = xe^{y/x} - y$, we find that

$$f(\lambda x, \lambda y) = (\lambda x)e^{\lambda y/\lambda x} - \lambda y$$

$$= \lambda f(x, y).$$

f is therefore of degree 1 in x and y.

THEOREM 2.2.1 *If the coefficients M and N are homogeneous of the same degree in x and y, then the equation*

$$M(x,y)\,dx + N(x,y)\,dy = 0 \tag{2.2.7}$$

can be reduced to a separable equation by the transformation $v = y/x$.

Proof Since M and N are of the same degree, say k, we have

$$M(x,y) = M(x,vx) = x^k M(1,v),$$

$$N(x,y) = N(x,vx) = x^k N(1,v),$$

and hence

$$\frac{M(x,y)}{N(x,y)} = \frac{M(1,v)}{N(1,v)} = f(v).$$

From $v = y/x$, we have

$$\frac{dy}{dx} = v + x\frac{dv}{dx}.$$

Thus Eq. (2.2.7) transforms into

$$v + x\frac{dv}{dx} = -f(v).$$

Consequently

$$\frac{dv}{f(v) + v} + \frac{dx}{x} = 0.$$

This is a separable equation. ∎

Example 2.2.2 Solve $y^2\,dx - x(x+y)\,dy = 0$.

Since the coefficients are homogeneous, we let $v = y/x$. We have

$$\frac{dy}{dx} = \frac{y^2}{x^2 + xy} = \frac{y^2/x^2}{1 + y/x}.$$

Thus the given equation is transformed into

$$v + x\frac{dv}{dx} = \frac{v^2}{1+v}.$$

Separating the variables, we have

$$\left(\frac{1}{v}+1\right)dv+\frac{dx}{x}=0,$$

the solution of which is

$$|xv|=ce^{-v}, \qquad c>0.$$

In terms of the original variable y, we have

$$y=ce^{-y/x}$$

for arbitrary c.

We should remark that the substitution $v=x/y$ can also be used. The proper choice $v=y/x$ or $v=x/y$ depending upon the coefficients may lead the given equation to a more manageable separable equation.

2.3   Exact Differential Equations

In Section 2.1 we have seen that a first-order differential equation can be written in the form

$$M(x,y)\,dx+N(x,y)\,dy=0. \tag{2.3.1}$$

We recall from calculus that if $F(x,y)$ has continuous first partial derivatives, dF is defined by

$$dF=F_x\,dx+F_y\,dy, \tag{2.3.2}$$

where, as usual, the subscript on F denotes the partial differentiation of F with respect to that variable. This immediately suggests the following definition.

DEFINITION 2.3.1   The differential $M\,dx+N\,dy$ for $M,N\in C(R)$ is called *exact* in a region R if there exists a function $F(x,y)\in C^1(R)$ such that $F_x=M$ and $F_y=N$. That is, a function F exists such that

$$dF=M\,dx+N\,dy. \tag{2.3.3}$$

Thus if the differential is exact, Eq. (2.3.1) becomes

$$dF=M\,dx+N\,dy=0.$$

Hence for a constant c

$$F(x,y) = c, \tag{2.3.4}$$

which is the *general integral* of Eq. (2.3.1).

Example 2.3.1   The differential $y\,dx + x\,dy$ is an exact differential in the entire xy plane since

$$d(xy) = y\,dx + x\,dy.$$

Thus the exact differential equation

$$y\,dx + x\,dy = 0$$

can be written as

$$d(xy) = 0.$$

The general integral of this equation is

$$xy = c,$$

where c is an arbitrary constant.

Now the question is under what condition the differential $M\,dx + N\,dy$ is exact, and if it is, how to determine the function $F(x,y)$. The answers to these questions will be clarified by the following theorems.

THEOREM 2.3.1   *If M_y and N_x are continuous in R, then a necessary condition for $M\,dx + N\,dy$ to be an exact differential is that $M_y = N_x$.*

Proof   Since the differential is exact, there exists $F(x,y)$ such that

$$M = F_x \quad \text{and} \quad N = F_y.$$

Thus $M_y = F_{xy}$ and $N_x = F_{yx}$. Because M_y and N_x are continuous by assumption, $F_{xy} = F_{yx}$ implies $M_y = N_x$.   ∎

THEOREM 2.3.2   *If M, N, M_y and N_x are continuous and $M_y = N_x$ for all (x,y) in a rectangular region R, then the differential $M\,dx + N\,dy$ is exact.*

Proof   To prove that the differential is exact is equivalent to proving the existence of a function $F(x,y)$ such that $F_x = M$ and $F_y = N$. Hence the function $F(x,y)$, if it exists, must satisfy

$$\frac{\partial F}{\partial x} = M(x,y).$$

Integrating this with respect to x, we obtain

$$F(x,y) = \int^x M(t,y)\, dt + G(y), \qquad (2.3.5)$$

where $G(y)$ is an arbitrary function of y. Now differentiation with respect to y yields

$$\frac{\partial F}{\partial y} = \frac{\partial}{\partial y} \int^x M(t,y)\, dt + \frac{dG}{dy}.$$

Using $F_y = N$, we obtain

$$\frac{dG}{dy} = N(x,y) - \frac{\partial}{\partial y} \int^x M(t,y)\, dt.$$

Integration then yields

$$G(y) = \int^y \left[N(x,s) - \frac{\partial}{\partial s} \int^x M(t,s)\, dt \right] ds.$$

Substituting this in Eq. (2.3.5), $F(x,y)$ becomes

$$F(x,y) = \int^x M(t,y)\, dt + \int^y \left[N(x,s) - \frac{\partial}{\partial s} \int^x M(t,s)\, dt \right] ds. \qquad (2.3.6)$$

This function is indeed the one that we seek, for

$$\frac{\partial F}{\partial x} = \frac{\partial}{\partial x} \int^x M(t,y)\, dt + \frac{\partial}{\partial x} \int^y \left[N(x,s) - \frac{\partial}{\partial s} \int^x M(t,s)\, dt \right] ds$$

$$= M(x,y) + \int^y \left[N_x(x,s) - \frac{\partial^2}{\partial x \partial s} \int^x M(t,s)\, dt \right] ds$$

$$= M(x,y) + \int^y \left[M_s(x,s) - \frac{\partial^2}{\partial s \partial x} \int^x M(t,s)\, dt \right] ds$$

$$= M(x,y) + \int^y \left[M_s(x,s) - \frac{\partial M}{\partial s}(x,s) \right] ds$$

$$= M(x,y)$$

and

$$\frac{\partial F}{\partial y} = \frac{\partial}{\partial y} \int^x M(t,y)\,dt + \frac{\partial}{\partial y} \int^y \left[N(x,s) - \frac{\partial}{\partial s} \int^x M(t,s)\,dt \right] ds$$

$$= \frac{\partial}{\partial y} \int^x M(t,y)\,dt + N(x,y) - \frac{\partial}{\partial y} \int^x M(t,y)\,dt$$

$$= N(x,y).$$

Thus the sufficiency condition is proved.   ■

We should remark here that in Theorem 2.3.2 it is not essential that the region R be rectangular but only that it be simply connected.[†]

Example 2.3.1   Find the general integral of

$$(3x^2 + y^2)\,dx + 2xy\,dy = 0.$$

In this case $M(x,y) = 3x^2 + y^2$, $N(x,y) = 2xy$. We see that $M_y = 2y = N_x$. Thus the equation is exact. Consequently, from (2.3.6) we find

$$F(x,y) = \int^x (3t^2 + y^2)\,dt + \int^y \left[2xs - \frac{\partial}{\partial s} \int^x (3t^2 + s^2)\,dt \right] ds.$$

Simplification yields

$$F(x,y) = x^3 + xy^2.$$

Thus the general integral is given by

$$x^3 + xy^2 = c.$$

When the differential equation,

$$M(x,y)\,dx + N(x,y)\,dy = 0, \tag{2.3.7}$$

is not exact, one can find a function $\mu(x,y)$ such that the differential equation

$$\mu(x,y)M(x,y)\,dx + \mu(x,y)N(x,y)\,dy = 0 \tag{2.3.8}$$

[†]A region R is said to be *simply connected* if every simple closed curve in R also has its interior in R.

is exact. The function $\mu(x,y)$ is called an *integrating factor*. The condition that Eq. (2.3.8) be exact is that

$$\frac{\partial}{\partial y}(\mu M) = \frac{\partial}{\partial x}(\mu N),$$

or

$$N\mu_x - M\mu_y + (N_x - M_y)\,\mu = 0. \tag{2.3.9}$$

Thus μ must satisfy this first-order partial differential equation.

In general, Eq. (2.3.9) is as difficult to solve as the original equation (2.3.7). Therefore, in practice, integrating factors can be found only for special types of equations (see Tenenbaum and Pollard [38]).

2.4 First-Order Linear Equations

A linear first-order equation is of the form

$$a(x)\frac{dy}{dx} + b(x)\,y = f(x),$$

where a, b and f are given functions of x. If $a(x) \neq 0$, the equation can be expressed in the standard form

$$\frac{dy}{dx} + p(x)\,y = q(x), \tag{2.4.1}$$

where $p(x) = b(x)/a(x)$ and $q(x) = f(x)/a(x)$ are both continuous functions of x defined on a certain interval I.

First consider the homogeneous case

$$\frac{dy}{dx} + p(x)\,y = 0.$$

We observe that $y = 0$ is a solution. For other solutions, we separate the equation to obtain

$$\frac{dy}{y} = -p(x)\,dx.$$

Integration yields

$$\ln|y| = -\int^x p(t)\,dt + \ln c$$

for $c > 0$. This can be written in the form

$$|y| = ce^{-\int^x p(t)\,dt}, \qquad c > 0.$$

Thus the general solution of the homogeneous first-order linear equation is given by

$$y = ce^{-\int^x p(t)\,dt}$$

for arbitrary values of c.

If we rewrite the solution in the form

$$ye^{\int^x p(t)\,dt} = c,$$

we immediately see after differentiation that

$$y'e^{\int^x p(t)\,dt} + pye^{\int^x p(t)\,dt} = 0,$$

which shows clearly that the integrating factor for the homogeneous equation is $\exp\int^x p(t)\,dt$.

Now since the nonhomogeneous term depends only on the independent variable x, we can solve the given equation (2.4.1) by multiplying it by the integrating factor $\exp\int^x p(t)\,dt$, resulting in

$$y'e^{\int^x p(t)\,dt} + p(t)\,ye^{\int^x p(t)\,dt} = q(t)e^{\int^x p(t)\,dt}.$$

Noting that the left side is an exact differential integration yields

$$ye^{\int^x p(t)\,dt} = \int^x q(t)e^{\int^t p(s)\,ds}\,dt + c,$$

where c is an arbitrary constant. Explicitly we write

$$y(x) = e^{-\int^x p(t)\,dt}\left[\int^x q(t)e^{\int^t p(s)\,ds}\,dt + c\right],$$

which is the general solution of Eq. (2.4.1). This proves the following theorem:

THEOREM 2.4.1   *If $p(x)$ and $q(x)$ are continuous on an interval I, the general solution $\phi(x)$ of Eq. (2.4.1) on I is given by*

$$\phi(x) = e^{-\int^x p(t)\,dt}\left[\int^x q(t)e^{\int^t p(s)\,ds}\,dt + c\right]. \qquad (2.4.2)$$

Example 2.4.1 *Solve the equation*

$$y' + xy = 2x.$$

This is a first-order linear equation, and hence the solution is given by

$$\phi(x) = e^{-\int^x t\,dt}\left[\int^x e^{\int^t s\,ds}2t\,dt + c\right]$$

$$= e^{-x^2/2}\left[\int^x e^{t^2/2}2t\,dt + c\right]$$

$$= e^{-x^2/2}\left[2e^{x^2/2} + c\right]$$

$$= 2 + ce^{-x^2/2}.$$

Example 2.4.2 Find the general solution of the *Bernoulli equation*

$$y' + a(x)y = b(x)y^n.$$

This is a nonlinear equation when n is different from 0 and 1. However, the solution can be obtained by setting $u = y^{1-n}$. The equation, rewritten in the form

$$y^{-n}y' + a(x)y^{1-n} = b(x),$$

then becomes

$$u' + (1-n)a(x)u = (1-n)b(x),$$

which is a linear first-order equation. The solution is thus given by

$$u(x) = e^{-P(x)}\left[\int^x (1-n)b(t)e^{P(t)}\,dt + c\right],$$

where $P(x) = (1-n)\int^x a(t)\,dt$.

2.5 Existence, Uniqueness and Continuity Theorems

We will now look into the existence of a solution to an initial-value problem

$$y' = f(x,y),$$

$$y(x_0) = y_0,$$

$$(2.5.1)$$

where f is a continuous function in a domain D, and let $(x_0, y_0) \in D$.

Let $\phi(x)$ be a solution on an interval I containing x_0. Then if ϕ is differentiable for all $x \in I$, we have

$$\phi'(x) = f[x, \phi(x)],$$

$$\phi(x_0) = y_0 \tag{2.5.2}$$

for all $x \in I$.

THEOREM 2.5.1 $\phi(x)$ *is a solution of the initial-value problem* (2.5.1) *on* I *if, and only if, it is a continuous solution of the integral equation*

$$\phi(x) = y_0 + \int_{x_0}^{x} f[t, \phi(t)] \, dt \tag{2.5.3}$$

on I.

Proof

(i) Suppose ϕ is a solution of the initial-value problem on I. Then

$$\phi'(x) = f[x, \phi(x)] \tag{2.5.4}$$

for all $x \in I$. Since ϕ is continuous on I and f is continuous in D, it follows that $f[x, \phi(x)]$ is continuous on I. Hence integration of (2.5.4) from x_0 to x yields

$$\phi(x) = y_0 + \int_{x_0}^{x} f[t, \phi(t) \, dt]$$

for all $x \in I$. Applying the initial condition $\phi(x_0) = y_0$, we see that ϕ is a solution of the integral equation (2.5.3) on I.

(ii) Suppose ϕ is a continuous solution of the integral equation (2.5.3) on I. Since $f[x, \phi(x)]$ is continuous for all $x \in I$, we see that by the fundamental theorem of integral calculus, differentiation of (2.5.3) yields

$$\phi'(x) = f[x, \phi(x)]$$

for all $x \in I$. We observe in (2.5.3) that $\phi(x_0) = y_0$. Thus ϕ is a solution of the initial-value problem (2.5.1).   ∎

We shall apply the *Picard method* of proving the existence of a solution of the initial-value problem. The method consists essentially of approximating the solution of the integral equation (2.5.3).

As an initial approximation one would naturally consider

$$\phi(x_0) = y_0,^\dagger$$

which is of course the prescribed initial condition (2.5.2). However, this can hardly be called an approximation, since it does not in general satisfy Eq. (2.5.3). So as a next step we compute the first approximation by substituting $\phi_1(t)$ for $\phi_0(t)$ in Eq. (2.5.3) resulting in

$$\phi_1(x) = y_0 + \int_{x_0}^{x} f[t, \phi_0(t)] \, dt.$$

If we continue the process and define successively the nth approximation, we obtain

$$\phi_n(x) = y_0 + \int_{x_0}^{x} f[t, \phi_{n-1}(t)] \, dt, \qquad n = 1, 2, 3, \ldots.$$

Now if $\{\phi_n\}$, a sequence of continuous functions, converges uniformly to $\phi(x)$ on I, and satisfies the integral equation

$$\phi(x) = y_0 + \int_{x_0}^{x} f[t, \phi(t)] \, dt$$

on I, then ϕ is a solution of the initial-value problem (2.5.1).

Thus our next task is to prove the existence of $\phi_n(x)$. Before we prove this, consider the following example.

Example 2.5.1   Consider the initial-value problem

$$y' = xy,$$

$$y(0) = 1.$$

The corresponding integral equation is

$$y(x) = 1 + \int_{0}^{x} t y(t) \, dt.$$

---

†Note that $\phi(x_0)$ denotes $\phi_0(x)$.

The successive approximations are given by

$$\phi_0(x) = 1,$$

$$\phi_1(x) = 1 + \int_0^x t\,dt = 1 + \frac{x^2}{2},$$

$$\phi_2(x) = 1 + \int_0^x t\left(1 + \frac{t^2}{2}\right) dt = 1 + \frac{x^2}{2} + \frac{x^4}{8},$$

and thus $\phi_n(x)$ is obtained by induction:

$$\phi_n(x) = 1 + \left(\frac{x^2}{2}\right) + \frac{1}{2!}\left(\frac{x^2}{2}\right)^2 + \cdots + \frac{1}{n!}\left(\frac{x^2}{2}\right)^n.$$

It can easily be seen that the right side is the partial sum of $\phi(x) = \exp[x^2/2]$. Since the series converges for all real values of x, $\phi(x)$ thus represents the solution of the given initial-value problem.

THEOREM 2.5.2 (Existence) *Let $f(x,y)$ be a continuous function in some domain D, and let f satisfy a* Lipschitz *condition (see Appendix I) in D, namely*

$$|f(x,y_1) - f(x,y_2)| \leqslant K|y_1 - y_2|, \qquad K > 0, \tag{2.5.5}$$

for all $(x,y_1),(x,y_2) \in D$. If (x_0,y_0) is a point in D, then there exists a solution $\phi(x)$ of the initial-value problem

$$y' = f(x,y),$$

$$y(x_0) = y_0,$$

on an interval $I : |x - x_0| \leqslant h$ for some $h > 0$.

Proof Let R be a rectangle

$$|x - x_0| \leqslant a, \qquad |y - y_0| \leqslant b, \qquad a > 0, \quad b > 0,$$

in D. Since f is continuous on a bounded and closed set R, it is necessarily bounded on R. Thus there exists a constant $M > 0$ such that

$$|f(x,y)| \leqslant M \tag{2.5.6}$$

for all $(x,y) \in R$.

Let h be defined by

$$h = \min\{a, b/M\}. \tag{2.5.7}$$

We will now prove by induction that $\phi_n(x)$ is continuous and satisfies

$$|\phi_n(x) - y_0| \leqslant M|x - x_0| \tag{2.5.8}$$

for all x in $I : |x - x_0| \leqslant h$.

The geometrical interpretation of the inequality (2.5.8) is that ϕ_n lies in $T \subset R$, bounded by the lines $y - y_0 = \pm M(x - x_0)$ and $x - x_0 = \pm h$, as shown in Figures 2.5-1 and 2.5-2.

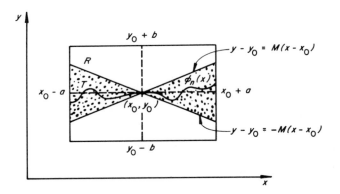

Figure 2.5-1

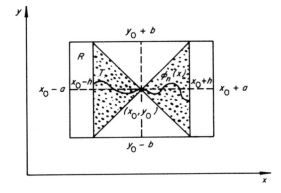

Figure 2.5-2

Since $h \leqslant b/M$, it follows from (2.5.8), which is assumed to hold, that

$$|\phi_n(x) - y_0| \leqslant Mh \leqslant b.$$

We also know that $h \leqslant a$, and hence the points $[x, \phi_n(x)]$ lie in R for all $x \in I$.

It is evident that ϕ_0 exists and is a continuous function on I that satisfies (2.5.8). Thus ϕ_1 is given by

$$\phi_1(x) = y_0 + \int_{x_0}^x f[t, y_0] dt.$$

Since f is continuous on R, $f(t, y_0)$ is continuous on I. Thus ϕ_1 exists and is continuous on I.

Next we see that

$$|\phi_1(x) - y_0| = \left| \int_{x_0}^x f(t, y_0) dt \right| \leqslant \left| \int_{x_0}^x |f(t, y_0)| dt \right| \leqslant M|x - x_0|,$$

which shows that ϕ_1 satisfies the inequality (2.5.8).

As stated before, we shall prove the existence and continuity of ϕ_n by mathematical induction. Suppose ϕ_n exists, is continuous on I, and satisfies (2.5.8). Since the points $(x, \phi_n) \in R$ for $x \in I$, $f(x, \phi_n)$ exists for $x \in I$. Moreover, f is continuous on R, and ϕ_n is continuous on I. Consequently

$$\phi_{n+1}(x) = y_0 + \int_{x_0}^x f[t, \phi_n(t)] dt$$

exists as a continuous function on I. Thus we have

$$|\phi_{n+1}(x) - y_0| \leqslant \left| \int_{x_0}^x |f[t, \phi_n(t)]| dt \right| \leqslant M|x - x_0|,$$

which shows that ϕ_{n+1} satisfies (2.5.8). Hence by induction we prove that ϕ_n exists, is continuous on I, and satisfies (2.5.8).

We observe that ϕ_n may be written in the form

$$\phi_n = y_0 + (\phi_1 - y_0) + (\phi_2 - \phi_1) + \cdots + (\phi_n - \phi_{n-1}),$$

which shows that $\phi_n(x)$ is the nth partial sum of the series

$$y_0 + \sum_{n=1}^{\infty} [\phi_n(x) - \phi_{n-1}(x)]. \qquad (2.5.9)$$

Thus proving the convergence of the sequence $\{\phi_n(x)\}$ is equivalent to proving the convergence of the series (2.5.9).

Since we have

$$\phi_2(x) - \phi_1(x) = \int_{x_0}^{x} \left[f(t, \phi_1(t)) - f(t, y_0) \right] dt,$$

it follows that

$$\left| \phi_2(x) - \phi_1(x) \right| \leqslant \left| \int_{x_0}^{x} \left| f(t, \phi_1(t)) - f(t, y_0) \right| dt \right|.$$

Since f satisfies the Lipschitz condition, we have

$$\left| \phi_2(x) - \phi_1(x) \right| \leqslant K \left| \int_{x_0}^{x} \left| \phi_1(t) - y_0 \right| dt \right|.$$

By virtue of (2.5.8), we obtain

$$\left| \phi_2(x) - \phi_1(x) \right| \leqslant MK \left| \int_{x_0}^{x} \left| t - x_0 \right| dt \right|.$$

If $x \geqslant x_0$, then

$$\left| \phi_2(x) - \phi_1(x) \right| \leqslant \frac{MK}{2} \left| x - x_0 \right|^2$$

This relation also holds true for the case $x \leqslant x_0$.

We will now prove by induction that

$$\left| \phi_n(x) - \phi_{n-1}(x) \right| \leqslant \frac{MK^{n-1}}{n!} \left| x - x_0 \right|^n \tag{2.5.10}$$

for all $x \in I$. Clearly this is true for $n = 1$ and $n = 2$.

Consider the case $x \geqslant x_0$. (A similar argument can be given for the case $x < x_0$.) Then

$$\phi_{n+1}(x) - \phi_n(x) = \int_{x_0}^{x} \left[f(t, \phi_n(t)) - f(t, \phi_{n-1}(t)) \right] dt,$$

and hence

$$\left| \phi_{n+1}(x) - \phi_n(x) \right| \leqslant \int_{x_0}^{x} \left| f(t, \phi_n(t)) - f(t, \phi_{n-1}(t)) \right| dt.$$

Again by using the Lipschitz condition, we obtain

$$\left|\phi_{n+1}(x)-\phi_n(x)\right| \leqslant K\left|\int_{x_0}^{x}\left|\phi_n(t)-\phi_{n-1}(t)\right|dt\right|. \qquad (2.5.11)$$

Because of the assumption (2.5.10), Eq. (2.5.11) becomes

$$\left|\phi_{n+1}(x)-\phi_n(x)\right| \leqslant \frac{MK^n}{n!}\left|\int_{x_0}^{x}\left|t-x_0\right|^n dt\right| = \frac{MK^n\left|x-x_0\right|^{n+1}}{(n+1)!},$$

which is just (2.5.10) for $n+1$. Hence the proof is complete.

For $|x-x_0| \leqslant h$, we note that

$$\frac{K^n\left|x-x_0\right|^n}{n!} \leqslant \frac{K^n h^n}{n!}.$$

Since the series $\sum_{n=1}^{\infty}K^n h^n/n!$ converges to e^{Kh}, the series (2.5.9) converges uniformly for all $x \in I$ by the Weierstrass M-test. Therefore the approximating sequence $\{\phi_n(x)\}$ converges uniformly to a limit function $\phi(x)$ for all $x \in I$. Since each $\phi_n(x)$ is continuous on I, $\phi(x)$ is continuous for all $x \in I$. Now $\phi_n(x)$ and hence $\phi(x)$ satisfy (2.5.8). Accordingly we have

$$\left|\phi(x)-y_0\right| \leqslant M\left|x-x_0\right|$$

which implies that $(x,\phi(x)) \in R$ for all $x \in I$.

What remains to be proved is that

$$\lim_{n \to \infty}\int_{x_0}^{x}f[t,\phi_n(t)]dt = \int_{x_0}^{x}f[t,\phi(t)]dt$$

for all $x \in I$. Consider

$$\left|\int_{x_0}^{x}f[t,\phi(t)]dt - \int_{x_0}^{x}f[t,\phi_n(t)]dt\right| \leqslant \left|\int_{x_0}^{x}\left|f[t,\phi(t)]-f[t,\phi_n(t)]\right|dt\right|$$

$$\leqslant K\left|\int_{x_0}^{x}\left|\phi(t)-\phi_n(t)\right|dt\right|$$

$$\leqslant K\left|x-x_0\right|\max_{t \in I}\left|\phi(t)-\phi_n(t)\right|$$

$$\leqslant Kh\max_{t \in I}\left|\phi(t)-\phi_n(t)\right|.$$

Since the sequence $\{\phi_n(t)\}$ converges uniformly to $\phi(t)$ on I, for any $\varepsilon > 0$ there exists a positive integer N such that

$$\max_{t \in I} |\phi(t) - \phi_n(t)| < \frac{\varepsilon}{Kh}$$

for all $n \geqslant N$. Hence for $n \geqslant N$, we have

$$\left| \int_{x_0}^{x} \{ f[t, \phi(t)] - f[t, \phi_n(t)] \} dt \right| < \varepsilon,$$

which completes the proof. ∎

THEOREM 2.5.3 (Uniqueness) *Let f be continuous and satisfy a Lipschitz condition in R. If a solution of the initial-value problem*

$$y' = f(x, y),$$

$$y(x_0) = y_0$$

exists, then it is unique.

Proof Suppose that $\phi(x)$ and $\psi(x)$ are two solutions of the initial-value problem. We shall show that $\psi(x) = \phi(x)$ for all $x \in I$. We express

$$\phi(x) = y_0 + \int_{x_0}^{x} f[t, \phi(t)] dt \qquad (2.5.12)$$

and

$$\psi(x) = y_0 + \int_{x_0}^{x} f[t, \psi(t)] dt \qquad (2.5.13)$$

for all $x \in I$.

Now, subtracting (2.5.12) from (2.5.13), we obtain

$$|\psi(x) - \phi(x)| \leqslant \left| \int_{x_0}^{x} |f[t, \psi(t)] - f[t, \phi(t)]| \, dt \right|. \qquad (2.5.14)$$

By virtue of the Lipschitz condition, this inequality becomes

$$|\psi(x) - \phi(x)| \leqslant K \left| \int_{x_0}^{x} |\psi(t) - \phi(t)| \, dt \right|. \qquad (2.5.15)$$

Since $\psi(x)$ and $\phi(x)$ are continuous, $\psi(x) - \phi(x)$ is continuous. Thus it is bounded on I, that is,

$$|\psi(x) - \phi(x)| \leqslant C$$

for some constant C. Hence (2.5.15) becomes

$$|\psi(x) - \phi(x)| \leqslant CK \left| \int_{x_0}^{x} dt \right| = CK |x - x_0| \qquad (2.5.16)$$

for all $x \in I$.

We shall prove by induction that

$$|\psi(x) - \phi(x)| \leqslant \frac{CK^n |x - x_0|^n}{n!} \qquad (2.5.17)$$

for all $x \in I$. In view of (2.5.16) it is evident that (2.5.17) holds true for $n = 1$. Now suppose that the inequality (2.5.17) is true. Then from (2.5.15) and (2.5.17) we have

$$|\psi(x) - \phi(x)| \leqslant \frac{CK^{n+1}}{n!} \left| \int_{x_0}^{x} |t - x_0|^n dt \right| = \frac{CK^{n+1} |x - x_0|^{n+1}}{(n+1)!}$$

for all $x \in I$. This is just (2.5.17) for n replaced by $n+1$, and hence the proof is complete.

For $|x - x_0| \leqslant h$, we see that

$$\frac{K^n |x - x_0|^n}{n!} \leqslant \frac{K^n h^n}{n!}.$$

Since the series $\sum_{n=1}^{\infty} K^n h^n / n!$ converges to e^{Kh}, it is necessary that

$$\lim_{n \to \infty} \frac{(Kh)^n}{n!} = 0.$$

It immediately follows from (2.5.17) that

$$|\psi(x) - \phi(x)| \leqslant \frac{C(Kh)^n}{n!} \qquad \text{for any } n,$$

and hence we have

$$0 \leqslant |\psi(x) - \phi(x)| \leqslant \lim_{n \to \infty} \frac{C(Kh)^n}{n!} = 0$$

for all $x \in I$. Thus $|\psi(x) - \phi(x)| = 0$, and hence $\phi(x) = \psi(x)$ for all $x \in I$. Therefore the function $\phi(x)$ is the unique solution of the initial-value problem. ∎

THEOREM 2.5.4 (Continuity) *Let f be a continuous function on*

$$R : |x - x_0| \leqslant a, \; |y - y_0| \leqslant b$$

and satisfy a Lipschitz condition. If in the initial-value problem

$$y' = f(x, y),$$

$$y(x_0) = y_0,$$

the initial value changes by a small amount, say

$$|y_0 - y_0^*| < \delta,$$

then the solution changes accordingly, that is,

$$|\phi(x) - \phi^*(x)| < \varepsilon.$$

Proof Since ϕ and ϕ^* are the solutions of the corresponding initial-value problems, we can immediately write

$$\phi(x) = y_0 + \int_{x_0}^{x} f[t, \phi(t)] \, dt,$$

$$\phi^*(x) = y_0^* + \int_{x_0}^{x} f[t, \phi^*(t)] \, dt.$$

Subtracting $\phi^*(x)$ from $\phi(x)$, we obtain

$$\phi(x) - \phi^*(x) = y_0 - y_0^* + \int_{x_0}^{x} \left[f(t, \phi(t)) - f(t, \phi^*(t)) \right] dt.$$

Since f satisfies a Lipschitz condition, we obtain for $x \geqslant x_0$

$$|\phi(x) - \phi^*(x)| \leqslant |y_0 - y_0^*| + K \int_{x_0}^{x} |\phi(t) - \phi^*(t)| \, dt. \qquad (2.5.18)$$

If we let

$$\eta(x) = \int_{x_0}^{x} |\phi(t) - \phi^*(t)| \, dt,$$

then the inequality (2.5.18) becomes

$$\eta'(x) - K\eta(x) \leqslant \delta.$$

This is a first-order differential inequality. Hence

$$\frac{d}{dx}\left[\eta(x)e^{-K(x-x_0)}\right] \leqslant \delta e^{-K(x-x_0)}.$$

Integration from x_0 to x yields

$$\eta(x)e^{-K(x-x_0)} \leqslant \frac{\delta}{K}\left[1 - e^{-K(x-x_0)}\right],$$

and thus

$$\eta(x) \leqslant \frac{\delta}{K}\left[e^{K(x-x_0)} - 1\right].$$

From (2.5.18) we have

$$|\phi(x) - \phi^*(x)| \leqslant \delta + K\frac{\delta}{K}\left[e^{K(x-x_0)} - 1\right] = \delta e^{K(x-x_0)}.$$

Since a similar proof holds for $x \leqslant x_0$, we have

$$|\phi(x) - \phi^*(x)| \leqslant \delta e^{K|x-x_0|}.$$

Therefore if we choose $\varepsilon = \delta e^{Kh}$ for $|x - x_0| \leqslant h$, we obtain

$$|\phi(x) - \phi^*(x)| \leqslant \varepsilon. \qquad \blacksquare$$

We have just proved that there exists a unique solution of the well-posed initial-value problem (2.5.1) for x in the neighborhood of the initial point x_0. Thus Theorem 2.5.2 is known as the *local existence theorem*.

The existence of a solution of the initial-value problem (2.5.1) under some hypotheses can also be proved for $|x - x_0| \leqslant a$ for large values of a. This theorem is known as the *global existence theorem* (see Coddington [7]).

EXERCISES

1. Show that $\phi(x) = e^x$ is a solution of $y'' = y'$ on a certain interval I.

2. Verify that $\phi(x) = 1/(x + c)$ are solutions of $y' = -y^2$ on certain intervals. Graph the solutions for $c = 0, \pm 1, \pm 2$.

3. Draw the direction field for the equation $y' = x^2 + y^2$.

4. By the method of separation of variables solve $y' = (\cos x)(y - 2)$ satisfying the initial condition $y(0) = 1$. Find the unique solution of the same equation satisfying $y(0) = 2$. Specify the interval on which the solution is defined in each case.

5. Solve the equation
$$y' = 1 + y^2$$
satisfying $y(0) = 1$. Specify the interval on which the solution is defined.

6. Consider the initial-value problem
$$y' = 3y^{2/3},$$
$$y(x_0) = y_0.$$
Discuss and sketch the solutions.

7. Solve the initial-value problem
$$y' = \alpha y - \beta y^2,$$
$$y(0) = y_0,$$
where α and β are small positive numbers. Show that
$$\lim_{x \to \infty} \phi(x) = \begin{cases} \alpha/\beta & \text{for} \quad y_0 > 0, \\ 0 & \text{for} \quad y_0 = 0. \end{cases}$$
For $y_0 < 0$, ϕ is unbounded as x approaches a certain value depending on y_0.

8. Solve the equation
$$(x^2 + y^2) y' + xy = 0$$
by using the change of variable $v = y/x$ and $v = x/y$.

9. Show that the equation
$$F(x, y)(xy' - y) - f(x) y^n = 0$$
can be solved by the substitution $v = y/x$, where F is homogeneous in x and y.

10. Solve the *linear fractional equation*
$$y' = \frac{ax + by}{cx + dy}, \qquad ad \neq bc.$$
Also obtain solutions by using polar coordinates.

11. Test for exactness and solve the following equations.

(a)
$$\left(\frac{1}{x} - \frac{1}{y}\right) dx + \frac{x}{y^2} dy = 0.$$

(b)
$$(y \cos x - \sin y) dx + (\sin x - x \cos y) dy = 0.$$

(c)
$$(1 - xy)^{-2} dx + \left[y^2 + x^2 (1 - xy)^{-2} \right] dy = 0.$$

12. If $M = yf(xy)$ and $N = xg(xy)$, show that $1/(Mx - Ny)$ is an integrating factor provided $Mx - Ny \neq 0$.

13. Show that $1/x^2, 1/y^2, 1/xy, 1/(x^2 \pm y^2)$ are the integrating factors of the equation $y' = y/x$, and obtain the solutions representing the same family of curves.

14. Show that the solution of the initial-value problem

$$y' - 2xy = 1,$$
$$y(0) = 1$$

is

$$\phi(x) = e^{x^2} \left(1 + \frac{\sqrt{\pi}}{2} \operatorname{erf}(x) \right)$$

where the *error function* is defined by

$$\operatorname{erf}(x) = \frac{2}{\sqrt{\pi}} \int_0^x e^{-t^2} dt$$

and is tabulated.

15. Describe the behavior of the solution of

$$y' + \frac{1}{x} y = \frac{\cos x}{x}$$

as $x \to 0$.

16. A function is said to be *periodic with period p* if

$$f(x + np) = f(x),$$

where n is an integer. Suppose that $f(x)$ is continuous and periodic with period p for all x. Show that if $\phi(x)$ is a solution of the homogeneous equation

$$y' + f(x)\, y = 0,$$

then $\phi(x+p)$ is also a solution. Show that for some constant c,

$$\phi(x+p) = c\phi(x)$$

for all x.

17. Consider the initial-value problem

$$y' = x + y,$$

$$y(0) = 0.$$

By the Picard method of successive approximations, show that the successive approximations $\phi_0, \phi_1, \ldots, \phi_n, \ldots$ exist for all x. Compute $\phi_0, \phi_1, \phi_2, \phi_3, \phi_4$ and compare with the exact solution.

18. Show that a unique solution exists for each of the following initial-value problems.

(a)
$$y' = x^2 + y^2,$$

$$y(0) = 0,$$

on the interval $|x| \leqslant \frac{1}{\sqrt{2}}$.

(b)
$$y' = 1 + y^2,$$

$$y(0) = 0,$$

on the interval $|x| \leqslant \frac{1}{2}$.

19. (Peano's existence theorem). Suppose $f(x, y)$ is continuous on the rectangle $|x - x_0| \leqslant h$, $|y - y_0| \leqslant k$, where $|f(x, y)| \leqslant M$. Prove that there exists at least one solution ϕ such that $\phi' = f(x, \phi)$ on the interval $|x - x_0| \leqslant \min(h, k/M)$, satisfying the initial condition $y(x_0) = y_0$.

20. An equation of the form

$$y = xp + f(p), \tag{A}$$

where $p = dy/dx$, is known as a *Clairaut equation*.

(a) Differentiate (A) with respect to x and obtain

$$\left[x + f'(p) \right] \frac{dp}{dx} = 0.$$

(b)   If $[x + f'(p)] \neq 0$, then $dp/dx = 0$, which gives $p = c$, and as a result $y = cx + f(c)$.

(c)   If $x + f'(p) = 0$, then a *singular solution* is obtained by eliminating p between the equations $x + f'(p) = 0$ and $y = xp + f(p)$.

(d)   Determine a one-parameter family of solutions of

$$y = xp + p^2.$$

Find the singular solution also.

21.   Any first-order equation

$$y' = a(x) + b(x)\, y + c(x)\, y^2$$

is called a *Riccati equation*. Suppose that a particular solution $y_1(x)$ of this equation is known.

(a)   By the substitution $y(x) = y_1(x) + 1/u(x)$, show that the Riccati equation is transformed into a linear first-order equation

$$\frac{du}{dx} = -(b + 2cy_1)u - c.$$

(b)   If the substitution is $y(x) = y_1(x) + u(x)$, show that Riccati's equation is reduced to a Bernoulli equation.

(c)   Solve $y' = 1 + x^2 - 2xy + y^2$ if $y_1(x) = x$.

Chapter 3.
Second-Order Linear Equations.
Oscillation and Separation
Theorems

3.1 Linear Differential Equations

A second-order linear differential equation may be written in the form

$$a_0(x)\, y'' + a_1(x)\, y' + a_2(x)\, y = g(x), \tag{3.1.1}$$

where a_0, a_1, a_2 are real-valued continuous functions defined on some interval I.

If $a_0 \neq 0$, then Eq. (3.1.1) may be rewritten as

$$y'' + a(x)\, y' + b(x)\, y = f(x), \tag{3.1.2}$$

where $a = a_1/a_0$, $b = a_2/a_0$ and $f = g/a_0$.

It is often convenient to introduce a differential operator notation in the the theory of linear differential equations.

DEFINITION 3.1.1 The operator

$$L = \frac{d^n}{dx^n} + a_{n-1}\frac{d^{n-1}}{dx^n} + \cdots + a_1\frac{d}{dx} + a_0$$

is said to be a *linear differential operator* if for any n times differentiable functions $y_1(x)$ and $y_2(x)$ and for any constants c_1 and c_2, it has the property

$$L\big[\,c_1\,y_1(x) + c_2\,y_2(x)\,\big] = c_1 L\big[\,y_1(x)\,\big] + c_2 L\big[\,y_2(x)\,\big].$$

Thus Eq. (3.1.2) may be written in the form

$$L\big[\,y\,\big] = f(x), \tag{3.1.3}$$

where L is the linear differential operator defined by $L[y] = d^2y/dx^2 + a\,dy/dx + by$. If $f(x) = 0$ for all $x \in I$, the resulting equation $L[y] = 0$ is called a *homogeneous equation*. Eq. (3.1.3) is called a *nonhomogeneous equation*.

We are now concerned with finding a solution of $L[y] = f(x)$ on the interval I, which may be finite or infinite and which may include one or both of its end points.

DEFINITION 3.1.2   A *solution* $\phi(x)$ of $L[y] = f(x)$ is a twice continuously differentiable function which satisfies $L\big[\phi(x)\big] = f(x)$.

We shall state the following fundamental existence-uniqueness theorem without proof. A more general result on the nth-order equation will be given in Chapter 5.

THEOREM 3.1.1 (Existence-uniqueness theorem)   *Let the functions $a(x)$, $b(x)$ and $f(x)$ be continuous on an interval I. For any $x_0 \in I$ and constants b_1 and b_2, there exists a unique solution of the initial-value problem*

$$L\big[\,y\,\big] = y'' + a(x)\,y' + b(x)\,y = f(x);$$
$$y(x_0) = b_1, \tag{3.1.4}$$
$$y'(x_0) = b_2.$$

First let us consider the second-order linear homogeneous equation

$$L\big[\,y\,\big] = y'' + a(x)\,y' + b(x)\,y = 0, \tag{3.1.5}$$

where $a(x)$ and $b(x)$ are continuous functions on an interval I.

The result that follows immediately from the definition of a linear differential operator applied to linear homogeneous differential equations is the following theorem.

THEOREM 3.1.2 *If ϕ_1 and ϕ_2 are solutions of $L[y]=0$, then a linear combination $c_1\phi_1 + c_2\phi_2$ with c_1 and c_2 as constants is also a solution of $L[y]=0$.*

Proof By virtue of the linearity of L, we have

$$L[c_1\phi_1 + c_2\phi_2] = c_1 L[\phi_1] + c_2 L[\phi_2].$$

By hypothesis $L[\phi_1]=0$ and $L[\phi_2]=0$. Hence

$$L[c_1\phi_1 + c_2\phi_2]=0. \qquad \blacksquare$$

We have just proved that $c_1\phi_1(x) + c_2\phi_2(x)$ satisfies the homogeneous differential equation $L[y]=0$. Next we will determine whether ϕ_1 and ϕ_2 are linearly independent.

DEFINITION 3.1.3 The functions f_1, $f_2,\ldots,f_n$ are said to be *linearly dependent* on an interval I if there exist constants c_1, $c_2,\ldots,c_n$, not all zero, such that

$$c_1 f_1(x) + c_2 f_2(x) + \cdots + c_n f_n(x) \equiv 0, \qquad (3.16)$$

for all $x \in I$.

Functions that are not linearly dependent are called *linearly independent*. That is, the functions f_1, $f_2,\ldots,f_n$ are linearly independent on I if the only constants that satisfy

$$c_1 f_1(x) + c_2 f_2(x) + \cdots + c_n f_n(x) = 0$$

are the constants $c_1 = c_2 = \cdots = 0$, for all $x \in I$.

The concept of linear independence is related to a determinant known as the *Wronskian*.

DEFINITION 3.1.4 The Wronskian of two differentiable functions $\phi_1(x)$ and $\phi_2(x)$ on an interval I is defined by the determinant

$$W(\phi_1,\phi_2;x) = \begin{vmatrix} \phi_1(x) & \phi_2(x) \\ \phi_1'(x) & \phi_2'(x) \end{vmatrix} = \phi_1(x)\phi_2'(x) - \phi_1'(x)\phi_2(x).$$

THEOREM 3.1.3 *Let ϕ_1 and ϕ_2 be the solutions of $L[y]=0$ on I. Then ϕ_1 and ϕ_2 are linearly independent on I if, and only if, the Wronskian $W(\phi_1,\phi_2;x) \neq 0$ for all $x \in I$.*

Proof   Suppose $c_1\phi_1 + c_2\phi_2 = 0$. Then for every $x \in I$ we have

$$c_1\phi_1(x) + c_2\phi_2(x) = 0,$$

$$c_1\phi_1'(x) + c_2\phi_2'(x) = 0.$$

Since $W \neq 0$ for any $x \in I$, we have for $x_0 \in I$

$$\begin{vmatrix} \phi_1(x_0) & \phi_2(x_0) \\ \phi_1'(x_0) & \phi_2'(x_0) \end{vmatrix} \neq 0.$$

Thus for $x = x_0$ the preceding system in c_1 and c_2 may be rewritten in the form

$$\phi_1(x_0)c_1 + \phi_2(x_0)c_2 = 0,$$

$$\phi_1'(x_0)c_1 + \phi_2'(x_0)c_2 = 0.$$

This is a homogeneous algebraic system of equations in c_1 and c_2. Since the determinant of the coefficients does not vanish, there exists a unique solution $c_1 = c_2 = 0$. Hence ϕ_1 and ϕ_2 are linearly independent on I.

Conversely, let ϕ_1 and ϕ_2 be linearly independent solutions on I. Let us assume that there exists a point $x_0 \in I$ such that $W(\phi_1, \phi_2; x_0) = 0$. Then the system of equations

$$c_1\phi_1(x_0) + c_2\phi_2(x_0) = 0,$$

$$c_1\phi_1'(x_0) + c_2\phi_2'(x_0) = 0, \tag{3.1.7}$$

for c_1 and c_2 has a nontrivial solution. Using such c_1 and c_2, we define $\chi = c_1\phi_1 + c_2\phi_2$. Then it is obvious from $L[y] = 0$ and (3.1.7) that

$$L[\chi] = 0,$$

$$\chi(x_0) = 0, \qquad \chi'(x_0) = 0.$$

Thus by the Uniqueness Theorem (3.1.1), we have $\chi(x) = 0$ for all values of $x \in I$. This implies that

$$c_1\phi_1(x) + c_2\phi_2(x) = 0$$

for all $x \in I$. This contradicts the hypothesis that ϕ_1 and ϕ_2 are linearly independent. Hence $W(\phi_1, \phi_2; x) \neq 0$ for all $x \in I$.   ∎

COROLLARY 3.1.3 *Let ϕ_1 and ϕ_2 be any two solutions of $L[y]=0$ on I. Then their Wronskian either vanishes identically or else is never zero on I.*
(The proof is left to the reader.)

We are now in a position to prove the following theorem.

THEOREM 3.1.4 *Let $\phi_1(x)$ and $\phi_2(x)$ be linearly independent solutions of $L[y]=0$ on an interval I. Then every solution of $L[y]=0$ can be expressed uniquely as*

$$\phi(x) = c_1\phi_1(x) + c_2\phi_2(x), \tag{3.1.8}$$

where c_1 and c_2 are constants.

Proof Suppose that $\phi(x)$ is any solution of $L[y]=0$ on I. At a point $x_0 \in I$ we calculate ϕ and ϕ' to obtain

$$\phi(x_0) = b_1,$$
$$\phi'(x_0) = b_2. \tag{3.1.9}$$

Let us assume that $\phi(x)$ can be expressed as a linear combination of $\phi_1(x)$ and $\phi_2(x)$, namely,

$$\phi(x) = c_1\phi_1(x) + c_2\phi_2(x),$$

for some constants c_1 and c_2. Then from (3.1.9) we have

$$c_1\phi_1(x_0) + c_2\phi_2(x_0) = b_1,$$
$$c_1\phi_1'(x_0) + c_2\phi_2'(x_0) = b_2.$$

Since the Wronskian $W(x_0) \neq 0$ for linearly independent functions $\phi_1(x)$ and $\phi_2(x)$ at x_0, c_1 and c_2 can be determined uniquely. Choosing such c_1 and c_2 we define the function $\chi(x) = c_1\phi_1(x) + c_2\phi_2(x)$. Obviously

$$L[\chi] = 0,$$
$$\chi(x_0) = b_1 = \phi(x_0),$$
$$\chi'(x_0) = b_2 = \phi'(x_0).$$

Thus ϕ and χ are both solutions of $L[y]=0$ on I and they satisfy the same initial conditions at x_0. By the Uniqueness Theorem (3.1.1), ϕ must be identically equal to χ on I. Hence

$$\phi(x) = c_1\phi_1(x) + c_2\phi_2(x)$$ ∎

Two solutions ϕ_1 and ϕ_2 are said to form a *fundamental set of* solutions of $L[y]=0$ on I. This family of solutions $c_1\phi_1 + c_2\phi_2$, which contains all solutions, is called the *general solution* of $L[y]=0$.

3.2   Linear Equations with Constant Coefficients

We consider the equation

$$L[y] = y'' + ay' + by = 0, \tag{3.2.1}$$

where a and b are constants. In searching for solutions, we first observe that:

1. $e^{\gamma x}$ is a solution of the first-order equation $y' = \gamma y$.
2. The exponential function possesses the property that its derivatives are multiples of the function itself.

This suggests trying $\phi(x) = e^{\lambda x}$ as a possible solution of $L[y]=0$ for an appropriate value of λ. If we assume $\phi(x) = e^{\lambda x}$, then substitution of this in Eq. (3.2.1) yields

$$(\lambda^2 + a\lambda + b)e^{\lambda x} = 0. \tag{3.2.2}$$

Since $e^{\lambda x}$ cannot vanish, for Eq. (3.2.1) to have a nontrivial solution,[†] we must have

$$p(\lambda) = \lambda^2 + a\lambda + b = 0.$$

$p(\lambda)$ is called the *characteristic polynomial* and $\lambda^2 + a\lambda + b = 0$ is called the *characteristic equation* of $L[y]=0$. We know that the polynomial $p(\lambda)$ has two roots, namely

$$\lambda_{1,2} = \frac{-a \pm \sqrt{a^2 - 4b}}{2}.$$

1. When $a^2 - 4b > 0$, λ_1 and λ_2 are real and distinct roots. Hence the general solution is

$$\phi(x) = c_1 e^{\lambda_1 x} + c_2 e^{\lambda_2 x} \tag{3.2.3}$$

[†] A trivial solution is a function $\phi(x)$ which is zero for all $x \in I$.

2. When $a^2 - 4b < 0$, λ_1 and λ_2 are complex roots. If $\lambda_{1,2} = \alpha \pm i\beta$ for real α and β, then the general solution is

$$\phi(x) = a_1 e^{(\alpha + i\beta)x} + a_2 e^{(\alpha - i\beta)x}.$$

Since it is a complex-valued solution, it is desirable to express it as a real-valued solution. Using the Euler formula

$$e^{\pm i\theta} = \cos\theta \pm i\sin\theta,$$

which holds for all real θ, we have

$$\phi(x) = a_1 e^{\alpha x}(\cos\beta x + i\sin\beta x) + a_2 e^{\alpha x}(\cos\beta x - i\sin\beta x)$$

$$= e^{\alpha x}\left[(a_1 + a_2)\cos\beta x + i(a_1 - a_2)\sin\beta x\right]$$

$$= e^{\alpha x}\left[c_1\cos\beta x + c_2\sin\beta x\right], \tag{3.2.4}$$

where $c_1 = a_1 + a_2$ and $c_2 = i(a_1 - a_2)$ are two new arbitrary constants.

3. When $a^2 - 4b = 0$, the roots are repeated, and hence $\lambda_1 = \lambda_2 = \lambda$ (say). Clearly, one of the solutions is $e^{\lambda x}$. In regard to finding the remaining solution, we have the following theorem:

THEOREM 3.2.1 *If λ is a root of multiplicity 2 of the characteristic polynomial $p(\lambda) = \lambda^2 + a\lambda + b$, then the function $xe^{\lambda x}$ is a solution of $L[y] = 0$.*

Proof From (3.2.2) we see that

$$L[e^{\lambda x}] = p(\lambda)e^{\lambda x}$$

Since λ is a repeated root of $p(\lambda)$, we have

$$p(\lambda) = p'(\lambda) = 0$$

We note that

$$\frac{\partial}{\partial\lambda} L[e^{\lambda x}] = L\left[\frac{\partial e^{\lambda x}}{\partial\lambda}\right] = L[xe^{\lambda x}].$$

Hence

$$L[xe^{\lambda x}] = \frac{\partial}{\partial \lambda} L[e^{\lambda x}]$$

$$= \frac{\partial}{\partial \lambda} p(\lambda)e^{\lambda x}$$

$$= [p'(\lambda) + xp(\lambda)]e^{\lambda x}$$

$$= 0.$$

which shows that $xe^{\lambda x}$ is a solution of $L[y] = 0$.   ∎

Thus the general solution is given by

$$\phi(x) = c_1 e^{\lambda x} + c_2 x e^{\lambda x}. \tag{3.2.5}$$

Example 3.2.1   Consider

$$y'' - 3y' + 2y = 0.$$

The characteristic equation corresponding to this differential equation is

$$\lambda^2 - 3\lambda + 2 = 0,$$

the roots of which are $\lambda_{1,2} = 1, 2$. Hence the general solution is

$$\phi(x) = c_1 e^x + c_2 e^{2x}.$$

Example 3.2.2   Given

$$y'' + y' + y = 0,$$

the characteristic equation is

$$\lambda^2 + \lambda + 1 = 0.$$

The roots are $\lambda_{1,2} = -\frac{1}{2} \pm (\sqrt{3}/2)i$. Hence the general solution is

$$\phi(x) = e^{-x/2}\left[c_1 \cos\frac{\sqrt{3}}{2}x + c_2 \sin\frac{\sqrt{3}}{2}x\right].$$

Example 3.2.3   Consider

$$y'' - 6y' + 9y = 0.$$

In this case $p(\lambda) = \lambda^2 - 6\lambda + 9$. The roots are $\lambda_{1,2} = 3,3$. Hence the general solution is

$$\phi(x) = c_1 e^{3x} + c_2 x e^{3x}.$$

The preceding results of second-order linear homogeneous equations can be extended to the nth order linear homogeneous equation

$$L[y] = y^{(n)} + a_{n-1} y^{(n-1)} + \cdots + a_1 y' + a_0 y = 0, \qquad (3.2.6)$$

where $a_{n-1}, \ldots, a_0$ are continuous functions on an interval I.

Any solution of Eq. (3.2.6) can be expressed as a linear combination of a fundamental set of solutions $\phi_1, \phi_2, \ldots, \phi_n$. Thus the general solution of Eq. (3.2.6) can be written as

$$\phi(x) = c_1 \phi_1(x) + c_2 \phi_2(x) + \cdots + c_n \phi_n(x).$$

Now consider the equation with constant coefficients

$$L[y] = 0. \qquad (3.2.7)$$

Then, as before, we assume a solution in the form

$$\phi(x) = e^{\lambda x}$$

Substituting this and its derivatives in Eq. (3.2.7), we obtain the characteristic equation

$$p(\lambda) = \lambda^n + a_{n-1} \lambda^{n-1} + \cdots + a_1 \lambda + a_0 = 0 \qquad (3.2.8)$$

(a) When $\lambda_1, \lambda_2, \ldots, \lambda_n$ are real and distinct roots of (3.2.8), then

$$e^{\lambda_1 x}, e^{\lambda_2 x}, \ldots, e^{\lambda_n x}$$

are linearly independent solutions of Eq. (3.2.7).

(b) When λ_i is a root of multiplicity $\kappa > 1$ of Eq. (3.2.8), then

$$e^{\lambda_i x}, x e^{\lambda_i x}, x^2 e^{\lambda_i x}, \ldots, x^{\kappa-1} e^{\lambda_i x}$$

are κ linearly independent solutions of Eq. (3.2.7).

(c)   When $\lambda_i = \alpha + i\beta$ and $\lambda_j = \alpha - i\beta$ are a pair of complex conjugate roots of multiplicity $m > 1$ of Eq. (3.2.8), then

$$e^{\alpha x} \cos \beta x, e^{\alpha x} \sin \beta x, xe^{\alpha x} \cos \beta x, xe^{\alpha x} \sin \beta x,$$

$$x^2 e^{\alpha x} \cos \beta x, x^2 e^{\alpha x} \sin \beta x, \ldots, x^{m-1} e^{\alpha x} \cos \beta x, x^{m-1} e^{\alpha x} \sin \beta x.$$

are $2m$ linearly independent solutions of Eq. (3.2.7).

Example 3.2.4   Consider the equation

$$y^{iv} + 3y''' + 3y'' + y' = 0. \tag{3.2.9}$$

The characteristic equation is

$$p(\lambda) = \lambda^4 + 3\lambda^3 + 3\lambda^2 + \lambda = \lambda(\lambda + 1)^3 = 0,$$

the roots of which are $\lambda_1 = 0$ and $\lambda_2 = -1$. λ_2 is a root of multiplicity 3. Thus the general solution of Eq. (3.2.9) is

$$\phi(x) = c_1 + (c_2 + c_3 x + c_4 x^2)e^{-x}.$$

3.3   Variation of Parameters

We shall now describe a method for determining a particular solution of the nonhomogeneous equation

$$L[y] = y'' + a(x) y' + b(x) y = f(x), \tag{3.3.1}$$

where a, b and f are continuous real-valued functions on an interval I.

Let ϕ_p be a particular solution of Eq. (3.3.1) and let ϕ be any other solution of Eq. (3.3.1). Then

$$L[\phi - \phi_p] = L[\phi] - L[\phi_p] = f - f = 0,$$

which shows that $\phi - \phi_p$ satisfies the associated homogeneous equation $L[y] = 0$. If ϕ_1 and ϕ_2 are linearly independent solutions of $L[y] = 0$, then by Theorem 3.2.4, $\phi - \phi_p$ can be expressed as a linear combination of ϕ_1 and ϕ_2 so that for any constants c_1 and c_2

$$\phi - \phi_p = c_1 \phi_1 + c_2 \phi_2.$$

Hence, we have

$$\phi(x) = c_1\phi_1(x) + c_2\phi_2(x) + \phi_p(x),$$

which is the general solution of $L[y] = f$.

The general solution of the associated homogeneous equation is often known as the *complementary solution*. If it is denoted by ϕ_c, we have

$$\phi_c(x) = c_1\phi_1(x) + c_2\phi_2(x).$$

A solution of the nonhomogeneous equation $L[y] = f$ is called a *particular solution*, which we have already denoted by ϕ_p. Thus the general solution of $L[y] = f$ may be written as

$$\phi(x) = \phi_c(x) + \phi_p(x).$$

Now we will present a method known as the *method of variation of parameters* for determining solutions of nonhomogeneous differential equations.

Suppose ϕ_1 and ϕ_2 are linearly independent solutions of the homogeneous equation $L[y] = 0$ on I. Then we know that the function

$$\phi(x) = c_1\phi_1(x) + c_2\phi_2(x)$$

is also a solution of $L[y] = 0$. The constants c_1 and c_2 are often called the *parameters*. The primary idea of this method is to vary these parameters in the hope of finding a particular solution of $L[y] = f$.

Assume ϕ_p of the form

$$\phi_p(x) = u_1(x)\phi_1(x) + u_2(x)\phi_2(x).$$

Differentiation of ϕ_p yields

$$\phi_p' = u_1'\phi_1 + u_2'\phi_2 + u_1\phi_1' + u_2\phi_2',$$

$$\phi_p'' = (u_1'\phi_1 + u_2'\phi_2)' + u_1\phi_1'' + u_2\phi_2'' + u_1'\phi_1' + u_2'\phi_2'.$$

Substituting these values in $L[y] = f$, we obtain

$$\left[(u_1'\phi_1 + u_2'\phi_2)' + u_1\phi_1'' + u_2\phi_2'' + u_1'\phi_1' + u_2'\phi_2'\right]$$

$$+ a(x)\left[(u_1'\phi_1 + u_2'\phi_2) + u_1\phi_1' + u_2\phi_2'\right]$$

$$+ b(x)\left[u_1\phi_1 + u_2\phi_2\right] = f(x).$$

Upon collecting terms, we obtain

$$u_1(\phi_1'' + a_1\phi_1' + b\phi_1) + u_2(\phi_2'' + a\phi_2' + b\phi_2)$$
$$+ (u_1'\phi_1 + u_2'\phi_2)' + (u_1'\phi_1' + u_2'\phi_2') + a(u_1'\phi_1 + u_2'\phi_2) = f. \quad (3.3.2)$$

Since ϕ_1 and ϕ_2 are solutions of $L[y]=0$, the first two terms in Eq. (3.3.2) vanish. Then the remaining equation is satisfied if

$$u_1'\phi_1 + u_2'\phi_2 = 0,$$
$$u_1'\phi_1' + u_2'\phi_2' = f. \quad (3.3.3)$$

This system of equations has a unique solution since the determinant of the system is the Wronskian

$$W(\phi_1, \phi_2; x) = \begin{vmatrix} \phi_1(x) & \phi_2(x) \\ \phi_1'(x) & \phi_2'(x) \end{vmatrix} \neq 0$$

for some $x \in I$. Thus we solve for u_1' and u_2', obtaining

$$u_1' = -\frac{\phi_2 f}{W},$$
$$u_2' = \frac{\phi_1 f}{W}. \quad (3.3.4)$$

Integration then yields

$$u_1(x) = -\int^x \frac{\phi_2(t)f(t)}{W(\phi_1, \phi_2; t)} \, dt + C_1,$$

$$u_2(x) = \int^x \frac{\phi_1(t)f(t)}{W(\phi_1, \phi_2; t)} \, dt + C_2.$$

Since C_1 and C_2 would only contribute a general solution of $L[y]=0$, we set $C_1 = C_2 = 0$. The particular solution ϕ_p therefore takes the form

$$\phi_p(x) = \int^x \frac{\phi_1(t)\phi_2(x) - \phi_1(x)\phi_2(t)}{W(\phi_1, \phi_2; t)} f(t) \, dt. \quad (3.3.5)$$

Summarizing the results, we have the following theorem:

THEOREM 3.3.1 *Let a, b and f be continuous functions on an interval I. Then the general solution of* $L[y] = f$ *is*

$$\phi(x) = \phi_c(x) + \phi_p(x),$$

where ϕ_c *is the complementary solution and* ϕ_p *is a particular solution given by* (3.3.5).

Example 3.3.1   Consider the equation $y'' + y = \sec x$.
   Here the complementary solution is

$$\phi_c(x) = c_1 \cos x + c_2 \sin x.$$

To find ϕ_p, we first determine the Wronskian

$$W = \begin{vmatrix} \cos x & \sin x \\ -\sin x & \cos x \end{vmatrix} = 1.$$

Thus using ϕ_p given by (3.3.5), we obtain

$$\phi_p(x) = -\cos x \int^x \sin t \sec t \, dt + \sin x \int^x \cos t \sec t \, dt.$$

Evaluation yields

$$\phi_p(x) = \cos x \ln|\cos x| + x \sin x.$$

The solution of the given equation is therefore

$$\phi(x) = c_1 \cos x + c_2 \sin x + \cos x \ln|\cos x| + x \sin x.$$

   We should remark here that the method of variation of parameters is readily applicable to equations whose complementary solutions can be found. For most equations with variable coefficients, only series solutions (which are treated in Chapter 4) are available. However, there are exceptions.
   Consider for example the *Euler equation*

$$x^2 y'' + axy' + by = 0.$$

where a and b are constants. If we let $x = e^t$, we find

$$y' = \frac{1}{x}\frac{dy}{dt},$$

$$y'' = -\frac{1}{x^2}\frac{dy}{dt} + \frac{1}{x^2}\frac{d^2y}{dt^2}.$$

Substituting y' and y'' in the Euler equation, we obtain

$$\frac{d^2y}{dt^2} + (a-1)\frac{dy}{dt} + by = 0,$$

which is an equation with constant coefficients. The characteristic equation is given by

$$\lambda^2 + (a-1)\lambda + b = 0,$$

and hence the solutions are as follows:

1. When the roots λ_1 and λ_2 are real and distinct,

$$\phi(t) = c_1 e^{\lambda_1 t} + c_2 e^{\lambda_2 t},$$

or in terms of the original variable x,

$$\phi(x) = c_1 x^{\lambda_1} + c_2 x^{\lambda_2}.$$

2. When the roots are equal, say $\lambda_1 = \lambda_2 = \lambda$,

$$\phi(t) = c_1 e^{\lambda t} + c_2 t e^{\lambda t},$$

or in terms of the original variable x,

$$\phi(x) = c_1 x^\lambda + c_2 x^\lambda \ln x.$$

3. When the roots are complex, $\lambda_{1,2} = \alpha \pm i\beta$,

$$\phi(t) = c_1 e^{\alpha t}\cos\beta t + c_2 e^{\alpha t}\sin\beta t,$$

or in terms of the original variable x,

$$\phi(x) = c_1 x^\alpha \cos(\beta \ln x) + c_2 x^\alpha \sin(\beta \ln x).$$

The application of the variation-of-parameters method is clear, for instance, if we consider the following example:

Example 3.3.2 Given

$$x^2 y'' - 2xy' + 2y = 6x^4,$$

the characteristic equation is

$$\lambda^2 - 3\lambda + 2 = 0,$$

and hence $\phi_1(x) = x$ and $\phi_2(x) = x^2$. Thus the Wronskian is

$$W = \begin{vmatrix} x & x^2 \\ 1 & 2x \end{vmatrix} = x^2.$$

and ϕ_p is given by

$$\phi_p(x) = -x \int^x \frac{t^2 6 t^2}{t^2} \, dt + x^2 \int^x \frac{t 6 t^2}{t^2} \, dt$$

$$= x^4.$$

Therefore the general solution of the given equation is

$$\phi(x) = c_1 x + c_2 x^2 + \tfrac{3}{10} x^6.$$

Example 3.3.3 [Falling Particle] Let us consider a particle of mass m falling from a height above the surface of the earth. Let x be the directed distance from the initial position above the earth. The forces acting on the particle are the force due to gravity, namely,

$$f_1 = mg,$$

where g is the acceleration due to gravity, and the force,

$$f_2 = -k \frac{dx}{dt},$$

due to air resistance. Here we assume that the air resistance is proportional to the speed. The negative sign is introduced since the resistance is against the motion of the particle. The constant k is a coefficient of friction of the air.

By Newton's second law of motion, we have

$$m\frac{d^2x}{dt^2} = mg - k\frac{dx}{dt},$$

or

$$\frac{d^2x}{dt^2} + \frac{k}{m}\frac{dx}{dt} = g,$$

·which is a second-order linear nonhomogeneous equation. The general solution is readily found to be

$$x(t) = c_1 + c_2 e^{-(k/m)t} + \frac{mg}{k}t.$$

Since the particle is initially at rest, the initial conditions are

$$x(0) = 0, \qquad \frac{dx}{dt}(0) = 0.$$

Application of the initial conditions to $x(t)$ yields

$$x(t) = \frac{m^2 g}{k^2}\left[e^{-(k/m)t} - 1\right] + \frac{mg}{k}t.$$

The velocity of the particle is

$$v(t) = \frac{dx}{dt} = \frac{mg}{k}\left[1 - e^{-(k/m)t}\right].$$

It is interesting to observe that when $t \to \infty$, the steady state velocity is

$$v(t) = \frac{mg}{k},$$

which is called the *limiting velocity*.

3.4   Method of Undetermined Coefficients

In determining a particular solution of $L[y] = f$ with constant coefficients, the so-called *method of undetermined coefficients* is easier and often faster than the method of variation of parameters. The disadvantage of this method is that f must possess a rather special form, namely, f itself must be a solution of some linear homogeneous equation with constant coefficients: $M[f]=0$. Thus f must be a linear combination of functions of

$$x^k e^{px},$$

$$x^k e^{px} \cos qx, \tag{3.4.1}$$

$$x^k e^{px} \sin qx,$$

where k is a nonnegative integer and p and q are real numbers.

Let ϕ_p be a solution of $L[y]=f(x)$. Since $M[f]=0$, ϕ_p is also a solution of

$$M[L[y]]=0. \tag{3.4.2}$$

Thus we see that ϕ_p is a linear combination of linearly independent solutions of $M[L[y]]=0$. However, not every linear combination satisfies $L[y]=f$. Thus we need to find a specific linear combination that is a solution of $L[y]=f$.

This method is sometimes known as the *annihilator method*, because the operator M annihilates the nonhomogeneous term $f(x)$ in $L[y]=f$ to give $M[f]=0$.

Example 3.4.1 Consider

$$L[y]=y''-2y'+y=2e^x+2x. \tag{3.4.3}$$

Since $2e^x+2x$ is a solution of

$$M[y]=y'''-y''=0,$$

we see that ϕ_p of $L[y]=2e^x+2x$ is also a solution of

$$M[L[y]]=y^v-3y^{iv}+3y'''-y''=0.$$

The characteristic equation is given by

$$\lambda^5-3\lambda^4+3\lambda^3-\lambda^2=0,$$

and hence the roots are $0,0,1,1,1$. These roots are simply the products of the roots of the characteristic polynomials for L and M. Hence ϕ_p must have the form

$$\phi_p=c_1+c_2x+c_3e^x+c_4xe^x+c_5x^2e^x.$$

Since $c_3e^x + c_4xe^x$ is a solution of $L[y]=0$, that is,

$$L[c_3e^x + c_4xe^x]=0,$$

we need only to assume ϕ_p in the form

$$\phi_p = c_1 + c_2x + c_5x^2e^x.$$

This can easily be seen from the fact that ϕ_p must satisfy $L[\phi_p]=f$. Thus

$$L[\phi_p] = L[c_1 + c_2x + c_5x^2e^x] + L[c_3e^x + c_4xe^x] = f(x),$$

and consequently

$$L[\phi_p] = L[c_1 + c_2x + c_5x^2e^x] = f(x). \tag{3.4.4}$$

Thus the problem now is to find the undetermined coefficients c_1, c_2 and c_5 by equating the coefficients[†] in Eq. (3.4.4). Now differentiation of ϕ_p yields

$$\phi_p' = c_2 + 2c_5xe^x + c_5x^2e^x,$$

$$\phi_p'' = 2c_5e^x + 4c_5xe^x + c_5x^2e^x.$$

Thus substituting these values in (3.4.3), we obtain

$$(2c_5e^x + 4c_5xe^x + c_5x^2e^x) - 2(c_2 + 2c_5xe^x + c_5x^2e^x)$$

$$+ (c_1 + c_2x + c_5x^2e^x) = 2e^x + 2x. \tag{3.4.5}$$

Equating the coefficients, we obtain

$$c_1 - 2c_2 = 0,$$

$$c_2 = 2,$$

$$2c_5 = 2,$$

and hence

$$\phi_p(x) = 4 + 2x + x^2e^x.$$

[†]Since the functions x^k, x^ke^{px} are linearly independent, Eq. (3.4.5) is satisfied if and only if the coefficient of each function for $k, p = 0, 1, 2, \ldots, n$ vanishes. This is accomplished by equating the coefficients in Eq. (3.4.5).

The method of undetermined coefficients can also be stated simply as follows: If f has the form

$$f(x) = \sum_{k=0}^{n} a_k x^k e^{px},$$

we assume

$$\phi_p(x) = \sum_{k=0}^{n} b_k x^k e^{px}.$$

If f has the form

$$f(x) = \sum_{k=0}^{n} a_k x^k e^{px} \cos qx,$$

or

$$f(x) = \sum_{k=0}^{n} a_k x^k e^{px} \sin qx,$$

we assume

$$\phi_p(x) = \sum_{k=0}^{n} b_k x^k e^{px} \cos qx + \sum_{k=0}^{n} c_k x^k e^{px} \sin qx.$$

If the assumed ϕ_p has any term which is a solution of the associated homogeneous equation, we multiply the entire expression by the lowest degree of x that changes the expression such that the new ϕ_p no longer contains a term that is a solution of the associated homogeneous equation.

For example, if $\phi_c(x) = k_1 + k_2 x$ and if $f(x) = a_0 + a_1 x + a_2 x^2$, then we assume ϕ_p of the form

$$\phi_p(x) = x^2 (b_0 + b_1 x + b_2 x^2).$$

Example 3.4.2 Consider

$$y'' - y' = 3x + 4e^x. \tag{3.4.6}$$

It is evident that

$$\phi_c(x) = k_1 + k_2 e^x.$$

Since f has the terms that are solutions of the associated homogeneous equation, we assume

$$\phi_p(x) = x(b_0 + b_1 x) + x(c_0 e^x)$$

$$= b_0 x + b_1 x^2 + c_0 x e^x.$$

Thus

$$\phi_p'(x) = b_0 + 2b_1 x + c_0 e^x + c_0 x e^x,$$

$$\phi_p''(x) = 2b_1 + 2c_0 e^x + c_0 x e^x.$$

Substituting these in Eq. (3.4.6), we obtain

$$(2b_1 + 2c_0 e^x + c_0 x e^x) - (b_0 + 2b_1 x + c_0 e^x + c_0 x e^x) = 3x + 4e^x.$$

Equating the coefficients, we have

$$2b_1 - b_0 = 0$$

$$-2b_1 = 3$$

$$c_0 = 4.$$

Hence

$$\phi_p(x) = -3x - \tfrac{3}{2}x^2 + 4xe^x.$$

Most of the results of second-order equations in the preceding sections can be extended to the nth order equation

$$L[y] = y^{(n)} + a_{n-1} y^{(n-1)} + \cdots + a_1 y' + a_0 y = f(x), \qquad (3.4.7)$$

where $a_{n-1}, a_{n-2}, \ldots, a_0$, and f are continuous functions on an interval I. A unique solution $y = \phi(x)$ exists satisfying Eq. (3.4.7) and the initial conditions

$$y(x_0) = b_1, \qquad y'(x_0) = b_2, \ldots, y^{(n-1)}(x_0) = b_n, \qquad (3.4.8)$$

for some point $x_0 \in I$, where $b_1, b_2, \ldots, b_n$ are the prescribed initial values [Existence-Uniqueness Theorem is stated in Chapter 5].

Thus the general solution of Eq. (3.4.7) can be written as

$$\phi(x) = c_1 \phi_1(x) + c_2 \phi_2(x) + \cdots + c_n \phi_n(x) + \phi_p(x),$$

where $\phi_1, \phi_2, \ldots, \phi_n$ are linearly independent solutions of the homogeneous equation $L[y] = 0$ and ϕ_p is a particular solution of Eq. (3.4.7).

Particular solutions can be determined by the method of variation of parameters. The method of undetermined coefficients can also be applied when f has the form of a solution of the homogeneous equation $L[y] = 0$ with constant coefficients.

Example 3.4.3 Find the general solution of

$$y''' - 6y'' + 11y' - 6y = x + e^x. \qquad (3.4.9)$$

The characteristic equation is

$$\lambda^3 - 6\lambda^2 + 11\lambda - 6 = 0.$$

Its roots are $\lambda_1 = 1$, $\lambda_2 = 2$, $\lambda_3 = 3$. Hence

$$\phi_1 = e^x, \qquad \phi_2(x) = e^{2x}, \qquad \phi_3(x) = e^{3x}.$$

Let

$$\phi_p(x) = A + Bx + Cxe^x,$$

$$\phi_p'(x) = B + Ce^x + Cxe^x,$$

$$\phi_p''(x) = 2Ce^x + Cxe^x,$$

$$\phi_p'''(x) = 3Ce^x + Cxe^x.$$

Substituting these values in Eq. (3.4.9) and equating the coefficients, we obtain

$$\phi_p(x) = -\tfrac{11}{36} - \tfrac{1}{6}x + \tfrac{1}{2}xe^x.$$

Hence

$$\phi(x) = C_1 e^x + C_2 e^{2x} + C_3 e^{3x} - \tfrac{11}{36} - \tfrac{1}{6}x + \tfrac{1}{2}xe^x.$$

3.5 Separation and Comparison Theorems

Although we cannot in general obtain explicit solutions of second-order equations, we can study the qualitative behavior of these solutions to some extent. Information such as the existence and relative position of zeros of the solution of an equation and the comparison of the number of zeros of two solutions of the same differential equation is important from the point of view of physical applications.

THEOREM 3.5.1 (Sturm separation theorem)   *If ϕ_1 and ϕ_2 are linearly independent solutions of $L[y]=0$ on I, then between any two successive zeros[†] of ϕ_1 there exists exactly one zero of ϕ_2. In other words, the zeros of ϕ_1 and ϕ_2 occur alternately.*

Proof Let x_1 and x_2 be the successive zeros of ϕ_1. Then $\phi_2(x_1) \neq 0$ and $\phi_2(x_2) \neq 0$, for otherwise the Wronskian $W(\phi_1, \phi_2, x) = \phi_1 \phi_2' - \phi_1' \phi_2$ would be zero there. Suppose that ϕ_2 does not vanish between x_1 and x_2. We consider the function ϕ_1/ϕ_2, which is twice continuously differentiable in (x_1, x_2) and vanishes at the end points. Thus by Rolle's theorem its first derivative must vanish at some point in (x_1, x_2). However,

$$\frac{d}{dx}\left(\frac{\phi_1}{\phi_2}\right) = \frac{\phi_1' \phi_2 - \phi_1 \phi_2'}{\phi_2^2} = -\frac{W(\phi_1, \phi_2; x)}{\phi_2^2} \neq 0.$$

This contradicts the assumption, and hence ϕ_2 vanishes at least once in (x_1, x_2). If it had two zeros, then ϕ_1 would have a zero between them, and x_1 and x_2 would not be consecutive zeros of ϕ_1. Thus ϕ_2 has only one zero in (x_1, x_2). Similarly ϕ_1 has exactly one zero between two successive zeros of ϕ_2. ∎

This theorem implies that the numbers of zeros of ϕ_1 and ϕ_2 for $L[y]=0$ on an interval I differ at most by one. To illustrate this, let us consider the following examples:

Example 3.5.1 Consider the equation

$$y'' + y = 0,$$

the solutions of which are

$$\phi_1(x) = \cos x,$$

$$\phi_2(x) = \sin x.$$

The zeros of ϕ_1 are $(n + \tfrac{1}{2})\pi$ and the zeros of ϕ_2 are $n\pi$, where n is an integer. These zeros alternate on $(-\infty, \infty)$ as shown in Figure 3.5-1.

[†]*A zero of $f(x)$ is the value of x when $f(x)=0$.*

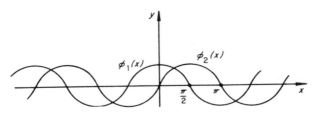

Figure 3.5-1

Example 3.5.2   The functions $\sinh x$ and $\cosh x$ are linearly independent solutions of

$$y'' - y = 0.$$

Thus the zeros of these functions alternate on $(-\infty, \infty)$. Here we see that $\sinh x$ has a zero at $x = 0$ and $\cosh x$ has no zero at all, as shown in Figure 3.5-2.

It is evident from the preceding examples that the Sturm separation theorem does not deal with the number of zeros of a solution. In the following theorems we will study the existence and the number of these zeros.

Before we proceed, it is worth mentioning that any second-order equation

$$a_0(x)\, y'' + a_1(x)\, y' + a_2(x)\, y = 0 \tag{3.5.1}$$

can be transformed into *normal form*,

$$u'' + q(x)u = 0, \tag{3.5.2}$$

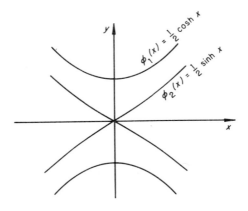

Figure 3.5-2

by the change of variable

$$y = ue^{-\frac{1}{2}\int^x (a_1/a_0)\,dt},\tag{3.5.3}$$

where

$$q(x) = \frac{a_2}{a_0} - \frac{1}{4}\frac{a_1^2}{a_0^2} - \frac{1}{2}\frac{a_1'a_0 - a_1 a_0'}{a_0^2}.$$

Now consider the following theorem:

THEOREM 3.5.2   *If $q(x) \leqslant 0$ in the interval (x_1, x_2), then any nontrivial solution $\phi(x)$ of the equation*

$$y'' + q(x)\,y = 0$$

has at most one zero in (x_1, x_2).

Proof   Suppose that $\phi(x_0) = 0$. Then $\phi'(x_0) \neq 0$, for if $\phi'(x_0) = 0$, then $\phi(x) = 0$ by the uniqueness theorem (Theorem 3.1.1). If $\phi'(x_0) > 0$, then for $x > x_0$, $\phi(x) > 0$ and hence $\phi''(x) = -q(x)\phi(x) \geqslant 0$. Thus $\phi(x)$ is a monotonic function, and therefore it has no zero for $x > x_0$. Similarly, ϕ has no zero for $x < x_0$. A similar argument holds for $\phi'(x_0) < 0$. Hence ϕ has at most one zero in (x_1, x_2). ∎

We shall now prove the celebrated comparison theorem due to Sturm.

THEOREM 3.5.3 (Sturm comparison theorem)   *Let $\phi(x)$ and $\psi(x)$ be nontrivial solutions of*

$$y'' + p(x)\,y = 0,$$

$$y'' + q(x)\,y = 0,$$

respectively, on an interval I where $p(x) > q(x)$ and $p(x) \neq q(x)$. Then between any two zeros of ψ there is at least one zero of ϕ.

Proof   Let x_1 and x_2 be the consecutive zeros of ψ. Suppose that ϕ does not vanish in (x_1, x_2). Since the zeros of a function y are the same as those of $-y$, we can assume ϕ to be positive on (x_1, x_2), for if $\phi < 0$, we can simply replace ϕ by $-\phi$. By the same argument we can also assume $\psi > 0$ on (x_1, x_2). Consequently we have

$$W(\phi, \psi; x_1) = \phi(x_1)\psi'(x_1) \geqslant 0, \qquad W(\phi, \psi; x_2) = \phi(x_2)\psi'(x_2) \leqslant 0.\tag{3.5.4}$$

However,

$$\frac{dW}{dx}(\phi,\psi;x) = \phi\psi'' - \phi''\psi$$

$$= \phi\psi(p-q) \geq 0 \qquad \text{on} \quad x_1 < x < x_2.$$

Hence W is nondecreasing on (x_1, x_2). This contradicts (3.5.4), and the proof is complete. ∎

In particular, if ϕ and ψ are both zero at x_1, the theorem shows that ϕ vanishes again before ψ does. That is to say, ϕ oscillates more rapidly than ψ.

Example 3.5.3 Show that every solution of

$$y'' + x^2 y = 0 \tag{3.5.5}$$

has infinitely many zeros on $[1, \infty)$.

Consider the equation

$$y'' + y = 0. \tag{3.5.6}$$

Its solution $\sin x$ has zeros at the points $x = k\pi$ for $k = 1, 2, 3, \ldots$. Since $x^2 \geq 1$ on $[1, \infty)$, by the Sturm comparison theorem a nontrivial solution of Eq. (3.5.5) has at least one zero between $k\pi$ and $(k+1)\pi$. Thus it has infinitely many zeros on $[1, \infty)$.

Example 3.5.4 The Bessel equation of order ν is given by

$$x^2 y'' + xy' + (x^2 - \nu^2) y = 0, \tag{3.5.7}$$

where ν is a nonnegative real number. With the change of variable $y = u/\sqrt{x}$, the Bessel equation is transformed into

$$u'' + \left(1 + \frac{1 - 4\nu^2}{4x^2}\right) u = 0. \tag{3.5.8}$$

It should be noted that the number of zeros of a solution of Eq. (3.5.8) is the same as the number of zeros of the corresponding solution of Eq. (3.5.7) on the interval $(0, \infty)$. Thus to find the number of zeros, we compare Eq. (3.5.8) with the equation

$$u'' + u = 0, \tag{3.5.9}$$

which has the solution

$$u(x) = \sin(x - \alpha),$$

where α is a positive real number. The zeros of this solution evidently are $\alpha, \alpha \pm \pi, \alpha \pm 2\pi, \ldots$.

Consider the following three cases:

1. $0 \leqslant \nu < \frac{1}{2}$. Here $1 + (1 - 4\nu^2)/4x^2 > 1$. Comparing Eq. (3.5.8) with Eq. (3.5.9) by the Sturm comparison theorem, there is at least one zero of any nontrivial solution of the Bessel equation in every subinterval of the positive x-axis of length π, and the distance between the consecutive zeros is less than π.

2. $\nu > \frac{1}{2}$. In this case $1 + (1 - 4\nu^2)/4x^2 < 1$. Thus if α and β are consecutive roots of any solution of the Bessel equation, there is a root of u of (3.5.9) between α and β. Since the root of u of (3.5.9) following α is $\alpha + \pi$, we have $\beta > \alpha + \pi$. Hence the consecutive roots of any solution of the Bessel equation for $\nu > \frac{1}{2}$ differ by more than π.

In both cases (1) and (2) we see that the distance between consecutive zeros of any nontrivial solution of the Bessel equation of order $\nu \neq \frac{1}{2}$ approach π as x tends to infinity.

3. $\nu = \frac{1}{2}$. Here the Bessel equation simply reduces to

$$u'' + u = 0.$$

Thus the general solution of Eq. (3.5.7) can be written explicitly as

$$y(x) = \frac{c}{\sqrt{x}} \sin(x - \alpha), \qquad c = \text{constant}.$$

Hence consecutive zeros of any solution of the Bessel equation of order $\nu = \frac{1}{2}$ are separated by an interval of length π.

3.6   Adjoint Forms. Lagrange Identity

In the next section and in Chapter 6, which deals with eigenvalue problems, we will be encountering second-order differential equations in self-adjoint forms. Since self-adjoint equations play a very important role in many areas of mathematical physics, we will here give a brief account of self-adjoint operators and the Lagrange identity.

Let us consider the equation

$$L[\,y\,] = a_0(x)\,y'' + a_1(x)\,y' + a_2(x)\,y = 0$$

defined on an interval I. Integrating $zL[y]$ by parts from a to x, we have

$$\int_a^x zL[y]\,dx = \left[(za_0)\,y' - (za_0)'y + (za_1)\,y\right]_a^x$$

$$+ \int_a^x \left[(za_0)'' - (za_1)' + (za_2)\right] y\,dx. \qquad (3.6.1)$$

Now if we define the second-order operator L^* by

$$L^*[z] = (za_0)'' - (za_1)' + (za_2) = a_0 z'' + (2a_0' - a_1)z' + (a_0'' - a_1' + a_2)z,$$

the relation (3.6.1) takes the form

$$\int_a^x (zL[y] - yL^*[z])\,dx = \left[a_0(y'z - yz') + (a_1 - a_0')\,yz\right]_a^x. \qquad (3.6.2)$$

The operator L^* is called the *adjoint operator* corresponding to the operator L. It can be readily verified that the adjoint of L^* is L itself. If L and L^* are the same, L is said to be *self-adjoint*. The necessary and sufficient condition for this is that

$$a_1 = 2a_0' - a_1,$$

$$a_2 = a_0'' - a_1' + a_2,$$

which is satisfied if

$$a_1 = a_0'.$$

Thus if L is self-adjoint, we have

$$L[y] = a_0\,y'' + a_0'\,y' + a_2\,y$$

$$= (a_0\,y')' + a_2\,y. \qquad (3.6.3)$$

In general $L[y]$ is not self-adjoint. But if we let

$$h(x) = \frac{1}{a_0}\exp\left\{\int^x \frac{a_1(t)}{a_0(t)}\,dt\right\}, \qquad (3.6.4)$$

then $h(x)L[y]$ is self-adjoint. Thus any second-order linear differential equation

$$a_0(x)\,y'' + a_1(x)\,y' + a_2(x)\,y = 0 \qquad (3.6.5)$$

can be made self-adjoint. Multiplying by $h(x)$, given by Eq. (3.6.4), Eq. (3.6.5) is transformed into the self-adjoint form

$$\frac{d}{dx}\left[p(x)\frac{dy}{dx}\right]+q(x)\,y=0, \qquad (3.6.6)$$

where

$$p(x)=\exp\left\{\int^x \frac{a_1(t)}{a_0(t)}\,dt\right\},$$

$$q(x)=\frac{a_2}{a_0}\exp\left\{\int^x \frac{a_1(t)}{a_0(t)}\,dt\right\}. \qquad (3.6.7)$$

For example, the self-adjoint form of the Legendre equation

$$(1-x^2)\,y''-2xy'+n(n+1)\,y=0$$

is

$$\frac{d}{dx}\left[(1-x^2)\frac{dy}{dx}\right]+n(n+1)\,y=0, \qquad (3.6.8)$$

and the self-adjoint form of the Bessel equation

$$x^2y''+xy'+(x^2-\nu^2)\,y=0$$

is

$$\frac{d}{dx}\left(x\frac{dy}{dx}\right)+\left(x-\frac{\nu^2}{x}\right)y=0. \qquad (3.6.9)$$

Many well-known equations of mathematical physics expressed in self-adjoint form are important in Sturm-Liouville theory.

Now if we differentiate both sides of Eq. (3.6.2), we obtain

$$zL[\,y\,]-yL^*[\,z\,]=\frac{d}{dx}\big[a_0(\,y'z-yz')+(a_1-a_0')\,yz\big], \qquad (3.6.10)$$

which is known as the *Lagrange identity* for the operator L.

If we consider the integral from a to b of Eq. (3.6.2), we obtain *Green's identity*,

$$\int_a^b (zL[\,y\,] - yL^*[\,z\,])\,dx = \big[\,a_0(\,y'z - yz') + (a_1 - a_0')\,yz\,\big]_a^b. \quad (3.6.11)$$

When L is self-adjoint, this relation becomes

$$\int_a^b (zL[\,y\,] - yL^*[\,z\,]) = \big[\,a_0(\,y'z - yz')\,\big]_a^b. \quad (3.6.12)$$

3.7 Prüfer Substitution. Second Sturm Comparison Theorem

One elegant method of locating the zeros of a solution of the self-adjoint second-order equation

$$\frac{d}{dx}\left[\,p(x)\frac{dy}{dx}\,\right] + q(x)\,y = 0, \qquad p(x) > 0, \quad (3.7.1)$$

is due to Prüfer. The method essentially consists of introducing the *Prüfer substitution*

$$py' = r\cos\theta, \qquad y = r\sin\theta. \quad (3.7.2)$$

The new dependent variables with nonvanishing Jacobian are

$$r^2 = (\,py'\,)^2 + y^2, \qquad r > 0, \quad (3.7.3)$$

$$\theta = \arctan(\,y/py'\,), \quad (3.7.4)$$

where $r(x)$ is called the amplitude and $\theta(x)$ the phase variable.

It is obvious that $r = 0$ is equivalent to $y = 0$, $y' = 0$ for a given x. Thus by the uniqueness theorem (Theorem 3.1.1), $y(x) = 0$.

To determine an equivalent system of differential equations for $r(x)$ and $\theta(x)$, we first differentiate (3.7.3) and then simplify to obtain

$$r'(x) = \left(\frac{1}{p} - q\right)r\sin\theta\cos\theta. \quad (3.7.5)$$

Again differentiation of (3.7.4) and simplification yield

$$\theta'(x) = \frac{1}{p}\cos^2\theta + q\sin^2\theta. \tag{3.7.6}$$

The system (3.7.5)–(3.7.6), which is equivalent to Eq. (3.7.1), is called the *Prüfer system* associated with the self-adjoint equation (3.7.1). When p, q are continuous in $[a,b]$, we write

$$f(x,\theta) = \frac{1}{p}\cos^2\theta + q\sin^2\theta,$$

and hence

$$\frac{\partial f}{\partial \theta} = \left(q - \frac{1}{p}\right)\sin 2\theta.$$

We see that f and f_θ are continuous and f satisfies a Lipschitz condition with the Lipschitz constant

$$K = \sup_{a<x<b} |f_\theta| \leqslant \sup_{a<x<b} |q(x)| + \sup_{a<x<b} \frac{1}{|p(x)|}.$$

Thus if the initial value $\theta(a) = \alpha$ is specified, then by the uniqueness theorem (Theorem 2.5.3) a unique solution $\theta(x)$ exists. When $\theta(x)$ is known, $r(x)$ may be found from (3.7.5) by a quadrature:

$$r(x) = r(a)\exp\left\{\int_a^x \left[\frac{1}{p(t)} - q(t)\right]\sin\theta(t)\cos\theta(t)\,dt\right\}.$$

We observe here that the solution depends on $r(a)$ and $\theta(a)$. Changing $r(a)$ would merely change $y(x)$ by a constant factor. Hence we can study the zeros of any solution of Eq. (3.7.1) by studying Eq. (3.7.6).

Since $r(x) > 0$, the zeros of any solution $\phi(x)$ occur at the points where $\sin\theta(x) = 0$. At each of these points $\theta = 0, \pm\pi, \pm 2\pi,\ldots$, we have $\cos^2\theta = 1$ and $d\theta/dx > 0$. Hence the curve $(r(x), \theta(x))$ in a polar coordinate system can cross the rays $\theta = n\pi$, $n = 0, \pm 1, \pm 2,\ldots$, only in a counterclockwise direction, as shown in Figure 3.7-1.

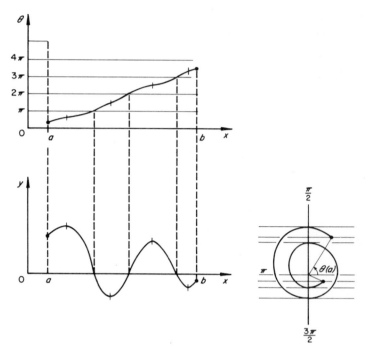

Figure 3.7-1

THEOREM 3.7.1 *Let $p(x) > 0$ and p, q be continuous on $[a, b]$. Then the only solution of*

$$L[y] = \frac{d}{dx}\left(p(x)\frac{dy}{dx}\right) + q(x)y = 0$$

which has an infinite number of zeros on $[a, b]$ is the trivial solution.

Proof Suppose $\phi(x)$ has infinitely many zeros on $[a, b]$. Then they would have a cluster point c. Let $\{x_n\}$ be a sequence of zeros for which $c = \lim_{n \to \infty} x_n$. Since $\phi(x)$ is continuous, we have

$$\phi(c) = \lim_{n \to \infty} \phi(x_n) = 0$$

and

$$\phi'(c) = \lim_{x_n \to c} \frac{\phi(x_n) - \phi(c)}{x_n - c} = 0.$$

Thus by the uniqueness theorem (Theorem 2.5.3), $\phi(x) = 0$. ∎

Alternatively, the preceding theorem states that in a finite interval a nontrivial solution can have but a finite number of zeros.

We shall now prove Sturm's second comparison theorem.

THEOREM 3.7.2   Let p'_1, p'_2, q_1 and q_2 be continuous on $[a,b]$, and let $0 < p_2(x) \leqslant p_1(x)$, $q_2(x) \geqslant q_1(x)$ on $[a,b]$. Let ϕ_1 and ϕ_2 be the nontrivial solutions of

$$\frac{d}{dx}(p_1\, y') + q_1\, y = 0,$$

$$\frac{d}{dx}(p_2\, y') + q_2\, y = 0,$$

respectively. If $\theta_2(a) \geqslant \theta_1(a)$, then $\theta_2(x) \geqslant \theta_1(x)$.

Proof   The two Prüfer equations are

$$\theta'_1 = \frac{1}{p_1}\cos^2\theta_1 + q_1 \sin^2\theta_1 = F_1\left(x, \theta_1\left(x\right)\right), \tag{3.7.7}$$

$$\theta'_2 = \frac{1}{p_2}\cos^2\theta_2 + q_2 \sin^2\theta_2 = F_2\left(x, \theta_2\left(x\right)\right). \tag{3.7.8}$$

By hypothesis it is evident that for all $x \in [a,b]$,

$$F_1\left(x, \theta\left(x\right)\right) \leqslant F_2\left(x, \theta\left(x\right)\right).$$

From (3.7.7) and (3.7.8) we have

$$(\theta_2 - \theta_1)' = F_2\left(x, \theta_2\left(x\right)\right) - F_1\left(x, \theta_1\left(x\right)\right)$$

$$\geqslant F_1\left(x, \theta_2\left(x\right)\right) - F_1\left(x, \theta_1\left(x\right)\right). \tag{3.7.9}$$

Thus

$$(\theta_1 - \theta_2)' \leqslant F_1\left(x, \theta_1\left(x\right)\right) - F_1\left(x, \theta_2\left(x\right)\right).$$

Let $\xi = \theta_1 - \theta_2$. Suppose $\theta_1(x) > \theta_2(x)$. If K is a Lipschitz constant for F_1, then we have

$$\xi' - K\xi \leqslant 0,$$

which is a first-order inequality. Hence

$$\frac{d}{dx}\left(\xi e^{-Kx}\right) \leqslant 0.$$

Integrating from a to x, we obtain

$$\xi(x)e^{-Kx} \leqslant \xi(a)e^{-Ka},$$

which implies that

$$\xi(x) \leqslant \xi(a)e^{K(x-a)}. \tag{3.7.10}$$

But $\xi(a) = \theta_1(a) - \theta_2(a) \leqslant 0$ by hypothesis, and $e^{K(x-a)} > 0$ for all $x \in [a,b]$; it follows from (3.7.10) that

$$\xi(x) \leqslant 0,$$

which contradicts the assumption that $\xi(x) > 0$. This completes the proof. ∎

COROLLARY 3.7.1 *If $q_2(x) > q_1(x)$ on (a,b), then $\theta_2(x) > \theta_1(x)$ on $(a,b]$.*

Proof Suppose for some $c > a$,

$$\theta_2(x) = \theta_1(x)$$

for $x \in [a,c]$. It is clear that (3.7.9) can hold for $q_2 > q_1$ only if $p_2(x) = p_1(x)$ over (a,c) and if

$$\theta_2 = \theta_1 = 0 \pmod{\pi}.$$

Thus Eqs. (3.7.7)–(3.7.8) clearly cannot hold. This contradicts our assumption.

We have just proved that there cannot exist $c > a$ such that $\theta_2(x) \geqslant \theta_1(x)$ on $[a,b]$. Thus there must exist a sequence of points $\{x_j\}$ with a as a cluster point such that $\theta_2(x_j) > \theta_1(x_j)$. Hence $\theta_2(x) > \theta_1(x)$ for $x > x_j$, and consequently $\theta_2(x) > \theta_1(x)$ on $(a,b]$. ∎

We are now in a position to prove the extension of the Sturm comparison theorem.

THEOREM 3.7.3 *Let $\phi_1(x)$ and $\phi_2(x)$ be any nontrivial solutions of*

$$L_1[y] = \frac{d}{dx}(p_1 y') + q_1 y = 0,$$

$$L_2[y] = \frac{d}{dx}(p_2 y') + q_2 y = 0,$$

respectively. Let $0 < p_2(x) \leqslant p_1(x)$ and $q_2(x) \geqslant q_1(x)$ for $x \in [a,b]$. Then ϕ_2 has a zero between any pair of consecutive zeros of ϕ_1.

Proof Let ϕ_1 have consecutive zeros at $x = x_1$ and $x = x_2$. Then for $\phi_1(x) > 0$,

$$\theta_1(x_1) = k\pi, \qquad \theta_1(x_2) = (k+1)\pi \qquad (3.7.11)$$

for some integer k. Since changing θ_2 by an integral multiple of π does not change ϕ_2, we assume without loss of generality that

$$\theta_2(x_1) - \theta_1(x_1) < \pi.$$

Hence

$$\theta_2(x_1) < (k+1)\pi.$$

But from Theorem 3.7.2 we have

$$\theta_2(x_2) > \theta_1(x_2),$$

and thus by (3.7.11),

$$\theta_2(x_2) > (k+1)\pi.$$

Consequently $\theta_2(x_2)$ must take on the value $(k+1)\pi$ at some point $x^* \in (x_1, x_2)$, and hence $\phi_2(x^*) = 0$. ∎

EXERCISES

1. Determine the solution of each of the following problems:

    (a) $y'' - 3y' + 2y = 0$.

    (b) $y''' + 2y'' - 8y' = 0$, $y(0) = 1$, $y'(0) = 0$, $y''(0) = 0$.

    (c) $y'' + 4y' + 4y = 0$.

    (d) $y^{iv} - 8y'' + 16y = 0$, $y(0) = 1$, $y'(0) = 0$, $y''(0) = 0$, $y'''(0) = 0$.

    (e) $y'' - 4y' + 7y = 0$.

    (f) $y'' + y' + y = 0$, $y(0) = 1$, $y'(0) = 0$.

    (g) $y^{iv} + 2y'' + y = 0$.

2. If $\phi = \xi + i\eta$ is a complex-valued solution of the equation

$$L[\,y\,] = a_0(x)\,y'' + a_1(x)\,y' + a_2(x)\,y = 0$$

with a_j as real-valued functions on a certain interval I, then ξ and η are real solutions of $L[\,y\,]=0$. Discuss the behavior of the solutions of $y'' + y' + 7y = 0$ on the interval $(-\infty, \infty)$.

3. Let ϕ_1 and ϕ_2 be two nontrivial solutions of $L[\,y\,]=0$ on an interval I. Then ϕ_1 and ϕ_2 are linearly dependent on I if and only if

$$W(\phi_1, \phi_2; x) = 0$$

for all $x \in I$. This statement is not true for more than two solutions.

4. (a) Test for linear dependence:

    (i) $f_1(x) = x,$ $f_2(x) = x^2 - x + 1,$ $f_3(x) = x^2 + 1.$
    (ii) $f_1(x) = e^x,$ $f_2(x) = e^{-x},$ $f_3(x) = \sin x.$

    (b) Let $y = u + iv$. Then $\bar{y} = u - iv$. If y and $\bar{y}$ are linearly independent, prove that u and v are linearly independent.

5. Show that the Wronskian of the linearly independent functions $\phi_1(x) = x^2$ and $\phi_2(x) = x|x|$ is zero everywhere. Does the result contradict Theorem 3.1.3?

6. Find the general solution of the Euler equation:

    (a) $2x^2 y'' + 3xy' - y = 0,\ 0 < x < \infty.$
    (b) $(x+2)^2 y'' + 3(x+2)\,y' - 3y = 0,\ -2 < x < \infty.$

7. Obtain the general solution of the following equations by the method of variation of parameters:

    (a) $y'' + y = \sec x \tan x.$
    (b) $y'' - 3y' + 2y = \sin(e^{-x}).$
    (c) $y'' + y = |x|.$

8. Show by the method of variation of parameters that a particular integral of the equation

$$y'' + y = f(x), \qquad 0 \leqslant x < \infty,$$

is given by

$$\phi_p(x) = \int_0^x f(\tau)\sin(x - \tau)\,d\tau.$$

9. (a) If a nontrivial solution ϕ_1 of $L[y] = a_0 y'' + a_1 y' + a_2 y = 0$ is known, a second solution ϕ_2 can be obtained by varying the parameter, that is, by letting $\phi_2(x) = u(x)\phi_1(x)$. Show that $L[y] = g(x)$ is reduced to

$$u'' + \left(\frac{2\phi_1'}{\phi_1} + \frac{a_1}{a_0} \right) u' = g(x),$$

which is a linear first-order equation in u'.

(b) Find a second solution of the equation

$$(1 - x^2) y'' - 2xy' + 2y = 0$$

on $0 < x < 1$ if $\phi_1(x) = x$.

10. By the method of undetermined coefficients determine a particular solution of each of the following equations:

(a) $y'' + y = e^x + x^2$.

(b) $y'' + 2y' + y = 2 + \sin x$.

(c) $y'' - 4y' + 4y = e^{2x}$.

11. Prove that if ϕ_1 and ϕ_2 are solutions of $L[y] = g_1(x)$ and $L[y] = g_2(x)$, respectively, on an interval I, then $\phi_1 + \phi_2$ is a solution of $L[y] = g_1 + g_2$.

12. The free damped motion of a mass on a spring at time t is governed by the equation

$$m\ddot{y} + c\dot{y} + ky = 0,$$

where the coefficients are constants. The dot, as usual, denotes differentiation with respect to time. The roots of the characteristic equation are

$$\lambda_{1,2} = \frac{-c \pm \sqrt{c^2 - 4mk}}{2m}.$$

Describe the behavior of the solution in the three different cases of $c^2 - 4mk$ positive, negative or zero.

13. Prove that between every pair of successive zeros of $\sin x$ there is one zero of $\sin x + \cos x$. Sketch the curves on $[-2\pi, 2\pi]$.

14. Show that every nontrivial solution of the equation

$$y'' + (\sinh x)\, y = 0$$

has at most one zero in $(-\infty, 0)$ and infinitely many zeros in $(0, \infty)$.

15. Suppose that $q(x) > 0$ and $q(x)$ is continuous in the interval $(0, \infty)$. Prove that every nontrivial solution of

$$y'' + q(x)\, y = 0$$

has infinitely many zeros in $(0, \infty)$.

16. Show that every nontrivial solution of the equation

$$y'' + e^x y = 0$$

has infinitely many zeros on $(0, \infty)$, whereas a nontrivial solution of the equation

$$y'' - e^x y = 0$$

has at most one zero on the interval $(0, \infty)$.

17. (Sonin-Polya theorem). Let $p(x) > 0$ and $q(x) \neq 0$ be continuously differentiable on an interval I. If $p(x)q(x)$ is nonincreasing (nondecreasing) on I, then the absolute values of the relative maxima and minima of every nontrivial solution of the equation

$$\frac{d}{dx}\left(p(x)\frac{dy}{dx}\right) + q(x)\, y = 0$$

are nondecreasing (nonincreasing) as x increases.

18. Transform the Laguerre equation

$$xy'' + (1 - x)\, y' + ny = 0, \qquad n = \text{constant}$$

into self-adjoint form and discuss the oscillatory behavior of the solution on $(1, \infty)$.

19. (a) Let $q(x) \leq 0$ in an interval I. Prove that no solution of the equation

$$\frac{d}{dx}\left(p\frac{dy}{dx}\right) + qy = 0$$

can oscillate in I.

(b) Find the interval in which a nontrivial solution of the Legendre equation

$$(1-x^2)\, y'' - 2xy' + 2y = 0$$

has at most one zero.

20. If $0 < m < q(x) < M$ for $a \leqslant x \leqslant b$, and if x_1 and x_2 are the successive zeros in (a,b) of a solution of

$$y'' + q(x)\, y = 0,$$

prove that

$$\frac{\pi}{\sqrt{M}} < x_2 - x_1 < \frac{\pi}{\sqrt{m}}\,.$$

21. Show that the solutions of the equation

$$y'' + y = 0$$

oscillate more rapidly than those of

$$x^2 y'' + xy' + y = 0$$

on the interval $(1, \infty)$.

22. (Osgood's theorem). Let $q(x)$ be continuously differentiable, and let $q(x) > 0$, $q'(x) \geqslant 0$ on an interval $[0, \infty)$. If x_1 and x_2 are two successive zeros of $\phi'(x)$ of a solution $\phi(x)$ of $y'' + q(x)\, y = 0$, prove that $|\phi(x_2)| \leqslant |\phi(x_1)|$.

23. Prove that if ϕ_1 and ϕ_2 are solutions of

$$\frac{d}{dx}\left(p(x) \frac{dy}{dx} \right) + q(x)\, y = 0,$$

then

$$p(\phi_1 \phi_2' - \phi_1' \phi_2) = \text{constant},$$

which is known as *Abel's identity*.

24. (Sturm's first comparison theorem). Let $p_1(x) \geqslant p_2(x) > 0$ and $q_2(x) \geqslant q_1(x)$ for $x \in [a, b]$, and let ϕ_j be a solution of

$$\frac{d}{dx}\left(p_j \frac{dy}{dx}\right) + q_j y = 0 \qquad \text{for} \quad j = 1, 2.$$

Suppose that

$$\frac{p_2(a)\phi_2'(a)}{\phi_2(a)} \leqslant \frac{p_1(a)\phi_1'(a)}{\phi_1(a)}.$$

If ϕ_1 has exactly n zeros on $(a, b]$, prove that ϕ_2 has at least n zeros on the same interval.

25. Determine all solutions of the equation

$$\theta' = h \cos^2\theta + k \sin^2\theta$$

for $h > 0$, $k > 0$.

Chapter 4.
Solution in Series
Legendre and Bessel Functions

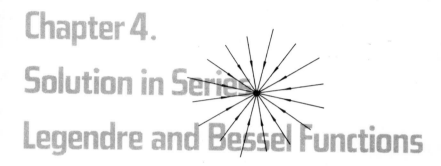

4.1 Solution at an Ordinary Point

In the preceding chapter we have shown how solutions were determined for second-order linear equations with constant coefficients. These solutions were obtained in closed form and in terms of elementary functions. However, with relatively few exceptions such as the Euler equation, it is not possible to find solutions of second- or higher-order equations with variable coefficients in simple closed form. Now we will present one of the powerful methods of determining solutions of differential equations known as the *power series method*.

Consider the linear homogeneous differential equation

$$y'' + p(x)\,y' + q(x)\,y = 0. \tag{4.1.1}$$

DEFINITION 4.1.1 If at a point $x = x_0$, the coefficients p and q are analytic,[†] then the point x_0 is called an *ordinary point* of the differential equation.

[†] A function $f(x)$ is said to be analytic at x_0 if it can be represented by a Taylor series

$$\sum_{n=0}^{\infty} \frac{f^{(n)}(x_0)}{n!}(x - x_0)^n,$$

which converges for all x in some open interval containing x_0.

Before proving the existence theorem, we shall first illustrate the procedure by the following example.

Example 4.1.1   Consider the initial-value problem

$$y'' + 3xy' + 3y = 0,$$
$$y(0) = 2, \qquad y'(0) = 3. \tag{4.1.2}$$

Here the coefficients are analytic everywhere. We shall endeavor to find the solution near the point $x = 0$.[†]

Assume a solution of the form

$$\phi(x) = \sum_{n=0}^{\infty} a_n x^n. \tag{4.1.3}$$

Then

$$\phi'(x) = \sum_{n=0}^{\infty} n a_n x^{n-1}$$

and

$$\phi''(x) = \sum_{n=0}^{\infty} n(n-1) a_n x^{n-2}.$$

Substitution of ϕ, ϕ' and ϕ'' in Eq. (4.1.2) yields

$$\sum_{n=0}^{\infty} n(n-1) a_n x^{n-2} + 3x \sum_{n=0}^{\infty} n a_n x^{n-1} + 3 \sum_{n=0}^{\infty} a_n x^n = 0$$

or

$$\sum_{n=0}^{\infty} n(n-1) a_n x^{n-2} + \sum_{n=0}^{\infty} (3n+3) a_n x^n = 0.$$

Rewriting the second series[‡] so that the power of x is $n-2$, we have

$$\sum_{n=0}^{\infty} n(n-1) a_n x^{n-2} + \sum_{n=2}^{\infty} (3n-3) a_{n-2} x^{n-2} = 0$$

[†]If one desires to find a solution near a point $x = x_0$, the solution may be assumed in the form $y(x) = \sum_0^\infty a_n (x - x_0)^n$. But then if we put $X = x - x_0$, we obtain $y(X) = \sum_0^\infty a_n X^n$, which is in the same form as (4.1.3). See Example 4.1.2.

[‡]Let $n = k - 2$ so that $\sum_{n=0}^\infty (3n+3) a_n x^n$ becomes $\sum_{k=2}^\infty (3k-3) a_{k-2} x^{k-2}$, which is the same as $\sum_{n=2}^\infty (3n-3) a_{n-2} x^{n-2}$.

or

$$\sum_{n=2}^{\infty} \left[n(n-1)a_n + (3n-3)a_{n-2} \right] x^{n-2} = 0.$$

In order for the power series to be identically zero, each of its coefficients must vanish. Hence

$$n(n-1)a_n + (3n-3)a_{n-2} = 0, \qquad n \geqslant 2,$$

which is called the *recurrence relation* for the coefficients a_n. It is obvious that all the coefficients can be determined in terms of two arbitrary coefficients. This is expected, since the equation under consideration is of second order. For convenience we choose a_0 and a_1 to be arbitrary coefficients.

Now, simplifying the recurrence relation, we obtain

$$a_n = -\frac{3}{n} a_{n-2}.$$

We arrange two columns: one for $n = 2, 4, 6, \ldots$ and the other for $n = 3, 5, 7, \ldots$. Thus we have

$$a_2 = -\frac{3}{2} a_0, \qquad\qquad a_3 = -\frac{3}{3} a_1,$$

$$a_4 = -\frac{3}{4} a_2, \qquad\qquad a_5 = -\frac{3}{5} a_3,$$

$$a_6 = -\frac{3}{6} a_4, \qquad\qquad a_7 = -\frac{3}{7} a_5,$$

$$\vdots \qquad\qquad\qquad\qquad \vdots$$

$$a_{2k} = -\frac{3}{2k} a_{2k-2}, \qquad\qquad a_{2k+1} = -\frac{3}{2k+1} a_{2k-1}.$$

First we take the product of corresponding members of the equations for every coefficient to obtain

$$a_2 a_4 a_6 \cdots a_{2k} = \frac{(-1)^k 3^k}{2^k k!} a_0 a_2 a_4 \cdots a_{2k-2}, \qquad k \geqslant 1.$$

Cancellation of the coefficients on both sides of the equation yields at once

$$a_{2k} = \frac{(-1)^k 3^k}{2^k k!} a_0, \qquad k \geqslant 1.$$

Similarly, from the remaining column in the array we obtain

$$a_{2k+1} = \frac{(-1)^k 3^k a_1}{3 \times 5 \times 7 \times \cdots \times (2k+1)}, \qquad k \geqslant 1.$$

Thus we have

$$\phi(x) = a_0 \left[1 + \sum_{k=1}^{\infty} \frac{(-3)^k x^{2k}}{2^k k!} \right] + a_1 \left[x + \sum_{k=1}^{\infty} \frac{(-3)^k 2^k k! x^{2k+1}}{(2k+1)!} \right].$$

Let

$$\phi_1(x) = 1 + \sum_{k=1}^{\infty} \frac{(-3)^k x^{2k}}{2^k k!},$$

$$\phi_2(x) = x + \sum_{k=1}^{\infty} \frac{(-3)^k 2^k k! x^{2k+1}}{(2k+1)!}.$$

Applying the ratio test to the series for ϕ_1 we see that

$$\lim_{k \to \infty} \left| \frac{(-3)^{k+1} x^{2k+2}}{2^{k+1}(k+1)!} \cdot \frac{2^k k!}{(-3)^k x^{2k}} \right| = \lim_{k \to \infty} \frac{3|x|^2}{2(k+1)} = 0,$$

for all finite x. Thus the series for ϕ_1 converges for $|x| < \infty$. Similarly we can show that the series for ϕ_2 converges for $|x| < \infty$.

To show that ϕ_1 and ϕ_2 are linearly independent, we need only to show that $W(\phi_1, \phi_2; 0) \neq 0$. It is obvious that

$$W(\phi_1, \phi_2; 0) = \begin{vmatrix} \phi_1(0) & \phi_2(0) \\ \phi_1'(0) & \phi_2'(0) \end{vmatrix}$$

$$= \begin{vmatrix} 1 & 0 \\ 0 & 1 \end{vmatrix} = 1 \neq 0.$$

Hence ϕ_1 and ϕ_2 are linearly independent for $|x| < \infty$, and consequently ϕ represents the general solution of Eq. (4.1.2).

The constants a_0 and a_1 can be determined from the initial conditions. Thus we have

$$\phi(0) = 2 = a_0,$$

$$\phi'(0) = 3 = a_1.$$

Hence the solution of the initial-value problem is

$$\phi(x) = 2\phi_1(x) + 3\phi_2(x).$$

The method just illustrated is valid in general when the coefficients of a linear differential equation are analytic. The solution so obtained always converges and is unique for an initial-value problem.

We will now prove the following theorems.

THEOREM 4.1.1 (Cauchy's inequality theorem) *If the power series $\sum_{n=0}^{\infty} a_n (x - x_0)^n$ has a radius of convergence $R > 0$, then there exists a constant $M > 0$ such that*

$$|a_n| r^n \leqslant M, \qquad n = 0, 1, 2, \ldots$$

for every x satisfying $|x - x_0| = r < R$.

Proof Since $\sum_{n=0}^{\infty} a_n (x - x_0)^n$ converges for $|x - x_0| = r < R$, a necessary condition for the series $\sum_{n=0}^{\infty} a_n r^n$ to converge is that

$$\lim_{n \to \infty} |a_n r^n| = 0.$$

Thus there exists an integer N such that for $n > N$,

$$|a_n| r^n \leqslant 1$$

Now if we choose

$$M = \max(|a_0|, |a_1| r, \ldots, |a_N| r^N; 1),$$

it is obvious that $|a_n| r^n \leqslant M$. ∎

THEOREM 4.1.2 (Existence) *Let the coefficients $p(x)$ and $q(x)$ have convergent power-series expansions in powers of $x - x_0$ on $|x - x_0| < R$,*

$R > 0$, *where R is the smaller radius of convergence of the series represent-*
ing p or q. Then there exists a unique solution

$$\phi(x) = \sum_{n=0}^{\infty} a_n (x - x_0)^n,$$

which converges for $|x - x_0| < R$, *of the initial-value problem*

$$L[\, y\,] = y'' + p(x)\, y' + q(x)\, y = 0, \tag{4.1.4}$$

$$y(x_0) = \alpha, \tag{4.1.5}$$

$$y'(x_0) = \beta, \tag{4.1.6}$$

where α *and* β *are constants.*

Proof Let $\phi(x) = \sum_{n=0}^{\infty} a_n (x - x_0)^n$ be convergent for $|x - x_0| < R$. Then

$$\phi'(x) = \sum_{n=0}^{\infty} n a_n (x - x_0)^{n-1},$$

$$\phi''(x) = \sum_{n=0}^{\infty} n(n-1) a_n (x - x_0)^{n-2},$$

and by hypothesis

$$p(x) = \sum_{n=0}^{\infty} p_n (x - x_0)^n, \tag{4.1.7}$$

$$q(x) = \sum_{n=0}^{\infty} q_n (x - x_0)^n \tag{4.1.8}$$

for $|x - x_0| < R$. Since ϕ must satisfy $L[\, y\,] = 0$, we have

$$\sum_{n=0}^{\infty} n(n-1) a_n (x - x_0)^{n-2} + \sum_{n=0}^{\infty} p_n (x - x_0)^n \sum_{n=0}^{\infty} n a_n (x - x_0)^{n-1}$$

$$+ \sum_{n=0}^{\infty} q_n (x - x_0)^n \sum_{n=0}^{\infty} a_n (x - x_0)^n = 0.$$

Shifting the indices, we have

$$\sum_{n=0}^{\infty} (n+2)(n+1)a_{n+2}(x-x_0)^n + \sum_{n=0}^{\infty} p_n(x-x_0)^n \sum_{n=0}^{\infty} (n+1)a_{n+1}(x-x_0)^n$$

$$+ \sum_{n=0}^{\infty} q_n(x-x_0)^n \sum_{n=0}^{\infty} a_n(x-x_0)^n = 0,$$

which may again be written in the form

$$\sum_{n=0}^{\infty} \left[(n+2)(n+1)a_{n+2} + \sum_{k=0}^{n} p_{n-k}(k+1)a_{k+1} + q_{n-k}a_k \right](x-x_0)^n = 0.$$

Thus a_n must satisfy, for $n = 0, 1, 2, \ldots$,

$$(n+2)(n+1)a_{n+2} = - \sum_{k=0}^{n} p_{n-k}(k+1)a_{k+1} + q_{n-k}a_k, \qquad (4.1.9)$$

which is the recurrence relation for the coefficients a_n.

With the coefficients a_n for $n \geqslant 2$ defined by the recurrence relation, we shall show that the series

$$\sum_{n=0}^{\infty} a_n(x-x_0)^n \qquad (4.1.10)$$

converges for $|x - x_0| < R$.

Since the series (4.1.7) and (4.1.8) are convergent for $|x - x_0| = r < R$, by Theorem 4.1.1 there exists a constant $M > 0$ such that

$$|p_n|r^n \leqslant M, \qquad |q_n|r^n \leqslant M, \qquad n = 0, 1, 2, \ldots.$$

Using the triangle inequality, we obtain from the recurrence relation (4.1.9)

$$(n+1)(n+2)|a_{n+2}| \leqslant \frac{M}{r^n} \sum_{k=0}^{n} \left[(k+1)|a_{k+1}| + |a_k| \right] r^k$$

$$\leqslant \frac{M}{r^n} \sum_{k=0}^{n} \left[(k+1)|a_{k+1}| + |a_k| \right] r^k + M|a_{n+1}|r \qquad (4.1.11)$$

for $n = 0, 1, 2, \ldots$.

Now we define

$$A_0 = |a_0|, \qquad A_1 = |a_1|,$$

and A_n for $n \geq 2$ by

$$(n+1)(n+2)A_{n+2} = \frac{M}{r^n} \sum_{k=0}^{n} \left[(k+1)A_{k+1} + A_k \right] r^k + MA_{n+1}r. \quad (4.1.12)$$

Comparing (4.1.11) and (4.1.12), we see that an induction yields

$$0 \leq |a_n| \leq A_n, \qquad n = 0, 1, 2, \ldots .$$

We shall now investigate the radius of convergence of the series

$$\sum_{n=0}^{\infty} A_n (x - x_0)^n. \quad (4.1.13)$$

This can be achieved by applying the ratio test. Thus by replacing n with $n-1$ and with $n-2$ in (4.1.12) for large n, we obtain respectively

$$n(n+1)A_{n+1} = \frac{M}{r^{n-1}} \sum_{k=0}^{n-1} \left[(k+1)A_{k+1} + A_k \right] r^k + MA_n r \quad (4.1.14)$$

and

$$(n-1)nA_n = \frac{M}{r^{n-2}} \sum_{k=0}^{n-2} \left[(k+1)A_{k+1} + A_k \right] r^k + MA_{n-1}r. \quad (4.1.15)$$

From (4.1.14) we have

$$n(n+1)A_{n+1} = \frac{M}{r^{n-1}} \sum_{k=0}^{n-2} \left[(k+1)A_{k+1} + A_k \right] r^k + M(nA_n + A_{n-1}) + MA_n r,$$

$$(4.1.16)$$

and we rewrite (4.1.15) in the form

$$\frac{(n-1)nA_n}{r} - MA_{n-1} = \frac{M}{r^{n-1}} \sum_{k=0}^{n-2} \left[(k+1)A_{k+1} + A_k \right] r^k. \quad (4.1.17)$$

Thus from (4.1.16) and (4.1.17) we obtain, after simplifying,

$$\frac{A_n}{A_{n+1}} = \frac{n(n+1)r}{(n-1)n + M(n+r)r}.$$

Thus

$$\lim_{n \to \infty} \frac{A_n}{A_{n+1}} = r,$$

and hence the series (4.1.13) converges for $|x - x_0| < r$. This implies that the series (4.1.10) converges for $|x - x_0| < r < R$. ∎

If instead of the homogeneous differential equation (4.1.4), the nonhomogeneous differential equation

$$L[\, y\,] = y'' + p(x)\, y' + q(x)\, y = f(x) \tag{4.1.18}$$

is used in the initial-value problem, then Theorem 4.1.2 can be proved in a similar manner, provided of course that f possesses a power-series expansion in powers of $x - x_0$ convergent for $|x - x_0| < R$.

Example 4.1.2 Find the power series solution of the equation

$$y'' + (x-2)^2\, y' - 7(x-2)\, y = 0 \tag{4.1.19}$$

about the point $x = 2$.

Let $t = x - 2$. Then Eq. (4.1.19) becomes

$$\frac{d^2 y}{dt^2} + t^2 \frac{dy}{dt} - 7ty = 0. \tag{4.1.20}$$

Now let $\phi(t)$ be a solution of the form

$$\phi(t) = \sum_{n=0}^{\infty} a_n t^n.$$

Substituting ϕ, ϕ' and ϕ'' in the new equation (4.1.20), we obtain

$$\sum_{n=0}^{\infty} n(n-1) a_n t^{n-2} + \sum_{n=0}^{\infty} n a_n t^{n+1} - \sum_{n=0}^{\infty} 7 a_n t^{n+1} = 0.$$

Thus

$$\sum_{n=0}^{\infty} n(n-1)a_n t^{n-2} + \sum_{n=0}^{\infty} (n-7)a_n t^{n+1} = 0.$$

Changing the exponent of t in the second term we have

$$\sum_{n=0}^{\infty} n(n-1)a_n t^{n-2} + \sum_{n=3}^{\infty} (n-10)a_{n-3} t^{n-2} = 0.$$

Combining like powers of t, we have

$$a_2 + \sum_{n=3}^{\infty} \left[n(n-1)a_n + (n-10)a_{n-3} \right] t^{n-2} = 0.$$

Hence $a_2 = 0$ and

$$a_n = \frac{-(n-10)}{n(n-1)} a_{n-3}, \qquad n \geqslant 3.$$

We arrange three columns as follows:

$$a_3 = \frac{-(-7)}{3 \cdot 2} a_0 \qquad\qquad a_4 = \frac{-(-6)}{4 \cdot 3} a_1 \qquad\qquad a_5 = \frac{-(-5)}{5 \cdot 4} a_2 = 0$$

$$a_6 = \frac{-(-4)}{6 \cdot 5} a_3 \qquad\qquad a_7 = \frac{-(-3)}{7 \cdot 6} a_4 \qquad\qquad a_8 = 0$$

$$a_9 = \frac{-(-1)}{9 \cdot 8} a_6 \qquad\qquad a_{10} = \frac{-(0)}{10 \cdot 9} a_7 = 0$$

$$\vdots \qquad\qquad\qquad \vdots \qquad\qquad\qquad \vdots$$

$$a_{3k} = \frac{-(3k-10)}{3k(3k-1)} a_{3k-3} \qquad a_{3k+1} = 0 \qquad\qquad a_{3k+2} = 0$$

Taking the product of corresponding members of the equations of every coefficient in the first column we obtain

$$a_3 a_6 a_9 \cdots a_{3k} = \frac{(-1)^k (-7)(-4)(-1)(2) \cdots (3k-10)}{3^k k! \, 2 \cdot 5 \cdot 8 \cdots (3k-1)} a_0 a_3 \cdots a_{3k-3}.$$

Cancellation of the coefficients on both sides of the equation yields

$$a_{3k} = \frac{(-1)^k(-28)a_0}{3^k k!(3k-7)(3k-4)(3k-1)}.$$

Thus we have

$$\phi(t) = a_0\left[1 + \sum_{k=1}^{\infty} \frac{(-1)^{k+1}28\,t^{3k}}{3^k k!(3k-7)(3k-4)(3k-1)}\right] + a_1\left[t + \frac{1}{2}t^4 + \frac{1}{28}t^7\right].$$

The solution in the original variable x appears as

$$\phi(x) = a_0\left[1 + \sum_{k=1}^{\infty} \frac{(-1)^{k+1}28\,(x-2)^{3k}}{3^k k!(3k-7)(3k-4)(3k-1)}\right]$$

$$+ a_1\left[(x-2) + \frac{1}{2}(x-2)^4 + \frac{1}{28}(x-2)^7\right]. \tag{4.1.21}$$

If we denote

$$\phi_1(x) = 1 + \sum_{k=1}^{\infty} \frac{(-1)^{k+1}28(x-2)^{3k}}{3^k k!(3k-7)(3k-4)(3k-1)},$$

and

$$\phi_2(x) = (x-2) + \frac{1}{2}(x-2)^4 + \frac{1}{28}(x-2)^7,$$

we can easily show that the series for ϕ_1 converges for all values of x. Since $W(\phi_1, \phi_2; 2) \neq 0$, ϕ_1 and ϕ_2 are linearly independent. Hence (4.1.21) represents the general solution of Eq. (4.1.19).

4.2 Legendre's Equation

Another example that is worth considering is the *Legendre equation*

$$(1-x^2)\,y'' - 2xy' + \nu(\nu+1)\,y = 0, \tag{4.2.1}$$

where ν is a real number. This equation arises in problems with spherical symmetry in mathematical physics. Its coefficients are analytic at $x=0$. Thus if we expand near the point $x=0$, the coefficients are

$$p(x) = -\frac{2x}{1-x^2} = -2x \sum_{m=0}^{\infty} x^{2m} = \sum_{m=0}^{\infty} (-2)x^{2m+1}$$

and

$$q(x) = \frac{\nu(\nu+1)}{1-x^2} = \nu(\nu+1) \sum_{m=0}^{\infty} x^{2m} = \sum_{m=0}^{\infty} \nu(\nu+1)x^{2m}.$$

We see that these series converge for $|x|<1$. According to the preceding theorem the solution of the Legendre equation on $|x|<1$ has convergent power series at $x=0$.

Now to find the solution near the ordinary point $x=0$, we assume

$$\phi(x) = \sum_{m=0}^{\infty} a_m x^m.$$

Then differentiation yields

$$\phi'(x) = \sum_{m=0}^{\infty} m a_m x^{m-1},$$

$$\phi''(x) = \sum_{m=0}^{\infty} m(m-1) a_m x^{m-2}.$$

Substituting ϕ, ϕ' and ϕ'' in the Legendre equation, we obtain

$$(1-x^2) \sum_{m=0}^{\infty} m(m-1)a_m x^{m-2} - 2x \sum_{m=0}^{\infty} m a_m x^{m-1} + \nu(\nu+1) \sum_{m=0}^{\infty} a_m x^m = 0.$$

Simplification gives

$$\sum_{m=0}^{\infty} \left[(m+1)(m+2)a_{m+2} + (\nu-m)(\nu+m+1)a_m \right] x^m = 0.$$

The coefficients in the power series must therefore satisfy the recurrence relation

$$a_{m+2} = -\frac{(\nu-m)(\nu+m+1)}{(m+1)(m+2)} a_m, \qquad m \geqslant 0. \tag{4.2.2}$$

This relation determines $a_2, a_4, a_6, \ldots$ in terms of a_0, and $a_3, a_5, a_7, \ldots$ in terms of a_1. Thus we write

$$a_2 = -\frac{\nu(\nu+1)}{1 \times 2} a_0, \qquad\qquad a_3 = -\frac{(\nu-1)(\nu+2)}{2 \times 3} a_1,$$

$$a_4 = -\frac{(\nu-2)(\nu+3)}{3 \times 4} a_2, \qquad\qquad a_5 = -\frac{(\nu-3)(\nu+4)}{4 \times 5} a_3,$$

$$\vdots \qquad\qquad\qquad\qquad \vdots$$

$$a_{2k} = -\frac{(\nu-2k+2)(\nu+2k-1)}{(2k-1)(2k)} a_{2k-2}, \qquad a_{2k+1} = -\frac{(\nu-2k+1)(\nu+2k)}{(2k)(2k+1)} a_{2k-1}.$$

Taking the product of the left and right sides of the above equations and canceling the like terms, we obtain

$$a_{2k} = \frac{(-1)^k \nu(\nu-2) \cdots (\nu-2k+2) \cdot (\nu+1)(\nu+3) \cdots (\nu+2k-1)}{(2k)!} a_0$$

and

$$a_{2k+1} = \frac{(-1)^k (\nu-1)(\nu-3) \cdots (\nu-2k+1) \cdot (\nu+2)(\nu+4) \cdots (\nu+2k)}{(2k+1)!} a_1.$$

Hence the solution of the Legendre equation is

$$\phi(x) = a_0 \left[1 + \sum_{k=1}^{\infty} \frac{(-1)^k \nu(\nu-2) \cdots (\nu-2k+2) \cdot (\nu+1)(\nu+3) \cdots (\nu+2k-1) x^{2k}}{(2k)!} \right]$$

$$+ a_1 \left[x + \sum_{k=1}^{\infty} \frac{(-1)^k (\nu-1)(\nu-3) \cdots (\nu-2k+1) \cdot (\nu+2)(\nu+4) \cdots (\nu+2k) x^{2k+1}}{(2k+1)!} \right]$$

$$= a_0 p_\nu(x) + a_1 q_\nu(x).$$

It can easily be proved that the functions $p_\nu(x)$ and $q_\nu(x)$ converge for $|x| < 1$ and are linearly independent.

Now consider the case in which $\nu = n$, with n a nonnegative integer. It is then evident from the recurrence relation (4.2.2) that when $m = n$,

$$a_{n+2} = a_{n+4} = \cdots = 0.$$

Consequently, when n is even, the series for $p_n(x)$ terminates with x^n, whereas the series for $q_n(x)$ does not terminate. When n is odd, it is the series for $q_n(x)$ which terminates with x^n, while that for $p_n(x)$ does not terminate. In the first case (n even), $p_n(x)$ is a polynomial of degree n; the same is true for $q_n(x)$ in the second case (n odd).

Thus for any nonnegative integer n, either $p_n(x)$ or $q_n(x)$, but not both, is a polynomial of degree n. Consequently, the general solution of the Legendre equation contains a polynomial solution $P_n(x)$ and an infinite-series solution $Q_n(x)$ for a nonnegative integer n. To find the polynomial solution $P_n(x)$ it is convenient to choose a_n so that $P_n(1) = 1$. Let this a_n be

$$a_n = \frac{(2n)!}{2^n (n!)^2}. \tag{4.2.3}$$

Rewriting the recurrence relation (4.2.2), we have

$$a_{n-2} = - \frac{(n-1)n}{2(2n-1)} a_n. \tag{4.2.4}$$

Substituting a_n from (4.2.3) into (4.2.4), we obtain

$$a_{n-2} = - \frac{(2n-2)!}{2^n (n-1)!(n-2)!}$$

and

$$a_{n-4} = \frac{(2n-4)!}{2^n 2!(n-2)!(n-4)!}.$$

It follows by induction that

$$a_{n-2k} = \frac{(-1)^k (2n-2k)!}{2^n k!(n-k)!(n-2k)!}.$$

Hence we may write $P_n(x)$ in the form

$$P_n(x) = \sum_{k=0}^{n} \frac{(-1)^k (2n-2k)!}{2^n k! (n-k)! (n-2k)!} x^{n-2k}, \qquad (4.2.5)$$

where $N = n/2$ when n is even and $N = (n-1)/2$ when n is odd. This polynomial $P_n(x)$ is called the *Legendre function of the first kind of order n*. It is also known as the *Legendre polynomial* of degree n.
The first few Legendre polynomials are

$$P_0(x) = 1,$$

$$P_1(x) = x,$$

$$P_2(x) = \tfrac{1}{2}(3x^2 - 1),$$

$$P_3(x) = \tfrac{1}{2}(5x^3 - 3x),$$

$$P_4(x) = \tfrac{1}{8}(35x^4 - 30x^2 + 3).$$

These polynomials are plotted in Fig. 4.2-1 for small values of x.

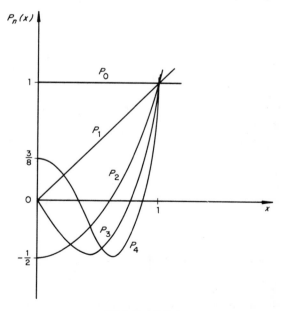

Figure 4.2-1

Recall that for a given nonnegative integer n, only one of the two solutions $p_n(x)$ and $q_n(x)$ of Legendre's equation is a polynomial, while the other is an infinite series. This infinite series, when appropriately normalized, is called the *Legendre function of the second kind*. It is defined for $|x| < 1$ by

$$Q_n(x) = \begin{cases} p_n(1)q_n(x) & \text{for } n \text{ even,} \\ -q_n(1)p_n(x) & \text{for } n \text{ odd.} \end{cases}$$

Thus when n is a nonnegative integer, the general solution of the Legendre equation is given by

$$\phi(x) = c_1 P_n(x) + c_2 Q_n(x).$$

4.3   Solution at a Regular Singular Point

Consider the linear differential equation

$$y^{(n)} + a_1(x) y^{(n-1)} + \cdots + a_{n-1}(x) y' + a_n(x) y = 0. \tag{4.3.1}$$

If one or more of the coefficients $a_1, a_2, \ldots, a_n$ is not analytic at $x = x_0$, the point $x = x_0$ is called a *singular point* of Eq. (4.3.1).

The singular point $x = x_0$ is called a *regular singular point* of Eq. (4.3.1) if the functions

$$(x - x_0)a_1(x), \quad (x - x_0)^2 a_2(x), \ldots, \quad (x - x_0)^n a_n(x) \tag{4.3.2}$$

are analytic at $x = x_0$.

If one or more of the functions in (4.3.2) is not analytic at $x = x_0$, the singular point $x = x_0$ is called an *irregular singular point*.

Here we are primarily interested in the second-order equation

$$y'' + p(x) y' + q(x) y = 0. \tag{4.3.3}$$

If x_0 is a regular point of Eq. (4.3.3), then the functions

$$(x - x_0) p(x), \qquad (x - x_0)^2 q(x)$$

are analytic at $x = x_0$. It is not so simple to find the solutions of initial-value problems near a singular point. The power-series method is no longer applicable. However, with a slight modification of the power-series method solutions near the singularities can be determined. This method is called the *Frobenius method*.

Before we justify this method, we first illustrate the procedure by the following example.

Example 4.3.1 Consider the equation

$$4xy'' + 3y' - 3y = 0 \qquad (4.3.4)$$

This can be written in the form

$$y'' + \frac{3}{4x}\, y' - \frac{3}{4x}\, y = 0.$$

Here $p(x) = 3/4x$, $q(x) = -3/4x$. Since the functions

$$(x-0)\left(\frac{3}{4x}\right) = \frac{3}{4},$$

$$(x-0)^2\left(\frac{-3}{4x}\right) = -\frac{3}{4}x$$

are analytic at $x=0$, the point $x=0$ is a regular singular point. We assume a solution in the form

$$\phi(x) = x^s \sum_{n=0}^{\infty} a_n x^n = \sum_{n=0}^{\infty} a_n x^{n+s}, \qquad (4.3.5)$$

where the exponent s may be any number.

Differentation of ϕ yields

$$\phi'(x) = \sum_{n=0}^{\infty} (n+s)a_n x^{n+s-1},$$

$$\phi''(x) = \sum_{n=0}^{\infty} (n+s)(n+s-1)a_n x^{n+s-2}.$$

Substitution of ϕ, ϕ' and ϕ'' into Eq. (4.3.4) yields

$$\sum_{n=0}^{\infty} 4(n+s)(n+s-1)a_n x^{n+s-1}$$

$$+ \sum_{n=0}^{\infty} 3(n+s)a_n x^{n+s-1} + \sum_{n=0}^{\infty} (-3)a_n x^{n+s} = 0.$$

Changing the power of x in the last term, we obtain

$$\sum_{n=0}^{\infty} [4(n+s)(n+s-1)+3(n+s)]a_n x^{n+s-1} + \sum_{n=1}^{\infty} (-3)a_{n-1}x^{n+s-1} = 0.$$

Hence the equations for the determination of s and a_n are

$$n=0: \qquad 4s(s-1)+3s=0, \qquad a_0 \neq 0, \tag{4.3.6}$$

$$n \geqslant 1: \qquad [4(n+s)(n+s-1)+3(n+s)]a_n - 3a_{n-1} = 0. \tag{4.3.7}$$

The equation (4.3.6) is called an *indicial equation*. It has two roots, $s_1 = 0$ and $s_2 = \frac{1}{4}$. This indicates that there are two possible solutions for the two values of s.

We consider first the case $s_1 = 0$. The recurrence relation (4.3.7) then becomes

$$(4n^2 - n)a_n - 3a_{n-1} = 0,$$

from which we find

$$a_1 = \frac{3}{1 \times 3} a_0,$$

$$a_2 = \frac{3}{2 \times 7} a_1,$$

$$a_3 = \frac{3}{3 \times 11} a_2,$$

$$\vdots$$

$$a_n = \frac{3}{n \times (4n-1)} a_{n-1}.$$

Thus taking the products of corresponding members of the equations and canceling like terms, we obtain

$$a_n = \frac{3^n}{n! \, 3 \times 7 \times 11 \times \cdots \times (4n-1)} a_0.$$

Hence for $a_0 = 1$,

$$\phi_1(x) = 1 + \sum_{n=1}^{\infty} \frac{3^n x^n}{n! \, 3 \times 7 \times 11 \times \cdots \times (4n-1)}.$$

In the case when $s_2 = \frac{1}{4}$, the recurrence relation is

$$n(4n+1)a_n - 3a_{n-1} = 0.$$

If we proceed as in the previous case, we arrive at

$$a_n = \frac{3^n a_0}{n!\, 5 \times 9 \times 13 \times \cdots \times (4n+1)},$$

and hence, taking $a_0 = 1$,

$$\phi_2(x) = x^{1/4}\left[1 + \sum_{n=1}^{\infty} \frac{3^n x^n}{n!\, 5 \times 9 \times 13 \times \cdots \times (4n+1)}\right].$$

It can be readily shown that $\phi_1(x)$ and $\phi_2(x)$ converge for $x \in (0, \infty)$ and they are linearly independent. Thus the general solution of Eq. (4.3.4) is given by

$$\phi(x) = c_1\phi_1(x) + c_2\phi_2(x).$$

4.4 Frobenius Method

Without loss of generality, consider the second-order differential equation with a regular singular point:

$$x^2 y'' + xp(x)\, y' + q(x)\, y = 0, \tag{4.4.1}$$

where the functions $p(x)$ and $q(x)$, which are analytic at $x = 0$, have the convergent power-series expansions

$$p(x) = \sum_{n=0}^{\infty} p_n x^n \quad \text{and} \quad q(x) = \sum_{n=0}^{\infty} q_n x^n \tag{4.4.2}$$

for $|x| < R$. We consider first $x > 0$, and assume a solution of Eq. (4.4.1) of the form

$$\phi(x) = \sum_{n=0}^{\infty} a_n x^{n+s}, \qquad a_0 \neq 0, \tag{4.4.3}$$

where the exponent s is to be determined. Then

$$\phi'(x) = \sum_{n=0}^{\infty} (n+s)a_n x^{n+s-1},$$

$$\phi''(x) = \sum_{n=0}^{\infty} (n+s)(n+s-1)a_n x^{n+s-2}.$$

Substitution of ϕ, ϕ', ϕ'', p and q into Eq. (4.4.1) yields

$$\sum_{n=0}^{\infty} (n+s)(n+s-1)a_n x^{n+s} + \left[\sum_{n=0}^{\infty} p_n x^n \right]\left[\sum_{n=0}^{\infty} (n+s)a_n x^{n+s} \right]$$

$$+ \left[\sum_{n=0}^{\infty} q_n x^n \right]\left[\sum_{n=0}^{\infty} a_n x^{n+s} \right] = 0,$$

which may be rewritten as

$$\sum_{n=0}^{\infty} (n+s)(n+s-1)a_n x^{n+s} + \sum_{n=0}^{\infty} \sum_{k=0}^{n} p_{n-k}(k+s)a_k x^{n+s}$$

$$+ \sum_{n=0}^{\infty} \sum_{k=0}^{n} q_{n-k}a_k x^{n+s} = 0$$

or

$$\sum_{n=0}^{\infty} \left[(n+s)(n+s-1)a_n + \sum_{k=0}^{n} (p_{n-k}(k+s) + q_{n-k})a_k \right] x^{n+s} = 0.$$

Thus ϕ given by (4.4.3) will satisfy Eq. (4.4.1) if

$$(n+s)(n+s-1)a_n + \sum_{k=0}^{n} \left[p_{n-k}(k+s) + q_{n-k} \right] a_k = 0 \qquad (4.4.4)$$

for $n = 0, 1, 2, \ldots$. Since $a_0 \neq 0$, we obtain for $n = 0$

$$s(s-1) + p_0 s + q_0 = 0, \qquad (4.4.5)$$

which is called the *indicial equation* of (4.4.1). The polynomial f defined by

$$f(s) = s(s-1) + p_0 s + q_0 \qquad (4.4.6)$$

is called the *indicial polynomial* of (4.4.1). From (4.4.5) it is evident that

$$f(s) = 0.$$

This quadratic equation has two roots s_1 and s_2, which are called the *characteristic exponents* of the differential equation (4.4.1).

Observing that

$$f(s+n) = (s+n)(s+n-1) + p_0(s+n) + q_0,$$

we write Eq. (4.4.4) as

$$f(s+n)a_n + \sum_{k=0}^{n-1} \left[p_{n-k}(k+s) + q_{n-k} \right] a_k = 0 \qquad (4.4.7)$$

for $n = 1, 2, 3, \ldots$. This is the *recurrence relation*. If we denote

$$g_n = \sum_{k=0}^{n-1} \left[p_{n-k}(k+s) + q_{n-k} \right] a_k,$$

then Eq. (4.4.7) may be written in the form

$$f(s+n)a_n + g_n = 0, \qquad n = 1, 2, 3, \ldots .$$

In terms of a_0 and s, a_n can be determined by

$$a_n(s) = -\frac{g_n(s)}{f(s+n)}, \qquad (4.4.8)$$

provided $f(s+n) \neq 0$. In fact, if we determine $a_1(s), a_2(s), \ldots, a_n(s)$ successively from (4.4.8), we find

$$a_n(s) = \frac{a_0 F_n(s)}{f(s+n)f(s+n-1)\cdots f(s+2)f(s+1)}, \qquad (4.4.9)$$

where $F_n(s)$ is a polynomial in s. If we write the indicial polynomial as

$$f(s) = (s-s_1)(s-s_2), \qquad (4.4.10)$$

then

$$f(s_1+n) = n\left[n + (s_1 - s_2) \right]. \qquad (4.4.11a)$$

If $\operatorname{Re} s_1 \geqslant \operatorname{Re} s_2,$[†] we immediately see that $f(s_1 + n) \neq 0$, and hence $a_n(s_1)$ exists for all $n = 1, 2, 3, \ldots$. Now if we let $a_0(s_1) = 1$, then

$$\phi_1(x) = x^{s_1} \sum_{n=0}^{\infty} a_n(s_1) x^n$$

is a solution of Eq. (4.4.1) provided the series converges.

If $\operatorname{Re} s_1 > \operatorname{Re} s_2$ and $s_1 - s_2$ is not a positive integer, we see from

$$f(s_2 + n) = n[n - (s_1 - s_2)] \tag{4.4.11b}$$

that $f(s_2 + n) \neq 0$ and hence $a_n(s_2)$ exist for all $n = 1, 2, 3, \ldots$. Again if we let $a_0(s_2) = 1$, then

$$\phi_2(x) = x^{s_2} \sum_{n=0}^{\infty} a_n(s_2) x^n$$

is another solution of Eq. (4.4.1) provided we can prove that the series is convergent.

For $x < 0$ the results remain valid in the interval if we replace x^{s_1} by $|x|^{s_1}$ and x^{s_2} by $|x|^{s_2}$ throughout the computations.

We shall now prove the convergence of the series representing $\phi_1(x)$ and $\phi_2(x)$. For given s_1 and s_2, we are essentially required to show that the series

$$\sum_{n=0}^{\infty} a_n(s) x^n, \qquad a_0(s) = 1,$$

converges for $0 < r < R$.

[†]If $s_1 = a + ib$ is a complex exponent, then $s_2 = a - ib$. Hence $s_1 - s_2 = 2ib$, which cannot be an integer. Thus one can assume

$$\Phi(x) = x^{a+ib} \sum_{n=0}^{\infty} C_n x^n,$$

and

$$\overline{\Phi}(x) = x^{a-ib} \sum_{n=0}^{\infty} \overline{C}_n x^n,$$

to obtain two real solutions,

$$\phi_1(x) = \frac{1}{2}(\Phi + \overline{\Phi}), \qquad \phi_2(x) = \frac{1}{2i}(\Phi - \overline{\Phi}).$$

For a detailed treatment, see Rabenstein [33].

Applying the inequality $|c + d| \geqslant |c| - |d|$ to (4.4.11a), we have

$$|f(s_1 + n)| = n|n + (s_1 - s_2)| \geqslant n(n - |s_1 - s_2|). \qquad (4.4.12)$$

Since the series in (4.4.2) are convergent for $|x| = r$, it follows from Theorem 4.1.1 that there exists a constant $M > 0$ such that

$$|p_n| \leqslant \frac{M}{r^n}, \qquad |q_n| \leqslant \frac{M}{r^n}, \qquad n = 0, 1, 2, \ldots. \qquad (4.4.13)$$

From (4.4.7), (4.4.12) and (4.4.13) we obtain

$$n(n - |s_1 - s_2|)a_n(s_1) \leqslant \sum_{k=0}^{n-1} \left[\frac{M(k + s_1)}{r^{n-k}} + \frac{M}{r^{n-k}} \right] |a_k(s_1)|$$

$$\leqslant M \sum_{k=0}^{n-1} (k + |s_1| + 1) r^{k-n} |a_k(s_1)| \qquad (4.4.14)$$

for $n = 1, 2, 3, \ldots$.

Let us define an integer N satisfying

$$N - 1 \leqslant |s_1 - s_2| < N$$

and define $A_0, A_1, \ldots, A_{N-1}$ by

$$A_0 = a_0(s_1) = 1, \quad A_1 = |a_1(s_1)|, \ldots, \quad A_{N-1} = |a_{N-1}(s_1)|$$

and

$$n(n - |s_1 - s_2|)A_n = M \sum_{k=0}^{n-1} (k + |s_1| + 1) r^{k-n} A_k \qquad (4.4.15)$$

for $n = N, N + 1, \ldots$. By comparing A_n from the above definition with (4.3.14), we find that

$$|a_n(s_1)| \leqslant A_n, \qquad n = 0, 1, 2, \ldots. \qquad (4.4.16)$$

We shall now show that the series

$$\sum_{n=0}^{\infty} A_n x^n \qquad (4.4.17)$$

converges for $|x| < r$. We first replace n by $n + 1$ in (4.4.15) to obtain

$$(n+1)(n+1-|s_1-s_2|)A_{n+1} = M \sum_{k=0}^{n} (k+|s_1|+1)r^{k-n-1}A_k. \quad (4.4.18)$$

Then from (4.4.15) and (4.4.18) for $n \geqslant N$ we have

$$\frac{A_n}{A_{n+1}} = \frac{r(n+1)(n+1-|s_1-s_2|)}{n(n-|s_1-s_2|)+M(n+|s_1|+1)}.$$

Thus

$$\lim_{n \to \infty} \frac{A_n}{A_{n+1}} = r,$$

and hence the series (4.4.17) converges for $|x| < r$. Consequently, by the comparison test, the series

$$\sum_{n=0}^{\infty} a_n(s_1)x^n, \qquad a_0(s_1) = 1, \quad (4.4.19)$$

converges for $|x| < r < R$.

In a similar manner, we can show that the series

$$\sum_{n=0}^{\infty} a_n(s_2)x^n, \qquad a_0(s_2) = 1 \quad (4.4.20)$$

converges for $|x| < R$ provided $s_1 - s_2$ is not a positive integer.

It can be shown [This is left as an exercise for the reader.] that the functions

$$\phi_1(x) = |x|^{s_1} \sum_{n=0}^{\infty} a_n(s_1)x^n, \qquad a_0(s_1) = 1,$$

$$\phi_2(x) = |x|^{s_2} \sum_{n=0}^{\infty} a_n(s_2)x^n, \qquad a_0(s_2) = 1,$$

are linearly independent for $|x| < R$.

We summarize the results by the following theorem:

THEOREM 4.4.1 *Let the coefficients $p(x)$ and $q(x)$ of the differential equation*

$$x^2y'' + xp(x)y' + q(x)y = 0$$

be analytic and have power-series expansions

$$p(x) = \sum_{n=0}^{\infty} p_n x^n, \qquad q(x) = \sum_{n=0}^{\infty} q_n x^n$$

in the interval $|x| < R$, $R > 0$. *Let* s_1 *and* s_2 *be the roots of the indicial equation*

$$f(s) = s(s-1) + p(0)s + q(0) = 0. \tag{4.4.21}$$

If $\operatorname{Re} s_1 > \operatorname{Re} s_2$ *for* $0 < |x| < R$, *then there is a convergent power-series solution*

$$\phi_1(x) = |x|^{s_1} \sum_{n=0}^{\infty} a_n x^n, \qquad a_0(s_1) = 1, \tag{4.4.22}$$

for $|x| < R$.

If $\operatorname{Re} s_1 > \operatorname{Re} s_2$ *and* $s_1 - s_2$ *is not a positive integer in* $0 < |x| < R$, *then there is a second linearly independent solution*

$$\phi_2(x) = |x|^{s_2} \sum_{n=0}^{\infty} b_n x^n, \qquad b_0(s_2) = 1, \tag{4.4.23}$$

where the power series converges for $|x| < R$.

The coefficients a_n *and* b_n *can be determined by substituting the solutions in the differential equation.*

The above theorem holds true for $\operatorname{Re} s_1 > \operatorname{Re} s_2$ if $s_1 - s_2$ does not differ by a positive integer. We shall now consider the special cases.

1. Exponents equal. Let $s_1 = s_2$. In this case we shall find a_n in

$$\phi(x, s) = x^s \sum_{n=0}^{\infty} a_n x^n \tag{4.4.24}$$

for $x > 0$. Here we regard ϕ as a function of x and s. Thus if L is the linear operator in (4.4.1), we have

$$L[\phi(x, s)] = a_0 f(s) x^s$$

$$+ x^s \sum_{n=1}^{\infty} \left\{ f(n+s)a_n + \sum_{k=0}^{n-1} [(k+s)p_{n-k} + q_{n-k}]a_k \right\} x^n$$

$$= a_0 f(s) x^s, \qquad a_0 \neq 0, \tag{4.4.25}$$

in which the series vanishes by virtue of the recurrence relation (4.4.7).

Differentiating (4.4.25) with respect to s, we obtain

$$L\left[\frac{\partial}{\partial s}\phi(x,s)\right]=\frac{\partial}{\partial s}L[\phi(x,s)]=a_0[f'(s)+f(s)\ln x]x^s.$$

Thus if $s=s_1$, then

$$\frac{\partial}{\partial s}L[\phi(x,s)]\Big|_{s=s_1}=a_0[f'(s_1)+f(s_1)\ln x]x^{s_1}.$$

Since $s=s_1$ is a root of $f(s)=0$ with multiplicity two, we have $f(s_1)=0$ and $f'(s_1)=0$. Hence

$$L\left[\frac{\partial}{\partial s}\phi(x,s)\right]\Big|_{s=s_1}=0,$$

and consequently

$$\phi_2(x)=\frac{\partial}{\partial s}\phi(x,s)\Big|_{s=s_1}$$

will yield a solution of Eq. (4.4.1) provided the series involved converges. Computing formally from (4.4.24), we find that

$$\frac{\partial\phi}{\partial s}(x,s)=\frac{\partial}{\partial s}\left[x^s\sum_{n=0}^{\infty}a_n(s)x^n\right]=(x^s\ln x)\sum_{n=0}^{\infty}a_n(s)x^n+x^s\sum_{n=0}^{\infty}a_n'(s)x^n.$$

Hence

$$\phi_2(x)=\frac{\partial}{\partial s}\phi(x,s)\Big|_{s=s_1}=x^{s_1}\ln x\sum_{n=0}^{\infty}a_n(s_1)x^n+x^{s_1}\sum_{n=0}^{\infty}a_n'(s_1)x^n.$$

In terms of ϕ_1, namely,

$$\phi_1(x)=x^{s_1}\sum_{n=0}^{\infty}a_n(s_1)x^n,\qquad a_0(s_1)=1,$$

ϕ_2 may be written in the form

$$\phi_2(x)=\phi_1(x)\ln x+x^{s_1}\sum_{n=0}^{\infty}a_n'(s_1)x^n. \tag{4.4.26}$$

Solutions for $x<0$ can be obtained by replacing x^{s_1} by $|x|^{s_1}$ and $\ln x$ by $\ln|x|$.

Since $a_0(s_1) = 1$, we have $a'_0(s_1) = 0$. Noting that $f(s_1 + n) \neq 0$ and $a_n(s) = -g_n(s)/f(s+n)$, $a'_n(s_1)$ exists for $n = 1, 2, 3, \ldots$. Hence the series in (4.4.26) is defined. Consequently, we obtain a second linearly independent solution in the form

$$\phi_2(x) = \phi_1(x)\ln|x| + |x|^{s_1+1} \sum_{n=0}^{\infty} c_n x^n \qquad (4.4.27)$$

for $0 < |x| < R$, where the coefficients c_n are determined directly from Eq. (4.4.1). The convergence of the series in (4.4.27) can be proved like that of the series (4.4.19).

2. *Exponents differ by a positive integer.* Let $s_1 - s_2 = m$, where m is a positive integer. We consider first the case $x > 0$. From (4.4.10) we have

$$f(s+m) = (s+m-s_1)(s+m-s_2)$$
$$= (s-s_2)(s+m-s_2),$$

since $s_1 = s_2 + m$. Thus by (4.4.9) it follows that

$$a_m(s) = \frac{a_0 F_m(s)}{(s-s_2)(s+m-s_2) f(s+m-1) \cdots f(s+2) f(s+1)}.$$

In view of (4.4.11b) $a_n(s_2)$ exists for all values of n except $n = m$. However, if F_m has a factor of $s - s_2$, then $a_m(s_2)$ is defined. In this case we have a second solution in the form

$$\phi_2(x) = x^{s_2} \sum_{n=0}^{\infty} a_n(s_2) x^n, \qquad a_0(s_2) = 1.$$

If F_m does not vanish when $s = s_2$, we choose $a_0 = s - s_2$, so that

$$a_m(s) = \frac{F_m(s)}{(s+m-s_2) f(s+m-1) \cdots f(s+2) f(s+1)}.$$

This shows that $a_n(s_2)$ is finite for all values of n.

Now let us define

$$\phi(x,s) = x^s \sum_{n=0}^{\infty} a_n(s) x^n$$

with $a_0 = s - s_2$. Recalling from (4.4.25) that

$$L[\phi(x,s)] = (s - s_2) f(s) x^s, \tag{4.4.28}$$

from which we immediately see that

$$L[\phi(x, s_2)] = 0.$$

Hence we determine a solution given by

$$\phi_2(x) = \phi(x, s_2).$$

By virtue of (4.4.9), namely

$$a_n(s) = \frac{(s - s_2) F_n(s)}{f(s+n) f(s+n-1) \cdots f(s+2) f(s+1)},$$

and

$$f(s_2 + n) = n(n - m) \neq 0 \qquad \text{for} \quad n = 1, 2, 3, \ldots, m-1,$$

we see that

$$a_1(s_2) = a_2(s_2) = \cdots = a_{m-1}(s_2) = 0. \tag{4.4.29}$$

Thus we have

$$\phi_2(x) = x^{s_2} \sum_{n=m}^{\infty} a_n(s_2) x^n$$

$$= x^{s_2 + m} \sum_{n=0}^{\infty} a_{m+n}(s_2) x^n$$

$$= x^{s_1} \sum_{n=0}^{\infty} c_n(s_2) x^n, \tag{4.4.30}$$

since $s_1 = s_2 + m$ and $c_n \equiv a_{m+n}$. It can be readily seen that ϕ_2 is just a constant multiple of $\phi_1(x)$, that is, $\phi_2(x) = c\phi_1(x)$ for some constant c.

We shall now find the second linearly independent solution ϕ_2 for $x > 0$. Differentiating (4.4.28) with respect to s, we obtain

$$\frac{\partial}{\partial s} L[\phi(x,s)] = L\left[\frac{\partial}{\partial s} \phi(x,s)\right] = f(s) x^s + (s - s_2)[f'(s) + f(s) \ln x] x^s$$

If we let $s = s_2$, we find that

$$\phi_2(x) = \frac{\partial \phi(x, s)}{\partial s}\bigg|_{s=s_2}$$

is a solution. Thus

$$\phi_2(x) = (x^{s_2} \ln x) \sum_{n=0}^{\infty} a_n(s_2) x^n + x^{s_2} \sum_{n=0}^{\infty} a_n'(s_2) x^n.$$

In view of (4.4.29) and (4.4.30), we have

$$\phi_2(x) = c\phi_1(x) \ln x + x^{s_2} \sum_{n=0}^{\infty} b_n x^n,$$

where $b_n = a_n'(s_2)$. For $x < 0$, x^{s_1}, x^{s_2} and $\ln x$ are replaced by $|x|^{s_1}$, $|x|^{s_2}$ and $\ln|x|$ respectively. Thus the solutions are given by

$$\phi_1(x) = |x|^{s_1} \sum_{n=0}^{\infty} a_n x^n,$$

$$\phi_2(x) = c\phi_1(x) \ln|x| + |x|^{s_2} \sum_{n=0}^{\infty} b_n x^n.$$

These solutions can readily be shown to be linearly independent and convergent for $|x| < R$.

4.5 Bessel's Equation

Here we will illustrate the application of the Frobenius method to Bessel's equation, which occurs frequently in problems of mathematical physics involving cylindrical symmetry.

The standard form of Bessel's equation is given by

$$x^2 y'' + xy' + (x^2 - \nu^2) y = 0, \tag{4.5.1}$$

where ν is a nonnegative real number. We shall first restrict our attention to $x > 0$. Since $x = 0$ is the regular singular point, a solution is taken in accordance with the Frobenius method to be

$$\phi(x) = \sum_{n=0}^{\infty} a_n x^{s+n}, \tag{4.5.2}$$

where the index s is to be determined. Substitution of this series into Eq. (4.5.1) then yields

$$[s^2 - \nu^2]a_0 x^s + [(s+1)^2 - \nu^2]a_1 x^{s+1}$$

$$+ \sum_{n=2}^{\infty} \{[(s+n)^2 - \nu^2]a_n + a_{n-2}\} x^{s+n} = 0. \quad (4.5.3)$$

The requirement that the coefficient of x^s vanish leads to the indicial equation

$$(s^2 - \nu^2)a_0 = 0, \quad (4.5.4)$$

from which it follows that $s = \pm \nu$ for arbitrary $a_0 \neq 0$. Since the leading term in the series (4.5.2) is $a_0 x^s$, it is clear that for $\nu > 0$ the solution of Bessel's equation corresponding to the choice $s = \nu$ vanishes at the origin, whereas the solution corresponding to $s = -\nu$ is infinite at that point.

We consider first the regular solution of Bessel's equation, that is, the solution corresponding to the choice $s = \nu$. The vanishing of the coefficient of x^{s+1} in Eq. (4.5.3) requires that

$$(2\nu + 1)a_1 = 0, \quad (4.5.5)$$

which in turn implies that $a_1 = 0$ (since $\nu \geqslant 0$). From the requirement that the coefficient of x^{s+n} in Eq. (4.5.3) be zero we obtain the two-term recurrence relation

$$a_n = -\frac{a_{n-2}}{n(2\nu + n)}. \quad (4.5.6)$$

Since $a_1 = 0$, it is obvious that $a_n = 0$ for $n = 3, 5, 7, \dots$. The remaining coefficients are given by

$$a_{2k} = \frac{(-1)^k a_0}{2^{2k}k!(\nu + k)(\nu + k - 1)\cdots(\nu + 1)} \quad (4.5.7)$$

for $k = 1, 2, 3, \dots$. This relation may also be written as

$$a_{2k} = \frac{(-1)^k 2^\nu \Gamma(\nu + 1)a_0}{2^{2k+\nu}k!\Gamma(\nu + k + 1)}, \qquad k = 1, 2, \dots,$$

where $\Gamma(\alpha)$ is the gamma function, whose properties are described in Appendix II.

Hence, the regular solution of Bessel's equation takes the form

$$\phi(x) = a_0 \sum_{k=0}^{\infty} \frac{(-1)^k 2^\nu \Gamma(\nu+1)}{2^{2k+\nu} k! \Gamma(\nu+k+1)} x^{2k+\nu}. \tag{4.5.9}$$

It is customary to choose

$$a_0 = \frac{1}{2^\nu \Gamma(\nu+1)} \tag{4.5.10}$$

and to denote the corresponding solution by $J_\nu(x)$. This solution, called the *Bessel function of the first kind of order ν*, is therefore given by

$$J_\nu(x) = \sum_{k=0}^{\infty} \frac{(-1)^k x^{2k+\nu}}{2^{2k+\nu} k! \Gamma(\nu+k+1)}. \tag{4.5.11}$$

To determine the irregular solution of the Bessel equation for $s = -\nu$ we proceed as above. In this way, we obtain as the analogue of Eq. (4.5.5) the relation

$$(-2\nu+1)a_1 = 0,$$

from which it follows that $a_1 = 0$ (the case $\nu = \frac{1}{2}$ is mentioned later). Using the recurrence relation

$$a_n = -\frac{a_{n-2}}{n(n-2\nu)}, \qquad n \geqslant 2, \tag{4.5.12}$$

we obtain as the irregular solution the *Bessel function of the first kind of order $-\nu$*:

$$J_{-\nu}(x) = \sum_{k=0}^{\infty} \frac{(-1)^k x^{2k-\nu}}{2^{2k-\nu} k! \Gamma(-\nu+k+1)}. \tag{4.5.13}$$

It can be easily proved that J_ν and $J_{-\nu}$ converge for all values of x, and are linearly independent if ν is not an integer. Thus the general solution of the

Bessel equation for nonintegral ν is

$$\phi(x) = c_1 J_\nu(x) + c_2 J_{-\nu}(x). \tag{4.5.14}$$

If ν is an integer, say $\nu = n$, then from Eq. (4.5.13), noting that when gamma functions in the coefficients of the first n terms become infinite, the coefficients become zero, we have

$$J_{-n}(x) = \sum_{k=n}^{\infty} \frac{(-1)^k x^{2k-n}}{2^{2k-n} k! \Gamma(-n+k+1)}$$

$$= (-1)^n \sum_{k=0}^{\infty} \frac{(-1)^k x^{2k+n}}{2^{2k+n} k! \Gamma(n+k+1)}$$

$$= (-1)^n J_n(x). \tag{4.4.15}$$

This shows that J_{-n} is not independent of J_n, and therefore a second linearly independent solution is required.

A number of distinct irregular solutions are discussed in the literature, but the one most commonly used, as defined by Weber, is

$$Y_\nu(x) = \frac{(\cos \nu\pi) J_\nu(x) - J_{-\nu}(x)}{\sin \nu\pi}. \tag{4.5.16}$$

For nonintegral ν, it is obvious that $Y_\nu(x)$, being a linear combination of $J_\nu(x)$ and $J_{-\nu}(x)$, is linearly independent of $J_\nu(x)$. When ν is a nonnegative integer n, $Y_\nu(x)$ is indeterminate. But

$$Y_n(x) = \lim_{\nu \to n} Y_\nu(x)$$

exists and is a solution of the Bessel equation. Moreover, it is linearly independent of $J_n(x)$ (for an extended treatment see Watson [39]). The function $Y_\nu(x)$ is called the *Bessel function of the second kind of order ν*. Thus the general solution of the Bessel equation is

$$\phi(x) = c_1 J_\nu(x) + c_2 Y_\nu(x), \qquad \text{for } \nu \geq 0. \tag{4.5.17}$$

Like elementary functions Bessel's functions are tabulated (See Jahnke and Emde [12]). The functions J_0, J_1, Y_0 and Y_1 are plotted for small values of x, as shown in Figure 4.5-1.

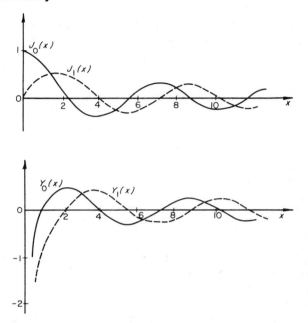

Figure 4.5-1

Bessel functions for $\nu = \pm \frac{1}{2}$ can readily be determined (see Exercise 11). In particular, these functions are expressible in terms of elementary functions:

$$J_{1/2}(x) = \sqrt{\frac{2}{\pi x}} \, \sin x, \qquad x > 0,$$

$$J_{-1/2}(x) = \sqrt{\frac{2}{\pi x}} \, \cos x, \qquad x > 0.$$

4.6 The Point at Infinity

It is sometimes necessary to determine the behavior of solutions of the differential equation

$$L[\,y\,] = y'' + p(x)\,y' + q(x)\,y = 0 \qquad (4.6.1)$$

for large values of the independent variable x. To study this equation in the neighborhood of infinity, we simply employ the substitution

$$x = \frac{1}{t} \qquad (4.6.2)$$

and investigate the transformed equation in the neighborhood of the point $t=0$.

Applying the substitution (4.6.2), we obtain

$$\frac{dy}{dx} = -t^2 \frac{dy}{dt},$$

$$\frac{d^2y}{dx^2} = t^4 \frac{d^2y}{dt^2} + 2t^3 \frac{dy}{dt},$$

so that the equation (4.6.1) becomes

$$\frac{d^2y}{dt^2} + \left[\frac{2}{t} - \frac{1}{t^2} P\left(\frac{1}{t}\right)\right] \frac{dy}{dt} + \frac{1}{t^4} q\left(\frac{1}{t}\right) y = 0. \qquad (4.6.3)$$

Equation (4.6.1) is said to have an ordinary point, a regular singular point or an irregular singular point at infinity if and only if Eq. (4.6.3) has an ordinary point, a regular singular point or an irregular singular point respectively at the point $t=0$.

To be more specific $t=0$ is an ordinary point if the coefficients

$$P(t) = \frac{2}{t} - \frac{1}{t^2} P\left(\frac{1}{t}\right),$$

$$Q(t) = \frac{1}{t^4} q\left(\frac{1}{t}\right)$$

are analytic at $t=0$. $t=0$ is a regular singular point if the coefficients $tP(t)$ and $t^2Q(t)$ are analytic at $t=0$, and, of course, $t=0$ is an irregular singular point if either or both of the coefficients $tP(t)$ and $t^2Q(t)$ are not analytic at $t=0$.

Example 4.6.1   Find the general solution of the equation

$$4x^3 \frac{d^2y}{dx^2} + 6x^2 \frac{dy}{dx} + y = 0 \qquad (4.6.4)$$

for large values of x.

First we rewrite the given equation in the form

$$\frac{d^2y}{dx^2} + \frac{3}{2x} \frac{dy}{dx} + \frac{1}{4x^3} y = 0. \qquad (4.6.5)$$

In this case $p(1/t) = \frac{3}{2}t$ and $q(1/t) = \frac{1}{4}t^3$, so that

$$P(t) = \frac{2}{t} - \frac{3}{2t} = \frac{1}{2t} \quad \text{and} \quad Q(t) = \frac{1}{4t}.$$

Then Eq. (4.6.5) is transformed into

$$4t\frac{d^2y}{dt^2} + 2\frac{dy}{dt} + y = 0,$$

which has a regular singularity at $t = 0$. Thus we can proceed according to the Frobenius method to obtain the general solution [see Exercise 6(a)]

$$\phi(t) = c_1 \sum_{n=0}^{\infty} \frac{(-1)^n}{(2n)!} t^n + c_2 \sum_{n=0}^{\infty} \frac{(-1)^n}{(2n+1)!} t^n.$$

In terms of the original variable x, the solution takes the form

$$\phi(x) = c_1 \sum_{n=0}^{\infty} \frac{(-1)^n}{(2n)!} x^{-n} + c_2 \sum_{n=0}^{\infty} \frac{(-1)^n}{(2n+1)!} x^{-n},$$

which can be easily identified as

$$\phi(x) = c_1 \cos x^{-1/2} + c_2 x^{1/2} \sin x^{-1/2}.$$

EXERCISES

1. Determine the general solution of each of the following equations near an ordinary point and specify the interval in which the solution is valid:

   (a) $y'' + xy' + y = 0$, $y(0) = 1$, $y'(0) = 2$.
   (b) $y'' + xy = 0$, $y(0) = 1$, $y'(0) = 0$.
   (c) $(x^2 + 4)y'' + 2xy' - 12y = 0$.
   (d) $y'' + x^2y' - 4xy = 0$.
   (e) $y'' - xy = 0$.
   (f) $y'' - y = \sin x$.

2. Expand the function $f(x,t) = (1 - 2xt + t^2)^{-1/2}$ in a power series and show that

$$f(x,t) = (1 - 2xt + t^2)^{-1/2} = \sum_{n=0}^{\infty} P_n(x) t^n$$

f is called the *generating function*.

3. An alternative formula for the Legendre polynomials is *Rodrigues' formula*

$$P_n(x) = \frac{1}{2^n n!} \frac{d^n}{dx^n} (x^2 - 1)^n.$$

Verify the validity of the formula.

4. Show that the Legendre polynomials are orthogonal on the interval $[-1, 1]$, that is,

$$\int_{-1}^{1} P_m(x) P_n(x) \, dx = 0 \qquad \text{for} \quad m \neq n.$$

When $m = n$, show that

$$\|P_n\|^2 = \int_{-1}^{1} \left[P_n(x) \right]^2 dx = \frac{2}{2n+1} \qquad \text{for} \quad n = 0, 1, 2, \ldots, .$$

5. (a) Show that any polynomial $g(x)$ of degree n can be represented in the form

$$g(x) = \sum_{k=0}^{n} c_k P_k(x),$$

where

$$c_k = \frac{2k+1}{2} \int_{-1}^{1} g(x) P_k(x) \, dx.$$

(b) Express $g(x) = 3x^2 + 2x + 1$ in the form

$$g(x) = c_0 P_0 + c_1 P_1(x) + c_2 P_2(x).$$

(c) Compute the zeros of $P_1(x)$, $P_2(x)$ and $P_3(x)$.

6. Classify the singular points and solve the following equations:

    (a) $4xy'' + 2y' + y = 0$.
    (b) $x^2 y'' + (x^2 + x/2) y' + xy = 0$.
    (c) $2x^2 y'' - xy' + (1+x) y = 0$.
    (d) $xy'' + 2y' - y = 0$.
    (e) $x^2 y'' + (2+3x)xy' - 2y = 0$.
    (f) $xy'' + y' + y = 0$.
    (g) $x^2 y'' + 3xy' + (1-2x) y = 0$.

7. Prove the convergence in Theorem 4.4.1.

8. Consider the equation with a regular singular point

    $$x^2 y'' + xp(x) y' + q(x) y = 0.$$

    If ϕ_1 is a solution on an interval I, determine ϕ_2 by the method of variation of parameters, that is, by letting $\phi_2 = u(x)\phi_1$, for the following cases:

    (a) Equal exponents.
    (b) Exponents differing by a positive integer.

9. Solve the equation

    $$x(x-1) y'' + (3x-1) y' + y = 0$$

    by applying the method stated in Exercise 8.

10. Solve the equation

    $$x(1-x) y'' + 2(1-x) y' + 2y = 0$$

    by applying the method stated in Exercise 8.

11. Show that for $x > 0$

    $$J_{1/2}(x) = \sqrt{\frac{2}{\pi x}} \sin x,$$

    $$J_{-1/2}(x) = \sqrt{\frac{2}{\pi x}} \cos x.$$

12. $J_0(x)$ is a solution of the equation

    $$x^2 y'' + xy' + x^2 y = 0$$

for $x > 0$. If $\phi = x^{1/2}J_0$, show that ϕ satisfies the equation

$$y'' + \left(1 + \frac{1}{4x^2}\right)y = 0 \qquad (A)$$

for $x > 0$.

Show that J_0 has infinitely many positive zeros by comparing (A) with

$$y'' + y = 0.$$

13. Prove that $J_\nu(x)$ and $J_{-\nu}(x)$ converge for all values of x. Discuss the behavior of $J_\nu(x)$ as $x \to 0$.

14. Prove that between any two positive consecutive zeros of J_ν, there is a zero of $J_{\nu+1}$.

15. Show that Bessel's function of the first kind satisfies the recurrence relations

(a) $J_{\nu+1} + J_{\nu-1} = (2\nu/x)J_\nu$.

(b) $J_{\nu+1} - J_{\nu-1} = -2J_\nu'$.

16. Show that

$$f(x,t) = e^{(t-1/t)x/2} = \sum_{n=-\infty}^{\infty} J_n(x)t^n$$

for $t \neq 0$.

17. If n is a nonnegative integer, show that

$$J_n(x) = \frac{1}{\pi}\int_0^\pi \cos(n\theta - x\sin\theta)\,d\theta,$$

which is Bessel's integral form for J_n.

18. Prove the orthogonality of the Bessel functions

$$\int_0^a xJ_\nu(\lambda_m x)J_\nu(\lambda_n x)\,dx = 0, \qquad m \neq n.$$

When $m = n$,

$$\int_0^a xJ_\nu^2(\lambda_n x)\,dx = \frac{a^2}{2}\left[J_{\nu+1}(\lambda_n a)\right]^2.$$

19. Obtain the solution in series which converge for large values of $|x|$ of the equation

$$4x^4 \frac{d^2y}{dx^2} + 4x^3 \frac{dy}{dx} + (1 - x^2)\, y = 0.$$

20. If $x^2 p(x) - 2x$, $x^4 q(x)$ and $x^4 f(x)$ are analytic in the neighborhood of infinity, show that infinity is an ordinary point of the equation

$$y'' + p(x)\, y' + q(x)\, y = f(x).$$

Chapter 5.
Systems of Equations

5.1 Systems of Equations. Existence Theorems

A system of first-order equations in general may be written in the form

$$\frac{dy_1}{dt} = f_1(t, y_1, y_2, \ldots, y_n),$$

$$\frac{dy_2}{dt} = f_2(t, y_1, y_2, \ldots, y_n), \qquad (5.1.1)$$

$$\vdots$$

$$\frac{dy_n}{dt} = f_n(t, y_1, y_2, \ldots, y_n),$$

where y_i are unknown functions and t is the independent variable. f_i are defined in some region R of $(n+1)$-dimensional space $(t, y_1, y_2, \ldots, y_n)$. If we introduce the vector notation

$$Y(t) = \begin{bmatrix} y_1(t) \\ y_2(t) \\ \vdots \\ y_n(t) \end{bmatrix}, \qquad F = \begin{bmatrix} f_1(t, y_1, y_2, \ldots, y_n) \\ f_2(t, y_1, y_2, \ldots, y_n) \\ \vdots \\ f_n(t, y_1, y_2, \ldots, y_n) \end{bmatrix},$$

then the system (5.1.1) simply takes the form

$$Y' = F(t, Y).$$ (5.1.2)

A differential equation of nth order such as

$$y^{(n)}(t) = f(t, y, \ldots, y^{(n-1)})$$

can be transformed into a system of first-order equations. This can be accomplished by introducing

$$y_1 = y,$$

$$y_2 = y',$$

$$y_3 = y'',$$

$$\vdots$$

$$y_n = y^{(n-1)}$$

to obtain

$$y_1' = y_2,$$

$$y_2' = y_3,$$

$$\vdots$$ (5.1.3)

$$y_{n-1}' = y_n,$$

$$y_n' = f(t, y_1, y_2, \ldots, y_n),$$

which is a special case of the system (5.1.1).

Another special case of the system (5.1.1) is the linear system

$$y_1' = a_{11}(t) y_1 + a_{12}(t) y_2 + \cdots + a_{1n}(t) y_n + g_1(t),$$

$$y_2' = a_{21}(t) y_1 + a_{22}(t) y_2 + \cdots + a_{2n}(t) y_n + g_2(t),$$

$$\vdots$$

$$y_n' = a_{n1}(t) y_1 + a_{n2}(t) y_2 + \cdots + a_{nn}(t) y_n + g_n(t).$$

In matrix notation this system appears in the form

$$Y' = AY + G,$$ (5.1.4)

where

$$
A = \begin{bmatrix}
a_{11} & a_{12} & \cdots & a_{1n} \\
a_{21} & a_{22} & \cdots & a_{2n} \\
\vdots & \vdots & & \vdots \\
a_{n1} & a_{n2} & \cdots & a_{nn}
\end{bmatrix}, \qquad
G = \begin{bmatrix}
g_1 \\
g_2 \\
\vdots \\
g_n
\end{bmatrix}.
$$

A is called the *coefficient matrix*. The system (5.1.4) is a nonhomogeneous linear system. When $G = 0$, we have a linear homogeneous system

$$
Y' = AY.
$$

THEOREM 5.1.1 (Existence and uniqueness) *Suppose that $F(t, Y)$ is continuous and satisfies a Lipschitz condition with respect to Y in some domain D of $(n + 1)$-dimensional (t, Y) space. If $(t_0, Y_0) \in D$, then there exists a unique solution $\Phi(t)$ on $J = |t - t_0| \leqslant h$, $h > 0$, such that $(t, \Phi(t)) \in D$ for $t \in J$ and*

$$
\Phi'(t) = F(t, \Phi(t)) \qquad \text{for all} \quad t \in J
$$

and

$$
\Phi(t_0) = Y_0.
$$

The proof is similar to the proof of Theorem 2.5.2 and is left to the reader.

THEOREM 5.1.2 (Continuity) *If $F(t, Y)$ is continuous and satisfies a Lipschitz condition with respect to Y in D, then the solution of the initial-value problem*

$$
Y' = F(t, Y),
$$

$$
Y(t_0) = Y_0
$$

varies continuously with the initial data (t_0, Y_0).

The proof is similar to the proof of Theorem 2.5.4 and is left to the reader.

5.2 Homogeneous Linear Systems

Consider the equation

$$Y' = A(t)Y, \qquad (5.2.1)$$

where $A(t)$ is an $n \times n$ coefficient matrix. We will now state without proof [it is left to the reader] the following theorem.

THEOREM 5.2.1 *If $a_{ij}(t)$ are continuous in some interval J, then there exists a unique solution of the system*

$$Y' = A(t)Y$$

satisfying the initial condition

$$Y(t_0) = E \qquad (5.2.2)$$

for any $t_0 \in J$, where E is a given vector.

The significant characteristic in the case of linear systems is that the solution is valid at all points on the interval J.

We will now focus our attention on the specific characteristics of linear systems.

THEOREM 5.2.2 *If $\Phi_1, \Phi_2, \ldots, \Phi_n$ are solutions of the system (5.2.1), then any linear combination $\Phi(t) = c_1\Phi_1 + c_2\Phi_2 + \cdots + c_n\Phi_n$ is also a solution for any constants c_j.*

Proof Differentiation of $\Phi(t)$ yields

$$\Phi' = \sum_{j=1}^{n} c_j \Phi'_j(t)$$

$$= A(t) \sum_{j=1}^{n} c_j \Phi_j(t)$$

$$= A(t)\Phi(t). \qquad \blacksquare$$

THEOREM 5.2.3 *Let Φ_j be the solutions of the system (5.2.1) satisfying $\Phi_j(t_0) = E_j$, where E_j are linearly independent vectors. Then Φ_j are linearly independent.*

Proof Suppose that Φ_j are linearly dependent. Then there exist c_j not all zero such that

$$c_1\Phi_1 + c_2\Phi_2 + \cdots + c_n\Phi_n = 0$$

for all $t \in J$. Since Φ_j are the solutions that satisfy $\Phi_j(t_0) = E_j$, we have

$$c_1\Phi_1(t_0) + c_2\Phi_2(t_0) + \cdots + c_n\Phi_n(t_0) = 0,$$

and consequently

$$c_1E_1 + c_2E_2 + \cdots + c_nE_n = 0.$$

Since E_j are linearly independent, we have $c_1 = c_2 = \cdots = c_n = 0$. This contradicts the assumption, and hence Φ_j are linearly independent. ∎

THEOREM 5.2.4 *Let Φ_j be n linearly independent solutions of the system (5.2.1). Then for every solution Φ there exists a unique linear combination of the Φ_j for $j = 1, 2, \ldots, n$.*

Proof Let Φ be any solution of the system (5.2.1) satisfying $\Phi(t_0) = E$. Let $\Phi_j(t_0) = E_j$. Since E_j are linearly independent, there exist c_j such that

$$E = c_1E_1 + c_2E_2 + \cdots + c_nE_n.$$

Hence the function

$$c_1\Phi_1 + c_2\Phi_2 + \cdots + c_n\Phi_n$$

is a solution of the system (5.2.1) which assumes the value E at t_0. By the uniqueness theorem, this function must be Φ. Therefore we have

$$\Phi = c_1\Phi_1 + c_2\Phi_2 + \cdots + c_n\Phi_n. \tag{5.2.3}$$

∎

In summary, we may state that the solution set of the system (5.2.1) forms an n-dimensional vector space over the complex field. The solution set $\{\Phi_j\}$ is said to form a *basis* or a *fundamental set*.

DEFINITION 5.2.1   The matrix function Ψ having Φ_j as column vectors is called a *solution matrix* of the system on an interval J. If Φ_j are linearly independent, then Ψ is called a *fundamental matrix* of the system on an interval J.

It is evident that Ψ is a solution matrix if and only if

$$\Psi' = A(t)\Psi \qquad (5.2.4)$$

If $\Psi(t_0) = I$, where I is the identity matrix, a solution matrix Ψ is called the *standard fundamental matrix.*

A simple test of whether a solution matrix is a fundamental matrix can be readily established. First we present what is known as *Abel's identity* or *Liouville's formula.*

THEOREM 5.2.5   *Let Ψ be a solution matrix of the system (5.2.1) on J. Then for some $t_0 \in J$,*

$$\det \Psi(t) = \det \Psi(t_0)\exp\left[\int_{t_0}^{t} \sum_{i=1}^{n} a_{ii}(\tau)\,d\tau\right]$$

for all $t \in J$.

Proof   Let Φ_j be the column vectors of Ψ. Let Φ_{ij} be the components of Φ_j, so that the system (5.2.1) may be expressed in the form

$$\Phi_{ij}' = \sum_{k=1}^{n} a_{ik}\Phi_{kj}, \qquad i,j = 1,2,\ldots,n. \qquad (5.2.5)$$

The derivative of $\det \Psi$ with respect to t is

$$(\det \Psi)' = \begin{vmatrix} \Phi_{11}' & \cdots & \Phi_{1n}' \\ \Phi_{21} & \cdots & \Phi_{2n} \\ \vdots & & \vdots \\ \Phi_{n1} & \cdots & \Phi_{nn} \end{vmatrix} + \begin{vmatrix} \Phi_{11} & \cdots & \Phi_{1n} \\ \Phi_{21}' & \cdots & \Phi_{2n}' \\ \vdots & & \vdots \\ \Phi_{n1} & \cdots & \Phi_{nn} \end{vmatrix} + \cdots + \begin{vmatrix} \Phi_{11} & \cdots & \Phi_{1n} \\ \Phi_{21} & \cdots & \Phi_{2n} \\ \vdots & & \vdots \\ \Phi_{n1}' & \cdots & \Phi_{nn}' \end{vmatrix}.$$

By virtue of (5.2.5) we have

$$(\det \Psi)' = \begin{vmatrix} \sum_{k=1}^{n} a_{1k}\Phi_{k1} & \cdots & \sum_{k=1}^{n} a_{1k}\Phi_{kn} \\ \Phi_{21} & \cdots & \Phi_{2n} \\ \vdots & & \vdots \\ \Phi_{n1} & \cdots & \Phi_{nn} \end{vmatrix} + \begin{vmatrix} \Phi_{11} & \cdots & \Phi_{1n} \\ \sum_{k=1}^{n} a_{2k}\Phi_{k1} & \cdots & \sum_{k=1}^{n} a_{2k}\Phi_{kn} \\ \vdots & & \vdots \\ \Phi_{n1} & \cdots & \Phi_{nn} \end{vmatrix}$$

$$+ \cdots + \begin{vmatrix} \Phi_{11} & \cdots & \Phi_{1n} \\ \Phi_{21} & \cdots & \Phi_{2n} \\ \vdots & & \vdots \\ \sum_{k=1}^{n} a_{nk}\Phi_{k1} & \cdots & \sum_{k=1}^{n} a_{nk}\Phi_{kn} \end{vmatrix}.$$

By elementary row operations (multiplying the second row by a_{12}, the third row by a_{13}, etc., and subtracting the sum of the last $n-1$ rows from the first) we can easily see that the first determinant is $a_{11} \det \Psi$. Evaluating the other determinants in a similar manner, we obtain

$$(\det \Psi)' = \sum_{i=1}^{n} a_{ii}(t) \det \Psi.$$

This is a first-order equation the solution of which is

$$\det \Psi(t) = \det \Psi(t_0) \exp \left[\int_{t_0}^{t} \sum_{i=1}^{n} a_{ii}(\tau) \, d\tau \right]. \tag{5.2.6}$$

$\blacksquare$

It should be noted here that since $\det \Psi(t_0)$ is arbitrary, either $\det \Psi(t) \neq 0$ or $\det \Psi(t) = 0$ for all $t \in J$.

THEOREM 5.2.6 Ψ *is a fundamental matrix of the system* (5.2.1) *if and only if* $\det \Psi(t) \neq 0$ *for every* $t \in J$.

Proof Let Φ be any solution of the system (5.2.1). Since Φ_i are the linearly independent column vectors of Ψ, we express

$$\Phi = c_1 \Phi_1 + c_2 \Phi_2 + \cdots + c_n \Phi_n,$$

with c_j not all zero. It can be easily seen that

$$\Phi = \Psi C,$$

where C is the column vector with components $c_1, c_2, \ldots, c_n$. For some $t_0 \in J$ this is a system of n equations with n unknowns c_j. The solution exists, and hence $\det \Psi(t_0) \neq 0$. Thus by (5.2.6), $\det \Psi(t) \neq 0$ for any $t \in J$. Conversely, if $\det \Psi(t) \neq 0$ for $t \in J$, it immediately follows that Φ_j are linearly independent for any $t \in J$, and hence Ψ is a fundamental matrix.   ∎

It should be remarked that the determinant of a matrix may be identically zero on some interval although its column vectors are linearly independent. This fact can be seen easily from the example

$$\Psi(t) = \begin{pmatrix} t & t^2 \\ 0 & 0 \end{pmatrix}.$$

The preceding theorem states that this cannot happen for the solutions of the system (5.2.1).

THEOREM 5.2.7 *If Ψ is a fundamental matrix of the system (5.2.1), then so is ΨC, where C is a constant nonsingular matrix. Every fundamental matrix of the system (5.2.1) is of this type for some nonsingular matrix C.*

The proof is left as an exercise (Exercise 8).

5.3 Nonhomogeneous Linear Systems

Consider the nonhomogeneous linear system

$$Y' = A(t)Y + G(t), \tag{5.3.1}$$

where A and G are continuous in an interval J. Let us assume that we can find a fundamental matrix $\Psi(t)$ of the homogeneous system $Y' = AY$. Then we can express the general solution of the system (5.3.1) as

$$\Phi(t) = \Psi C + \Phi^*(t), \tag{5.3.2}$$

where C is an arbitrary column vector and Φ^* is a particular solution.

Let a particular solution of the system (5.3.1) be of the form

$$\Phi^*(t) = \Psi(t)V(t), \tag{5.3.3}$$

where $V(t)$ is an undetermined vector function. Differentiation yields

$$\Phi^{*\prime} = \Psi' V + \Psi V'.$$

Since $\Psi' = A\Psi$, substitution in (5.3.1) yields

$$A\Psi V + \Psi V' = A\Psi V + G.$$

Thus we have

$$\Psi V' = G.$$

Since Ψ is nonsingular for every $t \in J$, we express

$$V' = \Psi^{-1} G.$$

Integration simply gives

$$V(t) = \int_{t_0}^{t} \Psi^{-1}(\tau) G(\tau) \, d\tau$$

for $t_0 \in J$. Hence (5.3.3) becomes

$$\Phi^*(t) = \Psi(t) \int_{t_0}^{t} \Psi^{-1}(\tau) G(\tau) \, d\tau, \tag{5.3.4}$$

and the general solution of the nonhomogeneous system (5.3.1) is given by

$$\Phi(t) = \Psi(t) C + \Psi(t) \int_{t_0}^{t} \Psi^{-1}(\tau) G(\tau) \, d\tau. \tag{5.3.5}$$

Thus we have the following theorem:

THEOREM 5.3.1 *If Ψ is a fundamental matrix of the associated homogeneous system $Y' = AY$, then*

$$\Phi(t) = \Psi(t) \int_{t_0}^{t} \Psi^{-1}(\tau) G(\tau) \, d\tau$$

is that solution of the nonhomogeneous system

$$Y' = A(t)Y + G(t)$$

satisfying $\Phi(t_0) = 0$ for any $t_0 \in J$.

The solution of the nonhomogeneous system satisfying $\Phi(t_0) = E$ *is given by*

$$\Phi(t) = E\Psi^{-1}(t_0)\Psi(t) + \Psi(t)\int_{t_0}^{t}\Psi^{-1}(\tau)G(\tau)\,d\tau \tag{5.3.6}$$

The proof for (5.3.6) follows immediately by direct verification.

5.4 Linear Systems with Constant Coefficients

Consider the homogeneous linear system

$$Y' = AY, \tag{5.4.1}$$

where A is an $n \times n$ constant matrix.

When $n = 1$, (5.4.1) is a first-order equation, the solution of which is e^{tA}. When $n > 1$, that is, when A is a matrix and Y is a vector, the solution retains the same form.

Now we will formally define the exponential of a matrix.

DEFINITION 5.4.1 Let A be any $n \times n$ matrix. Then the *exponential matrix* e^A is defined by the series

$$e^A = I + \sum_{k=1}^{\infty}\frac{A^k}{k!}$$

where A^k represents the kth power of A, and I is the $n \times n$ identity matrix.

Proof for convergence of the series for the exponential matrix and its properties are given in Appendix III.

THEOREM 5.4.1 *If A is an $n \times n$ constant matrix, then $\Psi(t) = e^{tA}$ is a fundamental matrix of the system $Y' = AY$ on J. If $\Phi(t_0) = E$, then the solution Φ is given by*

$$\Phi(t) = Ee^{(t-t_0)A}.$$

Proof Since $\Psi'(t) = Ae^{tA} = A\Psi$ for all $t \in J$, $\Psi(t) = e^{tA}$ is a solution. Moreover, $\Psi(0) = I$, and hence by Theorem 5.2.5, $\det\Psi(t) = e^{t\,\mathrm{tr}\,A}$. Thus Ψ is a fundamental matrix.

Let $\Phi(t)$ be any solution, and let $X(t) = \Phi(t)e^{-tA}$. Then

$$X'(t) = \Phi'(t)e^{-tA} - A\Phi(t)e^{-tA}$$

$$= \left[\Phi'(t) - A\Phi(t)\right]e^{-tA}$$

$$= 0.$$

Hence X is a constant vector C. Thus

$$X(t_0) = C = \Phi(t_0)e^{-t_0 A},$$

and consequently

$$\Phi(t) = Ce^{tA}$$

$$= \Phi(t_0)e^{-t_0 A}e^{tA}.$$

Since $t_0 A$ and tA commute, we have

$$\Phi(t) = \Phi(t_0)e^{(t-t_0)A}$$

$$= Ee^{(t-t_0)A}. \qquad \blacksquare$$

If we consider the nonhomogeneous system with constant coefficients

$$Y' = AY + G(t)$$

satisfying the initial condition $Y(t_0) = E$, it follows immediately from the previous results that the solution Φ is given by

$$\Phi(t) = Ee^{(t-t_0)A} + \int_{t_0}^{t} e^{(t-\tau)A}G(\tau)\,d\tau.$$

Although we have determined a solution matrix e^{tA} for a given matrix A, its calculation, in general, is quite difficult. Here we shall illustrate with two simple examples.

Example 5.4.1 Consider the matrix

$$A = \begin{pmatrix} 1 & 2 \\ 0 & 2 \end{pmatrix}.$$

Since

$$e^{tA} = I + tA + \frac{t^2}{2!}A^2 + \frac{t^3}{3!}A^3 + \cdots = \sum_{k=0}^{\infty} \frac{(tA)^k}{k!},$$

we have

$$e^{tA} = \begin{pmatrix} 1 & 0 \\ 0 & 1 \end{pmatrix} + t\begin{pmatrix} 1 & 2 \\ 0 & 2 \end{pmatrix} + \frac{t^2}{2!}\begin{pmatrix} 1 & 6 \\ 0 & 4 \end{pmatrix} + \frac{t^3}{3!}\begin{pmatrix} 1 & 14 \\ 0 & 8 \end{pmatrix} + \cdots$$

$$= \begin{pmatrix} e^t & f(t) \\ 0 & e^{2t} \end{pmatrix},$$

where

$$f(t) = 2t + \frac{6t^2}{2!} + \frac{14t^3}{3!} + \cdots .$$

We see that the nature of $f(t)$ is not obvious even in this simple example. If A is a diagonal matrix, e^{tA} can be determined with ease.

Example 5.4.2   Let

$$A = \begin{pmatrix} 1 & 0 \\ 0 & 2 \end{pmatrix}.$$

Then

$$e^{tA} = \sum_{k=0}^{\infty} \frac{t^k A^k}{k!} = \sum_{k=0}^{\infty} \frac{t^k}{k!}\begin{pmatrix} 1 & 0 \\ 0 & 2 \end{pmatrix}^k = \sum_{k=0}^{\infty} \frac{1}{k!}\begin{pmatrix} t^k & 0 \\ 0 & (2t)^k \end{pmatrix}.$$

Thus

$$e^{tA} = \begin{bmatrix} \displaystyle\sum_{k=0}^{\infty} \frac{t^k}{k!} & 0 \\ 0 & \displaystyle\sum_{k=0}^{\infty} \frac{(2t)^k}{k!} \end{bmatrix}$$

$$= \begin{pmatrix} e^t & 0 \\ 0 & e^{2t} \end{pmatrix}.$$

5.5   Eigenvalues and Eigenvectors

In this section we shall present a technique for determining a solution matrix for a system of equations.

Let $\Phi(t) = Be^{\lambda t}$ be a solution of the system $Y' = AY$, where A is a constant matrix and B a constant vector. Then Φ is a solution if and only if

$$B\lambda e^{\lambda t} = ABe^{\lambda t},$$

that is, since $e^{\lambda t} \neq 0$,

$$\lambda B = AB.$$

This implies that

$$(A - \lambda I)B = 0. \tag{5.5.1}$$

In order to obtain nontrivial solutions for the vector B we must have

$$\det(A - \lambda I) = 0 \tag{5.5.2}$$

This is a polynomial equation of degree n in λ, and hence there are n roots, not necessarily distinct and possibly complex. Equation (5.5.2) is called the *characteristic equation*, and

$$p(\lambda) = \det(A - \lambda I)$$

is called the *characteristic polynomial*. The roots λ_i of the characteristic equation are called the *eigenvalues* of A, and the corresponding vectors B_i are called the *eigenvectors* of A.

Example 5.5.1   Consider the system of equations

$$\begin{pmatrix} y'_1 \\ y'_2 \end{pmatrix} = \begin{pmatrix} 2 & 2 \\ 1 & 3 \end{pmatrix} \begin{pmatrix} y_1 \\ y_2 \end{pmatrix}. \tag{5.5.3}$$

The characteristic equation is

$$\det(A - \lambda I) = \begin{vmatrix} 2-\lambda & 2 \\ 1 & 3-\lambda \end{vmatrix} = (\lambda - 1)(\lambda - 4) = 0.$$

Thus the eigenvalues are $\lambda_1 = 1$ and $\lambda_2 = 4$.

For $\lambda_1 = 1$, the system (5.5.1) takes the form

$$\begin{pmatrix} 1 & 2 \\ 1 & 2 \end{pmatrix}\begin{pmatrix} b_1 \\ b_2 \end{pmatrix} = \begin{pmatrix} 0 \\ 0 \end{pmatrix},$$

where b_1 and b_2 are the components of B. The solution is $b_1 = -2\alpha$ and $b_2 = \alpha$ for arbitrary α, and hence the eigenvector is given by

$$B_1 = \begin{pmatrix} -2 \\ 1 \end{pmatrix}.$$

Thus the corresponding solution of (5.5.3) is

$$\Phi_1 = \begin{pmatrix} -2 \\ 1 \end{pmatrix} e^t.$$

The eigenvector corresponding to $\lambda_2 = 4$ is easily found to be

$$B_2 = \begin{pmatrix} 1 \\ 1 \end{pmatrix},$$

and hence the corresponding solution of (5.5.3) is

$$\Phi_2(t) = \begin{pmatrix} 1 \\ 1 \end{pmatrix} e^{4t}.$$

Thus a solution matrix $\Psi(t)$ is given by

$$\Psi(t) = \begin{pmatrix} -2e^t & e^{4t} \\ e^t & e^{4t} \end{pmatrix}.$$

Since $\det\Psi(t) \neq 0$ for $-\infty < t < \infty$, Ψ is a fundamental matrix. Therefore the general solution of the given system is given by

$$\Phi(t) = \Psi(t)C,$$

$$\begin{pmatrix} \phi_1(t) \\ \phi_2(t) \end{pmatrix} = c_1 \begin{pmatrix} -2e^t \\ e^t \end{pmatrix} + c_2 \begin{pmatrix} e^{4t} \\ e^{4t} \end{pmatrix},$$

where c_1 and c_2 are the components of C.

We may treat in a similar manner the system of equations whose characteristic roots are complex.

Example 5.5.2 Consider the system of equations

$$\begin{pmatrix} y_1' \\ y_2' \end{pmatrix} = \begin{pmatrix} 0 & 1 \\ -4 & 0 \end{pmatrix} \begin{pmatrix} y_1 \\ y_2 \end{pmatrix}. \tag{5.5.4}$$

Obviously the eigenvalues are $\lambda = \pm 2i$. For the case $\lambda = 2i$, we determine the eigenvector from the system

$$\begin{pmatrix} -2i & 1 \\ -4 & -2i \end{pmatrix} \begin{pmatrix} b_1 \\ b_2 \end{pmatrix} = \begin{pmatrix} 0 \\ 0 \end{pmatrix}.$$

The solution is $b_1 = \alpha$ and $b_2 = 2i\alpha$, where α is a scalar. Thus we obtain the corresponding eigenvector

$$B_1 = \begin{pmatrix} 1 \\ 2i \end{pmatrix}.$$

Similarly we determine the eigenvector associated with $\lambda = -2i$ to be

$$B_2 = \begin{pmatrix} 1 \\ -2i \end{pmatrix}.$$

Hence a solution matrix is given by

$$\Psi(t) = \begin{pmatrix} e^{2it} & e^{-2it} \\ 2ie^{2it} & -2ie^{-2it} \end{pmatrix}.$$

Since

$$\Phi_1 = \begin{pmatrix} e^{2it} \\ 2ie^{2it} \end{pmatrix} \quad \text{and} \quad \Phi_2 = \begin{pmatrix} e^{-2it} \\ -2ie^{-2it} \end{pmatrix}$$

are complex conjugates, $\Psi(t)$ is a fundamental matrix. Hence the solution of the system (5.5.4) is given by

$$\Phi(t) = c_1 \begin{pmatrix} 1 \\ 2i \end{pmatrix} e^{2it} + c_2 \begin{pmatrix} 1 \\ -2i \end{pmatrix} e^{-2it}$$

$$= \begin{pmatrix} (c_1 + c_2)\cos 2t \\ -2(c_1 + c_2)\sin 2t \end{pmatrix} + \begin{pmatrix} i(c_1 - c_2)\sin 2t \\ 2i(c_1 - c_2)\cos 2t \end{pmatrix}.$$

If we set $a_1 = c_1 + c_2$ and $a_2 = i(c_1 - c_2)$, we obtain

$$\Phi(t) = a_1 \begin{pmatrix} \cos 2t \\ -2\sin 2t \end{pmatrix} + a_2 \begin{pmatrix} \sin 2t \\ 2\cos 2t \end{pmatrix}.$$

So far we have encountered distinct roots of the characteristic equation $p(\lambda) = 0$. The roots of $p(\lambda) = 0$ may be repeated. Suppose that λ is a root of multiplicity m.

When the rank of the characteristic matrix $A - \lambda I$ is $n - m$, then there exist m linearly independent eigenvectors associated with eigenvalue λ. Thus there is no problem in finding a solution matrix. However, when the rank of $A - \lambda I$ is greater than $n - m$, the number of linearly independent eigenvectors associated with λ is less than m. In this case we consider a solution of the form

$$\Phi(t) = B(t)e^{\lambda t}, \tag{5.5.5}$$

where $B(t)$ is a polynomial of degree k given by

$$B_k(t) = P_0 + P_1 t + P_2 t^2 + \cdots + P_k t^k. \tag{5.5.6}$$

Substitution of (5.5.5) in $Y' = AY$ yields

$$(A - \lambda I)[P_0 + P_1 t + P_2 t^2 + \cdots + P_k t^k] = P_1 + 2P_2 t + \cdots + kP_k t^{k-1}.$$

In order for this equation to be valid for all t, we equate the coefficients of t to obtain

$$(A - \lambda I)P_k = 0,$$

$$(A - \lambda I)P_{k-1} = kP_k,$$

$$(A - \lambda I)P_{k-2} = (k-1)P_{k-1}, \tag{5.5.7}$$

$$\vdots$$

$$(A - \lambda I)P_0 = P_1.$$

Since $\det(A - \lambda I) = 0$ in the first system of (5.5.7), the remaining nonhomogeneous system can be solved, provided the rank of $A - \lambda I$ is equal to the rank of the augmented matrix formed by $A - \lambda I$ with nonhomogeneous terms in (5.5.7).

From a set of vectors $\{P_0, P_1, \ldots, P_k\}$ we determine the set of vectors $\{B_0, B_1, \ldots, B_k\}$, and from them we obtain a linearly independent set of solutions $\{\Phi_k\}$.

To simplify the computational procedure we let

$$P_k = Q_0,$$

$$P_{k-1} = kQ_1,$$

$$P_{k-2} = k(k-1)Q_2, \tag{5.5.8}$$

$$\vdots$$

$$P_0 = k!Q_k,$$

to obtain a new set of vectors $\{Q_0, Q_1, \ldots, Q_k\}$ satisfying

$$(A - \lambda I)Q_0 = 0,$$

$$(A - \lambda I)Q_1 = Q_0,$$

$$(A - \lambda I)Q_2 = Q_1, \tag{5.5.9}$$

$$\vdots$$

$$(A - \lambda I)Q_k = Q_{k-1}.$$

Example 5.5.3 Consider the system

$$Y' = AY$$

where

$$A = \begin{bmatrix} 2 & 0 & 0 \\ 3 & 2 & 0 \\ 5 & -2 & -1 \end{bmatrix}.$$

The characteristic matrix of A is given by

$$A - \lambda I = \begin{bmatrix} 2-\lambda & 0 & 0 \\ 3 & 2-\lambda & 0 \\ 5 & -2 & -1-\lambda \end{bmatrix},$$

and the characteristic equation is

$$(\lambda + 1)(\lambda - 2)^2 = 0.$$

Thus the eigenvalues are -1 of multiplicity 1, and 2 of multiplicity 2.

For the first eigenvalue $\lambda = -1$, we immediately obtain an eigenvector from $(A + I)B_1 = 0$:

$$B_1 = \begin{bmatrix} 0 \\ 0 \\ 1 \end{bmatrix}.$$

For $\lambda = 2$ we compute

$$A - 2I = \begin{bmatrix} 0 & 0 & 0 \\ 3 & 0 & 0 \\ 5 & -2 & -3 \end{bmatrix}.$$

This matrix clearly has the rank 2, and an eigenvector of A is given by

$$Q_0 = \begin{bmatrix} 0 \\ 3 \\ -2 \end{bmatrix}.$$

We calculate Q_1 from $(A - 2I)Q_1 = Q_0$, and obtain

$$\begin{bmatrix} 0 & 0 & 0 \\ 3 & 0 & 0 \\ 5 & -2 & -3 \end{bmatrix} \begin{bmatrix} q_1 \\ q_2 \\ q_3 \end{bmatrix} = \begin{bmatrix} 0 \\ 3 \\ -2 \end{bmatrix},$$

where q_i are the components of Q_1. Hence we have the eigenvector Q_1 given by

$$Q_1 = \begin{bmatrix} 1 \\ 2 \\ 1 \end{bmatrix}.$$

Since $B_0 = Q_0$ and $B_1 = Q_1 + Q_0 t$, the solutions are given by

$$\Phi_1(t) = \begin{bmatrix} 0 \\ 0 \\ 1 \end{bmatrix} e^{-t}, \qquad \Phi_2(t) = \begin{bmatrix} 0 \\ 3 \\ -2 \end{bmatrix} e^{2t}, \qquad \Phi_3(t) = \begin{bmatrix} 1 \\ 2+3t \\ 1-2t \end{bmatrix} e^{2t}.$$

Consequently, a solution matrix is

$$\Psi(t) = \begin{bmatrix} 0 & 0 & e^{2t} \\ 0 & 3e^{2t} & (2+3t)e^{2t} \\ e^{-t} & -2e^{2t} & (1-2t)e^{2t} \end{bmatrix}.$$

5.6   Diagonal and Jordan Matrices

When a matrix A is diagonalizable, calculation of a solution matrix Ψ is simplified considerably.

Let D be a diagonal matrix given by

$$D = \begin{bmatrix} d_1 & 0 & 0 & \cdots & 0 \\ 0 & d_2 & 0 & \cdots & 0 \\ 0 & 0 & d_3 & \cdots & 0 \\ \vdots & \vdots & \vdots & \ddots & \vdots \\ 0 & 0 & 0 & \cdots & d_n \end{bmatrix}.$$

Then

$$e^{tD} = I + \begin{bmatrix} d_1 & & & \\ & d_2 & & \\ & & \ddots & \\ & & & d_n \end{bmatrix} \frac{t}{1!} + \begin{bmatrix} d_1^2 & & & \\ & d_2^2 & & \\ & & \ddots & \\ & & & d_n^2 \end{bmatrix} \frac{t^2}{2!} + \cdots$$

$$+ \begin{bmatrix} d_1^k & & & \\ & d_2^k & & \\ & & \ddots & \\ & & & d_n^k \end{bmatrix} \frac{t^k}{k!} + \cdots$$

$$= \begin{bmatrix} e^{td_1} & & & \\ & e^{td_2} & & \\ & & \ddots & \\ & & & e^{td_n} \end{bmatrix}.$$

THEOREM 5.6.1   *If $A = PDP^{-1}$, where D is a diagonal matrix, then*

$$e^{tA} = Pe^{tD}P^{-1}.$$

Proof Since $A = PDP^{-1}$, we have $A^k = PD^kP^{-1}$ for any positive integer k. Thus we have

$$e^{tA} = I + \frac{t}{1!}A + \frac{t^2}{2!}A^2 + \cdots$$

$$= PIP^{-1} + P\frac{t}{1!}DP^{-1} + P\frac{t^2}{2!}D^2P^{-1} + \cdots$$

$$= P\left(I + \frac{tD}{1!} + \frac{t^2D^2}{2!} + \cdots\right)P^{-1}$$

$$= Pe^{tD}P^{-1}.$$ ■

Example 5.6.1 Consider the system $Y' = AY$, where

$$A = \begin{pmatrix} 2 & 2 \\ 1 & 3 \end{pmatrix}.$$

The matrix A has eigenvalues 1 and 4. The corresponding eigenvectors as columns in a matrix P are

$$P = \begin{pmatrix} -2 & 1 \\ 1 & 1 \end{pmatrix}.$$

We compute P^{-1} and determine that

$$P^{-1}AP = \begin{bmatrix} -\frac{1}{3} & \frac{1}{3} \\ \frac{1}{3} & \frac{2}{3} \end{bmatrix} \begin{pmatrix} 2 & 2 \\ 1 & 3 \end{pmatrix} \begin{pmatrix} -2 & 1 \\ 1 & 1 \end{pmatrix}$$

$$= \begin{pmatrix} 1 & 0 \\ 0 & 4 \end{pmatrix}.$$

Thus a fundamental matrix is

$$e^{tA} = Pe^{tD}P^{-1} = \begin{pmatrix} -2 & 1 \\ 1 & 1 \end{pmatrix} \begin{pmatrix} e^t & 0 \\ 0 & e^{4t} \end{pmatrix} \begin{bmatrix} -\frac{1}{3} & \frac{1}{3} \\ \frac{1}{3} & \frac{2}{3} \end{bmatrix}$$

$$= \begin{bmatrix} \frac{2}{3}e^t + \frac{1}{3}e^{4t} & -\frac{2}{3}e^t + \frac{2}{3}e^{4t} \\ -\frac{1}{3}e^t + \frac{1}{3}e^{4t} & \frac{1}{3}e^t + \frac{2}{3}e^{4t} \end{bmatrix}.$$

The general solution is therefore given by

$$\Phi(t) = e^{tA}C = \begin{bmatrix} c_1\left(\frac{2}{3}e^t + \frac{1}{3}e^{4t}\right) + c_2\left(-\frac{2}{3}e^t + \frac{2}{3}e^{4t}\right) \\ c_1\left(-\frac{1}{3}e^t + \frac{1}{3}e^{4t}\right) + c_2\left(\frac{1}{3}e^t + \frac{2}{3}e^{4t}\right) \end{bmatrix}$$

If we let $a_1 = -\frac{1}{3}(c_1 - c_2)$ and $a_2 = \frac{1}{3}(c_1 + 2c_2)$, then Φ takes the form

$$\Phi(t) = a_1\begin{pmatrix} -2 \\ 1 \end{pmatrix}e^t + a_2\begin{pmatrix} 1 \\ 1 \end{pmatrix}e^{4t}.$$

We note here that the constant vectors in the above expression are none other than the eigenvectors determined earlier. This is true in general. Thus for a diagonalizable matrix that has n linearly independent eigenvectors, we need not find e^{tA} explicitly.

A fundamental matrix of $Y' = AY$ can be expressed explicitly with use of the Jordan canonical form. Let J be a Jordan matrix. Then A is similar to J, i.e.,

$$J = P^{-1}AP = \begin{bmatrix} J_1 & & & \\ & J_2 & & \\ & & \ddots & \\ & & & J_n \end{bmatrix},$$

where P is a nonsingular constant matrix and the Jordan block J_i is given by

$$J_i = \begin{bmatrix} \lambda_i & 1 & & & \\ & \lambda_i & 1 & & \\ & & \ddots & \ddots & \\ & & & \ddots & 1 \\ & & & & \lambda_i \end{bmatrix}.$$

The elements λ_j for $j = 1, 2, \ldots, m$ are the eigenvalues of A, which need not all be distinct. Thus we see that

$$e^{tA} = e^{tPJP^{-1}} = Pe^{tJ}P^{-1} = P\begin{bmatrix} e^{J_1 t} & & & \\ & e^{J_2 t} & & \\ & & \ddots & \\ & & & e^{J_n t} \end{bmatrix}P^{-1}.$$

We may now express $J_i = \lambda_i I + N_i$, where

$$N_i = \begin{bmatrix} 0 & 1 & & & & \\ & 0 & 1 & & & \\ & & \ddots & \ddots & & \\ & & & \ddots & 1 & \\ & & & & 0 & 1 \\ & & & & & 0 \end{bmatrix}.$$

The matrix N_i has 1 in the superdiagonal and 0 elsewhere. We compute

$$e^{J_i t} = e^{\lambda_i t I + t N_i}$$

$$= e^{\lambda_i t} e^{t N_i}$$

$$= e^{\lambda_i t} \begin{bmatrix} 1 & t & \dfrac{t^2}{2!} & \cdots & \dfrac{t^{r-1}}{(r-1)!} \\[2mm] 0 & 1 & t & \cdots & \dfrac{t^{r-2}}{(r-2)!} \\[2mm] \vdots & \vdots & \vdots & & \vdots \\[2mm] 0 & 0 & 0 & \cdots & 1 \end{bmatrix},$$

where r is the order of J_i. Thus we can determine a fundamental matrix e^{tA} explicitly if the Jordan form of A is known.

5.7 Linear Equations with Periodic Coefficients. Floquet Theory

Let us consider the system

$$Y' = A(t)Y, \qquad -\infty < t < \infty, \tag{5.7.1}$$

where $A(t)$ is periodic with period ω, that is,

$$A(t+\omega) = A(t). \tag{5.7.2}$$

Let $\Psi(t)$ be a fundamental matrix that satisfies

$$\Psi'(t) = A(t)\Psi(t), \qquad (5.7.3)$$

$$\Psi(0) = I. \qquad (5.7.4)$$

Then

$$\Psi'(t+\omega) = A(t+\omega)\Psi(t+\omega) = A(t)\Psi(t+\omega)$$

and $\det \Psi(t+\omega) \neq 0$. Thus $\Psi(t+\omega)$ is a fundamental matrix with initial value $\Psi(\omega)$. As a consequence we have

$$\Psi(t+\omega) = \Psi(t)\Psi(\omega), \qquad (5.7.5)$$

which is evident because the right side satisfies (5.7.3) and has initial value $\Psi(\omega)$.

Let $\Psi(\omega)$ have distinct eigenvalues. Then there exists a nonsingular matrix S such that

$$S^{-1}\Psi(\omega)S = D,$$

where D is the diagonal matrix with distinct elements $\lambda_1, \lambda_2, \ldots, \lambda_n$.

Let $\Omega(t) = \Psi(t)S$. It is obvious that $\Omega' = A(t)\Omega$. In addition we have

$$\Omega(t+\omega) = \Psi(t+\omega)S$$

$$= \Psi(t)\Psi(\omega)S$$

$$= \Psi(t)SD$$

$$= \Omega(t)D. \qquad (5.7.6)$$

Thus if $\Phi_j(t)$ are the solutions of (5.7.1) and are the column vectors of $\Omega(t)$, then from (5.7.6) we see that

$$\Phi_j(t+\omega) = \lambda_j \Phi_j(t). \qquad (5.7.7)$$

Let R be a diagonal matrix with diagonal elements c_i such that

$$D = e^{\omega R}.$$

Thus we have $\lambda_i = e^{\omega c_i}$. Let P be defined by

$$P(t) = \Omega(t)e^{-tR}.$$

Then by using (5.7.6) we have

$$P(t+\omega) = \Omega(t+\omega)e^{-(t+\omega)R}$$

$$= \Omega(t)e^{\omega R}e^{-(t+\omega)R}$$

$$= \Omega(t)e^{-tR}$$

$$= P(t).$$

Hence the solutions of (5.7.1) are given by

$$\Phi_j(t) = P_j(t)e^{tc_j}, \qquad\qquad (5.7.8)$$

where P_j are the column vectors of P.

If the diagonalization is not possible, then $\Psi(\omega)$ can be transformed into the Jordan canonical form. In that case there exists a nonsingular matrix S such that

$$S^{-1}\Psi(\omega)S = J.$$

As in the previous case, if we let $\Omega(t) = \Psi(t)S$, then

$$\Omega(t+\omega) = \Omega(t)J.$$

Let λ_1 be an eigenvalue of multiplicity m. Then we can immediately determine

$$\Phi_1(t) = P_1(t)e^{tc_1},$$

where $P_1(t)$ is the first column vector of $P(t)$. By virtue of the form of J, the remaining solutions can be determined from

$$\Phi_k(t+\omega) = \lambda_1\Phi_k(t) + \Phi_{k-1}(t) \qquad\qquad (5.7.9)$$

with $k = 2, 3, \ldots, m$. To find $\Phi_2(t)$ we assume

$$\Phi_2(t) = Q(t)e^{tc_1}, \qquad\qquad (5.7.10)$$

where Q is an unknown column vector. Substitution of this value of Φ_2 in (5.7.9) yields

$$Q(t+\omega) - Q(t) = \frac{1}{\lambda_1}P_1(t).$$

This is clearly satisfied if

$$Q(t) = \frac{t}{\lambda_1 \omega} P_1(t).$$

Hence Φ_2 is given by

$$\Phi_2(t) = \frac{t}{\lambda_1 \omega} P_1(t) e^{tc_1},$$

and proceeding in a similar manner we obtain

$$\Phi_j(t) = \frac{t(t-\omega)(t-2\omega)\cdots(t-(j-2)\omega)}{(j-1)!(\lambda_1 \omega)^{j-1}} P_1(t) e^{tc_1}$$

with $j = 2, 3, \ldots, m$.

These results were mostly obtained by Floquet and are commonly known as the *Floquet theory*.

EXERCISES

1. Solve the following system of equations by first solving the independent equation.

    (a) $y_1' = y_1$,

    $y_2' = y_1 + y_2.$

    (b) $y_1' = 2y_1 + y_2$,

    $y_2' = -y_2.$

2. Obtain the general solution by the method of elimination, that is, elimination of all but one of the dependent variables by means of differentiation and algebraic substitution.

    (a) $y_1' = 2y_1 + y_2$,

    $y_2' = y_1 - y_2 + t$

    (b) $y_1' = y_1 + 2y_2$,

    $y_2' = 3y_1 + 2y_2.$

3. Transform the equation

$$y'' + 4y' + 40y = 0$$

into a system of equations and solve. Apply the initial conditions $y(0) = 1$, $y'(0) = 0$.

4. Discuss the existence and uniqueness of the solution of the following initial-value problems

    (a) $y_1' = y_1 + e^t y_2,$
        $y_2' = (\sin t)\, y_1 + t^2 y_2,$
        $y_1(0) = 1, \qquad y_2(0) = 0.$

    (b) $y_1' = y_1 + t y_2 + e^t y_3,$
        $y_2' = y_2 - t^2 y_3,$
        $y_3' = t y_1 - y_2 + y_3.$
        $y_1(0) = 1,\ y_2(0) = 0,\ y_3(0) = 0.$

5. The system of equations

$$y_1' = y_1 + \varepsilon y_2,$$
$$y_2' = \varepsilon y_1 + y_2$$

when $\varepsilon = 0$ is reduced to

$$y_1' = y_1,$$
$$y_2' = y_2.$$

Determine the solutions Φ_1 and Φ_2 of the systems satisfying $y_1(0) = 1$ and $y_2(0) = -1$, and show that $\Phi_1 \to \Phi_2$ as $\varepsilon \to 0$ for all real values of t.

6. Show that

$$\Psi(t) = \begin{pmatrix} \cos t & \sin t \\ -\sin t & \cos t \end{pmatrix}$$

is a fundamental matrix for the system

$$Y' = AY \qquad \text{with } A = \begin{pmatrix} 0 & 1 \\ -1 & 0 \end{pmatrix}.$$

7. Show that

$$\Psi(t) = \begin{pmatrix} e^t & e^{2t} \\ e^t & 2e^{2t} \end{pmatrix}$$

is a fundamental matrix for the system

$$Y' = AY \qquad \text{with } A = \begin{pmatrix} 0 & 1 \\ -2 & 3 \end{pmatrix}.$$

8. Prove Theorem 5.2.7. If Ψ is a fundamental matrix, show that $C\Psi$, where C is a constant matrix, need not be a solution matrix.

9. Verify that

$$\Phi(t) = E\Psi^{-1}(t_0)\Psi(t) + \Psi(t)\int_{t_0}^t \Psi^{-1}(\tau)G(\tau)\,d\tau$$

is the solution of the system

$$Y' = A(t)Y + G(t),$$

$$Y(t_0) = E.$$

10. Suppose that $A(t)$ is continuous and periodic with period 2π, that is, $A(t+2\pi) = A(t)$ for $|t| < \infty$. Prove that if $\Phi(t)$ is a fundamental matrix, so also is $\Phi(t+2\pi)$ for $|t| < \infty$.

11. Find a fundamental matrix of the system $Y' = AY$ by using an exponential matrix if

   (a) $A = \begin{pmatrix} 2 & 0 \\ 0 & 4 \end{pmatrix}$.

   (b) $A = \begin{pmatrix} 2 & 1 \\ 0 & 2 \end{pmatrix}$.

   (c) $A = \begin{bmatrix} 2 & 1 & 0 \\ 0 & 2 & 1 \\ 0 & 0 & 2 \end{bmatrix}$.

12. Find the general solution of each of the following systems by the method of eigenvalues.

   (a) $y_1' = 6y_1 - 7y_2,$
       $y_2' = y_1 - 2y_2.$
   (b) $y_1' = y_1 + y_2 - 2y_3,$
       $y_2' = -y_1 + 2y_2 + y_3,$
       $y_3' = y_2 - y_3.$
   (c) $y_1' = 2y_1 + y_3,$
       $y_2' = y_2,$
       $y_3' = y_1 + 2y_3.$

(d) $y_1' = 2y_1 - y_2,$

$\quad\;\; y_2' = 2y_1 + 4y_2.$

(e) $y_1' = y_1 - y_2,$

$\quad\;\; y_2' = 5y_1 - 3y_2.$

(f) $y_1' = 3y_1 + y_2 - y_3,$

$\quad\;\; y_2' = y_1 + 3y_2 - y_3,$

$\quad\;\; y_3' = 3y_1 + 3y_2 - y_3.$

(g) $y_1' = y_3,$

$\quad\;\; y_2' = y_1 - 3y_3,$

$\quad\;\; y_3' = y_2 + 3y_3.$

13.   Solve the nonhomogeneous linear system

(a) $y_1' = y_1 + 2y_2 + e^t,$

$\quad\;\; y_2' = y_1 + y_2 - 2e^t.$

(b) $y_1' = y_1 + y_2 + 2t,$

$\quad\;\; y_2' = 4y_1 + y_2 - \sin t.$

14.   Determine a solution of the system

$$tY' = AY$$

for $t > 0$ by assuming a solution of the form

$$Y(t) = Bt^\lambda,$$

where λ and B are constant.

    Show by the variation-of-parameters method that a particular solution of the nonhomogeneous equation

$$tY' = AY + G(t)$$

for $t > 0$ is given by

$$\Phi(t) = \Psi(t) \int \Psi^{-1}(\tau) \frac{G(\tau)}{\tau} d\tau.$$

15.   Write the equation

$$y'' + py' + qy = 0,$$

for constant p, q, in the form

$$Y' = AY$$

and determine a fundamental matrix for the case

(a) $p^2 - 4q \neq 0$ and   (b) $p^2 - 4q = 0$.

16. Let $P^{-1}AP = B$. If λ is an eigenvalue of A and X is a corresponding eigenvector, prove that λ is also an eigenvalue of B, and $P^{-1}X$ is a corresponding eigenvector.

17. Let A be a lower triangular $n \times n$ matrix. If Φ is a solution of $Y' = AY$, then

$$\phi_i(t) = \sum_{j=1}^{i} p_{ij}(t)e^{a_{ii}t}, \qquad i = 1, 2, \ldots, n,$$

where $p_{ij}(t)$ are polynomials.

18. Prove that

(a) If all eigenvalues of A have negative real part, every solution of $Y' = AY$ approaches zero as t tends to infinity.
(b) If some eigenvalue of A has positive real part, $Y' = AY$ has an unbounded solution for all $t \geq 0$.
(c) If all eigenvalues of A have negative and zero parts, $Y' = AY$ has a bounded solution for all $t \geq 0$.

19. Let Φ be a solution of

$$Y' = AY + G(t),$$

where G has a period $\omega > 0$. Prove that the system has a unique solution with period ω if and only if $Y' = AY$ has no solution with period ω except $Y = 0$.

20. Let $|G(t)| \leq Me^{at}$ for $t > T \geq 0$ and for some constants M and a in

$$Y' = AY + G$$

Prove that for some constants K and b,

$$|\Phi(t)| \leq Ke^{bt}.$$

Chapter 6
Boundary-Value Problems

6.1 Two-Point Boundary-Value Problem

A *boundary-value problem* consists in finding an unknown solution which satisfies an ordinary differential equation and appropriate boundary conditions at two or more points. This is in contrast to an initial-value problem, such as we studied earlier, for which a unique solution exists for an equation satisfying prescribed initial conditions at one point.

The linear *two-point boundary-value problem*, in general, may be written in the form

$$L[\,y\,] = f(x), \qquad a < x < b$$

$$U_i[\,y\,] = \alpha_i, \qquad 1 \leqslant i \leqslant n, \tag{6.1.1}$$

where L is the linear operator of order n and U_i is the boundary operator defined by

$$U_i[\,y\,] = \sum_{j=1}^{n} a_{ij} y^{(j-1)}(a) + \sum_{j=1}^{n} b_{ij} y^{(j-1)}(b). \tag{6.1.2}$$

Here a_{ij}, b_{ij} and α_i are constants. The treatment of this problem can be found in Coddington and Levinson [8]. More complicated boundary conditions occur in practice. Treating a general differential system is rather complex and difficult.

147

A large class of boundary-value problems that occur often in physical science consists of the second-order equations of the type

$$y'' = f(x, y, y'), \qquad a < x < b$$

with the boundary conditions

$$U_1[\, y\,] = a_1\, y(a) + a_2\, y'(a) = \alpha,$$

$$U_2[\, y\,] = b_1\, y(b) + b_2\, y'(b) = \beta$$

where a_1, a_2, b_1, b_2, α and β are constants. The existence and uniqueness of solutions to this problem are treated by Keller [21]. Here we are interested in considering a special case where the linear boundary-value problem consists of the differential equation

$$L[\, y\,] = y'' + p(x)\, y' + q(x)\, y = f(x) \tag{6.1.3}$$

and the boundary conditions

$$U_1[\, y\,] = a_1\, y(a) + a_2\, y'(a) = \alpha,$$
$$U_2[\, y\,] = b_1\, y(b) + b_2\, y'(b) = \beta, \tag{6.1.4}$$

where the constants a_1 and a_2, and likewise b_1 and b_2, are not both zero, and α and β are constants.

In general a boundary-value problem may not possess a solution, and if it does, the solution may not be unique. We will illustrate this with a simple problem.

Example 6.1.1 We first consider the boundary-value problem

$$y'' + y = 1,$$

$$y(0) = 0, \qquad y\!\left(\frac{\pi}{2}\right) = 0.$$

By the variation of parameters method we find a unique solution

$$\phi(x) = 1 - \cos x - \sin x.$$

We observe that the solution of the associated homogeneous boundary-value problem

$$y'' + y = 0,$$

$$y(0) = 0, \qquad y\left(\frac{\pi}{2}\right) = 0$$

is trivial.

Next we consider the boundary-value problem

$$y'' + y = 1,$$

$$y(0) = 0, \qquad y(\pi) = 0.$$

The general solution is

$$\phi(x) = c_1 \cos x + c_2 \sin x + 1.$$

Applying the boundary conditions we see that

$$\phi(0) = c_1 + 1 = 0,$$

$$\phi(\pi) = -c_1 + 1 = 0.$$

This is not possible, and hence the boundary-value problem has no solution. However, if we consider its associated homogeneous boundary-value problem

$$y'' + y = 0,$$

$$y(0) = 0, \qquad y(\pi) = 0$$

we can easily determine that solutions exist and are given by

$$\phi(x) = c_2 \sin x,$$

where c_2 is an arbitrary constant.

We are thus led to the following alternative theorem.

THEOREM 6.1.1 *Let $p(x)$, $q(x)$ and $f(x)$ be continuous on $[a,b]$. Then either the boundary-value problem*

$$L[y] = f,$$

$$U_1[y] = \alpha, \qquad U_2[y] = \beta \tag{6.1.5}$$

has a unique solution for any given constants α and β, or else the associated homogeneous boundary-value problem

$$L[y] = 0,$$

$$U_1[y] = 0, \qquad U_2[y] = 0 \tag{6.1.6}$$

has a nontrivial solution.

Proof Let $\phi_1(x)$ and $\phi_2(x)$ be the respective solutions of the initial-value problems

$$L[\phi_1(x)] = 0, \qquad \phi_1(a) = a_2, \quad \phi_1'(a) = -a_1,$$

$$L[\phi_2(x)] = 0, \qquad \phi_2(b) = b_2, \quad \phi_2'(b) = -b_1. \tag{6.1.7}$$

Let $\psi(x)$ be the solution of the initial-value problem

$$L[\psi(x)] = f(x), \qquad \psi(a) = \psi'(a) = 0. \tag{6.1.8}$$

Then by Theorem 3.1.1, the solutions ϕ_1, ϕ_2 and ψ exist. Thus for any constants c_1 and c_2 the function

$$\phi(x) = c_1 \phi_1(x) + c_2 \phi_2(x) + \psi(x)$$

obviously satisfies the differential equation $L[y(x)] = f(x)$. In order for $\phi(x)$ to satisfy the boundary conditions in (6.1.5) we must have

$$U_1[\phi] = c_2 [a_1 \phi_2(a) + a_2 \phi_2'(a)] = \alpha,$$

$$U_2[\phi] = c_1 [b_1 \phi_1(b) + b_2 \phi_1'(b)] + [b_1 \psi(b) + b_2 \psi'(b)] = \beta.$$

If we substitute a_1, a_2, b_1 and b_2 from (6.1.7), we obtain

$$U_1[\phi] = c_2 [-\phi_1'(a)\phi_2(a) + \phi_1(a)\phi_2'(a)] = \alpha,$$

$$U_2[\phi] = c_1 [-\phi_2'(b)\phi_1(b) + \phi_2(b)\phi_1'(b)] + U_2[\psi] = \beta.$$

If ϕ_1 and ϕ_2 are linearly independent, then the Wronskian $W = \phi_1 \phi_2' - \phi_1' \phi_2 \neq 0$ for any $x \in [a, b]$. Hence for any given constants α and β, c_1 and c_2 are uniquely determined.

If ϕ_1 and ϕ_2 are linearly dependent, then $k_1 \phi_1 + k_2 \phi_2 = 0$ for some constants k_1 and k_2. Thus we have $\phi_2 = k\phi_1$ with $k = -k_1/k_2$, and consequently

$$U_1[\phi_1] = \left[-\phi_1'(a)\phi_1(a) + \phi_1(a)\phi_1'(a) \right] = 0,$$

$$U_2[\phi_1] = k\left[-\phi_1'(b)\phi_1(b) + \phi_1(b)\phi_1'(b) \right] = 0.$$

It is evident in this case that $U_1[\phi_2] = U_2[\phi_2] = 0$. Since ϕ_1 and ϕ_2 satisfy the homogeneous differential equation and the homogeneous boundary conditions, the only nontrivial solution that can exist is the solution of the associated homogeneous boundary-value problem (6.1.6). ∎

The homogeneous differential system that has a nontrivial solution is the central theme of the study of eigenvalue problems, which will be treated in Chapter 7.

6.2 Green's Functions

In the present section we will first introduce Green's functions. Let us now consider the linear nonhomogeneous ordinary differential equation of second order:[†]

$$L[\,y\,] = -f(x) \tag{6.2.1}$$

in $[a,b]$, where $L = (d/dx)[p(x)(d/dx)] + q(x)$, with the homogeneous boundary conditions

$$a_1 y(a) + a_2 y'(a) = 0, \tag{6.2.2}$$

$$b_1 y(b) + b_2 y'(b) = 0, \tag{6.2.3}$$

where the constants a_1 and a_2, and likewise b_1 and b_2, are not both zero. We shall assume that f and q are continuous and that p is continuously differentiable and does not vanish in the interval $[a,b]$. We first present a heuristic argument for the Green's functions.

We consider a flexible cable which is stretched horizontally by a constant tension T. Since the cable has no resistance to bending, the only internal force is the tension T acting in the direction of the tangent of the deflection curve.

Let $y(x)$ be the vertical displacement of the cable. Let $\rho(x)$ be the continuously distributed load per unit length. Thus the load $\rho(x)\Delta x$ supported by the cable in the interval $(x, x + \Delta x)$ is in equilibrium with the

---

[†]The minus sign is introduced for consistency with the usual notation.

vertical component of the tension T. If we assume that the vertical displacement is small compared with the length of the cable, we have the equilibrium equation for an element between x and $x + \Delta x$,

$$T\left[\, y'(x + \Delta x) - y'(x)\,\right] - \rho(x)\Delta x = 0.$$

Dividing this equation by Δx, we obtain

$$\frac{y'(x + \Delta x) - y'(x)}{\Delta x} = \frac{\rho(x)}{T}.$$

Thus in the limit as $\Delta x \to 0$ we have

$$y''(x) = \rho(x)/T,$$

which may be written as

$$L[\, y\,] = y''(x) = -g(x),$$

where $g(x) = -\rho(x)/T$.

If we assume that the ends of the cable are connected to the end supports such that the vertical reactions are proportional to the displacements, the boundary conditions take the form

$$Ty'(a) = -a_1\, y(a),$$
$$Ty'(b) = -b_1\, y(b),$$

which may be written as

$$a_1\, y(a) + a_2\, y'(a) = 0,$$
$$b_1\, y(b) + b_2\, y'(b) = 0,$$

where $a_2 = b_2 = T$. There are other boundary conditions one of which, for example, is a fixed end. If the end at $x = a$ is fixed, then $y(a) = 0$.

We will now consider the boundary-value problem (6.2.1–6.2.3). If we denote by $G(x, \xi)$ the deflection of a cable at x due to a unit concentrated force applied at the point ξ, then the deflection at x due to a uniformly distributed force $f(\xi)$ per unit length over an elemental interval $(\xi, \xi + d\xi)$ is given by $f(\xi)G(x, \xi)d\xi$. Thus because of the linearity of the problem, the deflection of the cable at x due to the distribution of force $f(\xi)$ over the entire interval $[a, b]$ is given by the integral

$$y = \phi(x) = \int_a^b G(x, \xi) f(\xi) d\xi. \tag{6.2.4}$$

The function $G(x, \xi)$ is called the *influence function* or *Green's function*. It is evident that $G(x, \xi)$ must be defined and continuous in $[a, b]$ and must satisfy the prescribed boundary conditions. By its very definition, $G(x, \xi)$ is a solution of the equation

$$L[y] = -f_\varepsilon(x), \tag{6.2.5}$$

where $f_\varepsilon(x)$ is the function which vanishes outside the interval $|x - \xi| < \varepsilon$, and in the interval $|x - \xi| < \varepsilon$ it satisfies the relation

$$\int_{\xi - \varepsilon}^{\xi + \varepsilon} f_\varepsilon(x) dx = 1. \tag{6.2.6}$$

Thus for all $x \neq \xi$, $G(x, \xi)$ satisfies the homogeneous equation

$$L[y] = 0.$$

When $x = \xi$, we have from Eq. (6.2.5) the following relation after integration:

$$\int_{\xi - \varepsilon}^{\xi + \varepsilon} \frac{d}{dx} \left[p(x) G'(x, \xi) \right] dx + \int_{\xi - \varepsilon}^{\xi + \varepsilon} q(x) G(x, \xi) dx = - \int_{\xi - \varepsilon}^{\xi + \varepsilon} f_\varepsilon(x) dx,$$

or

$$p(x) G'(x, \xi) \Big|_{\xi - \varepsilon}^{\xi + \varepsilon} + \int_{\xi - \varepsilon}^{\xi + \varepsilon} q(x) G(x, \xi) dx = -1.$$

If we now assume that $G(x, \xi)$ is continuously differentiable except at $x = \xi$, then in the limit as ε approaches zero, we obtain

$$\frac{dG(x, \xi)}{dx} \Bigg|_{x = \xi -}^{x = \xi +} = -\frac{1}{p(\xi)}, \tag{6.2.7}$$

which states that the derivative of $G(x, \xi)$ has a jump discontinuity at $x = \xi$.

This heuristic discussion leads us to the following definition of the Green's function.

DEFINITION 6.2.1 The *Green's function* for the differential expression $L[y]$ under given homogeneous boundary conditions is the function $G(x,\xi)$ satisfying the following conditions:

(i) $G(x,\xi)$ is continuous for all values of x, and its first and second derivatives are continuous for all $x \neq \xi$ in $a \leqslant x, \xi \leqslant b$.

(ii) At the point $x = \xi$, the first derivative of $G(x,\xi)$ has a jump discontinuity given by

$$\frac{dG(x,\xi)}{dx}\bigg|_{x=\xi-}^{x=\xi+} = -\frac{1}{p(\xi)}.$$

(iii) For fixed ξ, $G(x,\xi)$ satisfies the prescribed boundary conditions. Moreover, $G(x,\xi)$ is the solution of the associated homogeneous equation

$$L[y] = 0$$

except at the point $x = \xi$.

With this definition in mind, we state the fundamental theorem for the Green's function.

THEOREM 6.2.1 *If $f(x)$ is continuous in the interval $[a,b]$, then the function*

$$\phi(x) = \int_a^b G(x,\xi) f(\xi) d\xi$$

is a solution of the boundary-value problem

$$L[y] = -f(x),$$

$$a_1 y(a) + a_2 y'(a) = 0,$$

$$b_1 y(b) + b_2 y'(b) = 0.$$

Proof First, we differentiate $\phi(x)$ with respect to x by Leibnitz's Rule,[†] and obtain

$$\phi'(x) = \int_a^x G'(x,\xi) f(\xi) d\xi + G(x,x-) f(x) + \int_x^b G'(x,\xi) f(\xi) d\xi$$

$$- G(x,x+) f(x).$$

[†]See W. Kaplan, *Advanced Calculus*, Addison-Wesley, 1953, p. 220.

Since $G(x,\xi)$ is continuous in ξ, we have

$$G(x,x-)=G(x,x+).$$

Thus $\phi'(x)$ may be written

$$\phi'(x)=\int_a^b G'(x,\xi)f(\xi)\,d\xi.$$

Since G satisfies the boundary conditions, we have

$$a_1\phi(a)+a_2\phi'(a)=\int_a^b\left[a_1G(a,\xi)+a_2G'(a,\xi)\right]f(\xi)\,d\xi.$$

$$=0.$$

Similarly

$$b_1\phi(b)+b_2\phi'(b)=0.$$

Differentiating ϕ' again with respect to x,

$$\phi''(x)=\int_a^x G''(x,\xi)f(\xi)\,d\xi+G'(x,x-)f(x)$$

$$+\int_x^b G''(x,\xi)f(\xi)\,d\xi-G'(x,x+)f(x)$$

$$=\int_a^b G''(x,\xi)f(\xi)\,d\xi+f(x)\left[G'(x,x-)-G'(x,x+)\right].$$

But we may write condition (6.2.7) in an equivalent form (see Exercise 16)

$$\frac{dG}{dx}(x,\xi)\Big|_{\xi=x-}^{\xi=x+}=\frac{1}{p(x)}.\tag{6.2.8}$$

Hence ϕ'' becomes

$$\phi''(x)=\int_a^b G''(x,\xi)f(\xi)\,d\xi-f(x)\left[G'(x+,x)-G'(x-,x)\right]$$

$$=\int_a^b G''(x,\xi)f(\xi)\,d\xi-\frac{f(x)}{p(x)}.$$

Therefore

$$L[\phi] = p(x)\phi''(x) + p'(x)\phi'(x) + q(x)\phi(x)$$

$$= -f(x) + \int_a^b \big[p(x)G''(x,\xi) + p'(x)G'(x,\xi)$$

$$+ q(x)G(x,\xi) \big] f(\xi)\, d\xi$$

$$= -f(x) + \int_a^b L[G] f(\xi)\, d\xi.$$

Since by the definition of G, $L[G] = 0$, we have

$$L[\phi] = -f(x). \qquad \blacksquare$$

To express the Green's function in two intervals separated by $x = \xi$, we let

$$G(x,\xi) = \begin{cases} G_1(x,\xi) & \text{for} \quad \xi < x \leqslant b, \\ G_2(x,\xi) & \text{for} \quad a \leqslant x < \xi. \end{cases} \qquad (6.2.9)$$

Then from the continuity condition we must have

$$G_1(\xi,\xi) = G_2(\xi,\xi),$$

and from the condition (6.2.7)

$$\frac{dG}{dx}(x,\xi)\bigg|_{x=\xi-}^{x=\xi+} = \frac{dG_1}{dx}(x,\xi)\bigg|_{x=\xi+} - \frac{dG_2}{dx}(x,\xi)\bigg|_{x=\xi-} = -\frac{1}{p(\xi)}. \qquad (6.2.10)$$

Similarly, if we take ξ as the variable, we may define

$$G(x,\xi) = \begin{cases} G_1(x,\xi) & \text{for} \quad a \leqslant \xi < x, \\ G_2(x,\xi) & \text{for} \quad x < \xi \leqslant b, \end{cases} \qquad (6.2.11)$$

where G_1 and G_2 are continuous. Thus

$$G_1(x,x) = G_2(x,x).$$

It follows from the condition (6.2.8) that

$$\frac{dG}{dx}(x,\xi)\bigg|_{\xi=x-}^{\xi=x+} = \frac{dG_2}{dx}(x,\xi)\bigg|_{\xi=x} - \frac{dG_1}{dx}(x,\xi)\bigg|_{\xi=x} = \frac{1}{p(x)}. \qquad (6.2.12)$$

Example 6.2.1 Consider the problem

$$y'' = -x,$$
$$y(0) = 0, \qquad\qquad\qquad\qquad (6.2.13)$$
$$y(1) = 0.$$

For a fixed value of ξ, the Green's function $G(x,\xi)$ satisfies the associated homogeneous equation

$$G'' = 0$$

in $0 < x < \xi$, $\xi < x < 1$, and the boundary conditions

$$G(0,\xi) = 0,$$
$$G(1,\xi) = 0.$$

In addition, it satisfies

$$\frac{dG}{dx}(x,\xi)\bigg|_{x=\xi-}^{x=\xi+} = -\frac{1}{p(\xi)}.$$

Now if we choose $G(x,\xi)$ such that

$$G(x,\xi) = \begin{cases} G_1(x,\xi) = (1-x)\xi & \text{for } \xi \leqslant x \leqslant 1, \\ G_2(x,\xi) = x(1-\xi) & \text{for } 0 \leqslant x \leqslant \xi. \end{cases}$$

It can be seen that $G'' = 0$ over the intervals $0 < x < \xi$, $\xi < x < 1$. Also

$$G_1(1,\xi) = 0,$$
$$G_2(0,\xi) = 0.$$

Moreover,

$$G_1'(x,\xi) - G_2'(x,\xi) = -\xi - (1-\xi) = -1,$$

which is the value of the jump $-1/p(\xi)$, because in this case $p=1$. Hence from Theorem 6.2.1, keeping in mind that ξ is the variable in $G(x,\xi)$, the solution of (6.2.13) is

$$
\begin{aligned}
\phi(x) &= \int_0^x G(x,\xi)f(\xi)\,d\xi + \int_x^1 G(x,\xi)f(\xi)\,d\xi \\
&= \int_0^x (1-x)\xi^2\,d\xi + \int_x^1 x(1-\xi)\xi\,d\xi \\
&= \frac{x}{6}(1-x^2).
\end{aligned}
$$

6.3   Construction of Green's Functions

In the above example, we see that the solution was obtained immediately as soon as the Green's function was selected properly. Thus the real problem is not that of finding the solution but that of determining the Green's function for the problem. We will now show that by construction there exists a Green's function for $L[y]$ satisfying the prescribed boundary conditions.

We first assume that the associated homogeneous equation satisfying the conditions (6.2.2) and (6.2.3) has the trivial solution only, as in Example 6.2.1. We construct the solution $\phi_1(x)$ of

$$L[y]=0$$

satisfying $a_1 y(a) + a_2 y'(a) = 0$. We see that $c_1\phi_1(x)$ is the most general such solution, where c_1 is an arbitrary constant.

In a similar manner we let $c_2\phi_2(x)$, with c_2 as an arbitrary constant, be the most general solution of

$$L[y]=0$$

satisfying $b_1 y(b) + b_2 y'(b) = 0$. Thus ϕ_1 and ϕ_2 exist in the interval (a,b) and are linearly independent. For, if they were linearly dependent, then $\phi_1 = c\phi_2$, which shows that ϕ_1 would satisfy both the boundary conditions at $x=a$ and $x=b$. This contradicts our assumption about the trivial solution. Consequently, the Green's function can take the form

$$
G(x,\xi) = \begin{cases} c_1(\xi)\phi_1(x) & \text{for} \quad x<\xi, \\ c_2(\xi)\phi_2(x) & \text{for} \quad x>\xi. \end{cases}
\tag{6.3.1}
$$

Since $G(x, \xi)$ is continuous at $x = \xi$, we have

$$c_2(\xi)\phi_2(\xi) - c_1(\xi)\phi_1(\xi) = 0. \tag{6.3.2}$$

The discontinuity in the derivative of G at that point requires that

$$\frac{dG}{dx}(x, \xi)\Big|_{x=\xi-}^{x=\xi+} = c_2(\xi)\phi_2'(\xi) - c_1(\xi)\phi_1'(\xi) = -\frac{1}{p(\xi)}. \tag{6.3.3}$$

Solving Eqs. (6.3.2) and (6.3.3) for c_1 and c_2, we find

$$c_1(\xi) = \frac{-\phi_2(\xi)}{p(\xi)\,W(\phi_1, \phi_2; \xi)},$$

$$\tag{6.3.4}$$

$$c_2(\xi) = \frac{-\phi_1(\xi)}{p(\xi)\,W(\phi_1, \phi_2; \xi)},$$

where $W(\phi_1, \phi_2; \xi)$ is the Wronskian given by $W(\phi_1, \phi_2; \xi) = \phi_1(\xi)\phi_2'(\xi) - \phi_2(\xi)\phi_1'(\xi)$. Since the two solutions are linearly independent, the Wronskian differs from zero.

Now we will prove that $p(\xi)\,W(\phi_1, \phi_2; \xi)$ is a constant differing from zero. Since $\phi_1(x)$ and $\phi_2(x)$ are solutions of the associated homogeneous equation, we have

$$\frac{d}{dx}(p\phi_1') + q\phi_1 = 0,$$

$$\frac{d}{dx}(p\phi_2') + q\phi_2 = 0.$$

Multiplying the first equation by ϕ_2 and the second by ϕ_1, and subtracting, we obtain

$$\phi_1\frac{d}{dx}(p\phi_2') - \phi_2\frac{d}{dx}(p\phi_1') = 0,$$

which can be written in the form

$$\frac{d}{dx}\big[\,p(\phi_1\phi_2' - \phi_2\phi_1')\,\big] = 0.$$

Integration yields

$$p(\phi_1\phi_2' - \phi_2\phi_1') = \text{constant} = C. \tag{6.3.5}$$

Hence the Green's function is given by

$$G(x,\xi) = \begin{cases} -\phi_1(x)\phi_2(\xi)/C & \text{for } x \leqslant \xi, \\ -\phi_2(x)\phi_1(\xi)/C & \text{for } x \geqslant \xi. \end{cases} \tag{6.3.6}$$

Thus we state the following theorem:

THEOREM 6.3.1   *If the associated homogeneous boundary-value problem of (6.2.1–6.2.3) has the trivial solution only, then the Green's function exists and is unique.*

The proof for uniqueness of Green's function is left as an exercise for the reader.

Example 6.3.1   Consider the problem

$$y'' + y = -1,$$

$$y(0) = 0, \tag{6.3.7}$$

$$y\left(\frac{\pi}{2}\right) = 0.$$

The solution of $L[y] = dy'/dx + y = 0$ satisfying $y(0) = 0$ is

$$\phi_1(x) = \sin x, \qquad 0 \leqslant x < \xi,$$

and the solution of $L[y] = 0$ satisfying $y(\pi/2) = 0$ is

$$\phi_2(x) = \cos x, \qquad \xi < x \leqslant \frac{\pi}{2}.$$

The Wronskian of ϕ_1 and ϕ_2 is then given by

$$W(\xi) = \phi_1(\xi)\phi_2'(\xi) - \phi_2(\xi)\phi_1'(\xi) = -1.$$

Since in this case $p = 1$, (6.3.6) becomes

$$G(x,\xi) = \begin{cases} \sin x \cos \xi & \text{for } x \leqslant \xi, \\ \cos x \sin \xi & \text{for } x \geqslant \xi. \end{cases}$$

Therefore the solution of (6.3.7) is

$$\phi(x) = \int_0^x G(x,\xi) f(\xi) d\xi + \int_x^{\pi/2} G(x,\xi) f(\xi) d\xi$$

$$= \int_0^x \cos x \sin \xi \, d\xi + \int_x^{\pi/2} \sin x \cos \xi \, d\xi$$

$$= -1 + \sin x + \cos x.$$

Although it can be seen in the formula (6.3.6) that the Green's function $G(x,\xi)$ is symmetric in x and ξ, we present here an independent proof of symmetry of the Green's function.

THEOREM 6.3.2 *The Green's function for a boundary-value problem (6.2.1–6.2.3) is symmetric, that is, $G(x,\xi) = G(\xi,x)$.*

Proof Consider the Green's functions

$$G = G(x,\xi),$$

$$H = G(x,\eta)$$

for $a < \xi < \eta < b$. Since L is a self-adjoint operator, the Lagrange identity (3.6.10) is given by

$$GL[H] - HL[G] = \frac{d}{dx} \left[p(H'G - HG') \right]. \tag{6.3.8}$$

Noting that G and H satisfy

$$L[G] = 0, \qquad L[H] = 0,$$

we have

$$\frac{d}{dx} \left[p(H'G - HG') \right] = 0.$$

Integrating over the intervals $[a,\xi]$, $[\xi,\eta]$ and $[\eta,b]$, we find

$$p(H'G - HG')\big|_a^\xi + p(H'G - HG')\big|_\xi^\eta + p(H'G - HG')\big|_\eta^b = 0.$$

Expansion and rearrangement yield

$$p(\xi)G(\xi,\xi)\big[H'(\xi-,\eta)-H'(\xi+,\eta)\big]+p(\xi)H(\xi,\eta)\big[G'(\xi+,\xi)-G'(\xi-,\xi)\big]$$

$$+P(\eta)G(\eta,\xi)\big[H'(\eta-,\eta)-H'(\eta+,\eta)\big]$$

$$+p(\eta)H(\eta,\eta)\big[G'(\eta+,\xi)-G'(\eta-,\xi)\big]+\big[p(x)(H'G-HG')\big]_a^b=0.$$

$$(6.3.9)$$

Since G and H satisfy the same homogeneous boundary conditions, the last term vanishes. In view of the continuity of G' and H' everywhere except at $x=\xi$ and $x=\eta$ respectively, we have

$$G'(\eta+,\xi)-G'(\eta-,\xi)=0,$$

$$H'(\xi-,\eta)-H'(\xi+,\eta)=0$$

and

$$G'(\xi+,\xi)-G'(\xi-,\xi)=-1/p(\xi),$$

$$H'(\eta+,\eta)-H'(\eta-,\eta)=-1/p(\eta).$$

Thus Eq. (6.3.9) becomes

$$G(\eta,\xi)=H(\xi,\eta),$$

which by the definition of H implies that

$$G(\eta,\xi)=G(\xi,\eta). \qquad\blacksquare$$

6.4   Nonhomogeneous Boundary Conditions

The solution of the more general two-point boundary-value problem

$$L[y]=-f(x), \tag{6.4.1}$$

$$U_1[y]=a_1\,y(a)+a_2\,y'(a)=\alpha, \tag{6.4.2}$$

$$U_2[y]=b_1\,y(b)+b_2\,y'(b)=\beta \tag{6.4.3}$$

may be obtained in a very simple manner.

Let $G_1(x)$ and $G_2(x)$ be the respective solutions of

$$\left.\begin{array}{l} L[G_1]=0, \\ U_1[G_1]=1, \\ U_2[G_2]=0, \end{array}\right\} \qquad (6.4.4)$$

$$\left.\begin{array}{l} L[G_2]=0, \\ U_1[G_2]=0, \\ U_2[G_2]=1. \end{array}\right\} \qquad (6.4.5)$$

It can be easily verified that the solution of the problem (6.4.1)–(6.4.3) is

$$\phi(x)= \int_a^b G(x,\xi) f(\xi) d\xi + \alpha G_1(x) + \beta G_2(x). \qquad (6.4.6)$$

Example 6.4.1   Consider the problem

$$y'' = -f(x),$$

$$y(0)=0, \qquad (6.4.7)$$

$$y(1)+y'(1)=2.$$

The solution of $y''=0$ that satisfies $y(0)=0$ in $0 \leqslant x < \xi$ is

$$\phi_1(x)=x,$$

and the solution of $y''=0$ that satisfies $y(1)+y'(1)=0$ in $\xi < x \leqslant 1$ is

$$\phi_2(x)=2-x.$$

The Wronskian of ϕ_1 and ϕ_2 is given by

$$W = \phi_1(\xi)\phi_2'(\xi) - \phi_2(\xi)\phi_1'(\xi)$$

$$= -2.$$

Since in this case $p=1$, (6.3.6) becomes

$$G(x,\xi)= \begin{cases} (2-\xi)x/2, & 0 \leqslant x \leqslant \xi, \\ \xi(2-x)/2, & \xi \leqslant x \leqslant 1. \end{cases}$$

In this case we need to determine $G_2(x)$ only, since α in (6.4.6) is zero. The function $G_2(x)$ that satisfies the problem

$$y'' = 0,$$

$$y(0) = 0,$$

$$y(1) + y'(1) = 1$$

is readily found to be $G_2(x) = x/2$. Hence the solution of the problem (6.4.7) is given by

$$\phi(x) = \frac{2-x}{2} \int_0^x \xi f(\xi) + \frac{x}{2} \int_x^1 (2 - \xi) f(\xi) \, d\xi + x.$$

6.5   Generalized Green's Function

In the preceding discussions we have assumed that the associated homogeneous problem has a trivial solution only. However, this is not always the case. For example, if we consider the problem

$$y'' + y = -1,$$

$$y(0) = 0, \qquad y(\pi) = 0,$$

the solution of the associated homogeneous equation that satisfies $y(0) = 0$ is obviously $\phi = \sin x$, which also satisfies $y(\pi) = 0$. Hence the Green's function does not exist in the usual sense.

In the succeeding theorem, we introduce a generalized Green's function that is appropriate to nonhomogeneous problems associated with homogeneous problems having nontrivial solutions.

THEOREM 6.5.1   *The nonhomogeneous boundary-value problem*

$$L[y] = \frac{d}{dx} [p(x) y'] + q(x) y = -f(x), \qquad (6.5.1)$$

$$a_1 y(a) + a_2 y'(a) = 0,$$
$$b_1 y(b) + b_2 y'(b) = 0 \qquad (6.5.2)$$

has a solution

$$\phi(x) = \int_a^b G(x, \xi) f(\xi) \, d\xi \qquad (6.5.3)$$

if and only if

$$\int_a^b f(\xi)\phi_0(\xi)\,d\xi = 0, \tag{6.5.4}$$

where ϕ_0 is a normalized solution, that is,

$$\int_a^b \phi_0^2(x)\,dx = 1, \tag{6.5.5}$$

of the associated homogeneous problem. The function $G(x,\xi)$, called the generalized Green's function, is a solution of

$$L[G] = \phi_0(x)\phi_0(\xi), \tag{6.5.6}$$

except at $x = \xi$, satisfying the boundary conditions (6.5.2). $G(x,\xi)$ is continuous at $x = \xi$, and $G'(x,\xi)$ is continuous everywhere except at $x = \xi$. At $x = \xi$, $G'(x,\xi)$ possesses a jump discontinuity of magnitude $-1/p(\xi)$. In addition, $G(x,\xi)$ satisfies the condition

$$\int_a^b G(x,\xi)\phi_0(x)\,dx = 0. \tag{6.5.7}$$

Proof Multiplying both sides of $L[\phi] = -f$ by ϕ_0 and integrating from a to b, we obtain

$$\int_a^b \phi_0 L[\,y\,]\,dx = -\int_a^b f(x)\phi_0(x)\,dx. \tag{6.5.8}$$

But from (3.6.12) and the boundary conditions we have

$$\int_a^b \big(\phi_0 L[\phi] - \phi L[\phi_0]\big)\,dx = 0.$$

Since $L[\phi_0] = 0$, we obtain

$$\int_a^b \phi_0 L[\phi]\,dx = 0. \tag{6.5.9}$$

Hence from (6.5.8) we have

$$\int_a^b f(x)\phi_0(x)\,dx = 0. \tag{6.5.10}$$

This is the necessary condition for the existence of a solution of (6.5.1). The sufficient condition will be given later.

Let ϕ be a solution of $L[\phi] = \phi_0(\xi)\phi_0(x)$ satisfying the boundary conditions (6.5.2). Then if we multiply both sides of this equation by $\phi_0(x)$ and integrate from a to b, we obtain

$$\int_a^b \phi_0(x) L[\phi]\, dx = \phi_0(\xi) \int_a^b \phi_0^2(x)\, dx.$$

But from (6.5.9) the left side vanishes, and hence

$$\phi_0(\xi) \int_a^b \phi_0^2(x)\, dx = 0. \tag{6.5.11}$$

Consequently $\phi_0(x) = 0$, which contradicts our assumption that $\phi_0(x)$ is a nontrivial solution of the associated homogeneous problem. This implies that $L[\phi] = \phi_0(\xi)\phi_0(x)$ does not possess a nontrivial solution that satisfies the same boundary conditions (6.5.2). To avoid this situation, let us consider the general solution of $L[\phi] = \phi_0(\xi)\phi_0(x)$, namely

$$\phi(x) = c_1(\xi)\phi_1(x) + c_2(\xi)\phi_2(x) + \phi_0(\xi)\phi_p(x),$$

where ϕ_1 and ϕ_2 are linearly independent solutions of $L[\phi] = 0$ and $\phi_p(x)$ is a particular solution of $L[\phi] = \phi_0(\xi)\phi_0(x)$.

We first determine c_1 in terms of c_2 by the boundary condition at $x = a$ and consider the function

$$G_1(x,\xi) = c_1(\xi, c_2(\xi))\phi_1(x) + c_2(\xi)\phi_2(x) + \phi_0(\xi)\phi_p(x).$$

Similarly we determine c_1^* in terms of c_2^* by the boundary condition at $x = b$ and consider the function

$$G_2(x,\xi) = c_1^*(\xi, c_2^*(\xi))\phi_1(x) + c_2^*(\xi)\phi_2(x) + \phi_0(\xi)\phi_p(x).$$

Then we determine $c_2^*(\xi)$ in terms of $c_2(\xi)$ by the continuity condition

$$G_1(\xi,\xi) = G_2(\xi,\xi).$$

Now we construct a generalized Green's function

$$G(x,\xi) = \begin{cases} G_1(x,\xi), & a \leqslant x \leqslant \xi, \\ G_2(x,\xi), & \xi \leqslant x \leqslant b, \end{cases} \tag{6.5.12}$$

in which $c_2(\xi)$ is still to be determined.

We will next prove that if ϕ_0 is normalized, then

$$\frac{dG}{dx}(x,\xi)\Big|_{x=\xi-}^{x=\xi+} = -\frac{1}{p(\xi)}. \tag{6.5.13}$$

It follows from the Lagrange identity (3.6.10) that

$$\phi_0 L[G] - GL[\phi_0] = \frac{d}{dx}\big[\, p(G'\phi_0 - G\phi_0')\,\big].$$

But $L[G] = \phi_0(\xi)\phi_0(x)$ and $L[\phi_0] = 0$, so we have

$$\phi_0(\xi)\phi_0^2(x) = \frac{d}{dx}\big[\, p(G'\phi_0 - G\phi_0')\,\big].$$

Integrating from a to b, we obtain

$$\int_a^b \phi_0(\xi)\phi_0^2(x)\,dx = \big[\, p(G'\phi_0 - G\phi_0')\,\big]_a^\xi + \big[\, p(G'\phi_0 - G\phi_0')\,\big]_\xi^b.$$

Since

$$\int_a^b \phi_0^2(x)\,dx = 1, \tag{6.5.14}$$

the above equation becomes

$$\phi_0(\xi) = p(\xi)G'(\xi-)\phi_0(\xi) - p(\xi)G(\xi-)\phi_0'(\xi)$$
$$- p(\xi)G'(\xi+)\phi_0(\xi) + p(\xi)G(\xi+)\phi_0'(\xi)$$
$$+ \big[\, p(G'\phi_0 - G\phi_0'\,\big]_a^b.$$

Since G and ϕ_0 satisfy the boundary conditions at a and b, the last term vanishes. By virtue of the continuity of G, we have $G(\xi-) = G(\xi+)$. Thus we have

$$\phi_0(\xi) = p(\xi)\phi_0(\xi)\big[\, G'(\xi-,\xi) - G'(\xi+,\xi)\,\big].$$

Hence

$$\frac{dG}{dx}(x,\xi)\Big|_{x=\xi-}^{x=\xi+} = -\frac{1}{p(\xi)}.$$

Thus far the function $G(x,\xi)$ has been determined up to an arbitrary function $c_2(\xi)$. To determine c_2 for a particular function G, we require that

$$\int_a^b G(x,\xi)\phi_0(x)\,dx = 0. \qquad (6.5.15)$$

This condition is used in order for G to be symmetric.

To show that G is symmetric, let $H = G(x,\eta)$, where $\xi < \eta$. We then have

$$L[G] = \phi_0(\xi)\phi_0(x),$$

$$L[H] = \phi_0(\eta)\phi_0(x).$$

By virtue of (6.5.15) it immediately follows that

$$\int_a^b (GL[H] - HL[G])\,dx = 0.$$

Following the proof of Theorem 6.3.2, we can easily prove that the generalized Green's function is symmetric, that is,

$$G(x,\xi) = G(\xi,x). \qquad (6.5.16)$$

Finally we will show that

$$\phi(x) = \int_a^b G(x,\xi)f(\xi)\,d\xi \qquad (6.5.17)$$

is a solution of the nonhomogeneous boundary-value problem (6.5.1)–(6.5.2). To do so, we find the derivatives of $\phi(x)$ from (6.5.17) to obtain

$$L[\phi] = \int_a^b L[G(x,\xi)]f(\xi)\,d\xi + p(x)f(x)[G'(x,x-) - G'(x,x+)]$$

$$= \phi_0(x)\int_a^b \phi_0(\xi)f(\xi)\,d\xi - f(x)$$

$$= -f(x). \qquad \blacksquare$$

To illustrate the construction of the generalized Green's function, we present the following example.

Example 6.5.1   Consider the problem

$$y'' = -f(x),$$

$$y(0) = 0,$$

$$y(1) - y'(1) = 0.$$

The normalized solution of the associated homogeneous problem is readily determined to be

$$\phi_0(x) = \sqrt{3}\, x.$$

We will then determine the Green's function from the equation

$$y'' = 3\xi x,$$

whose solution is

$$\phi(x) = \frac{\xi x^3}{2} + a(\xi)x + b(\xi).$$

Thus we have

$$G_1(x, \xi) = \frac{\xi x^3}{2} + a_1(\xi)x + b_1(\xi),$$

$$G_2(x, \xi) = \frac{\xi x^3}{2} + a_2(\xi)x + b_2(\xi).$$

After applying the boundary conditions

$$G_1(0, \xi) = 0,$$

$$G_2(1, \xi) - G_2'(1, \xi) = 0,$$

we obtain

$$G_1(x, \xi) = \frac{\xi x^3}{2} + a_1(\xi)x,$$

$$G_2(x, \xi) = \frac{\xi x^3}{2} + a_2(\xi)x + \xi.$$

Now we determine a_1 in terms of a_2 by the continuity condition $G_1(\xi,\xi) = G_2(\xi,\xi)$, resulting in $a_1(\xi) = a_2(\xi) + 1$. Then using the condition

$$\int_0^1 G(x,\xi)\phi_0(x)\,dx = 0,$$

we obtain

$$a_2(\xi) = \frac{\xi^3}{2} - \frac{9}{5}\xi.$$

Thus the Green's function takes the form

$$G(x,\xi) = \begin{cases} \dfrac{\xi x^3}{2} + \dfrac{\xi^3 x}{2} - \dfrac{9}{2}\xi x + x, & 0 \le x \le \xi, \\[2mm] \dfrac{\xi x^3}{2} + \dfrac{\xi^3 x}{2} - \dfrac{9}{2}\xi x + \xi, & \xi \le x \le 1, \end{cases}$$

and hence the solution of the given problem is

$$\phi(x) = \int_0^x \left(\frac{\xi^3 x}{2} + \frac{\xi x^3}{2} - \frac{9}{2}\xi x + \xi \right) f(\xi)\,d\xi$$

$$+ \int_x^1 \left(\frac{\xi^3 x}{2} + \frac{\xi x^3}{2} - \frac{9}{2}\xi x + x \right) f(\xi)\,d\xi$$

provided $\displaystyle\int_0^1 xf(x)\,dx = 0$ is satisfied. For extended treatment, see Sagan [39].

EXERCISES

1. Find the Green's functions for the following boundary-value problems:

(a) $L[y] = y'' = 0,$
     $y(0) = 0, \qquad y'(1) = 0.$

(b) $L[y] = (1 - x^2)\,y'' - 2xy' = 0,$
     $y(0) = 0, \qquad y'(1) = 0.$

(c) $L[y] = y'' + a^2 y = 0, \qquad a$ a constant,
     $y(0) = 0, \qquad y(1) = 0.$

2. Determine the solution of each of the following boundary-value problems:

(a) $y'' + y = 1,$
   $y(0) = 0, \qquad y(1) = 0.$

(b) $y'' + 4y = e^x,$
   $y(0) = 0, \qquad y'(1) = 0.$

(c) $y'' = \sin x,$
   $y(0) = 0, \qquad y(1) + 2y'(1) = 0.$

3. Determine the solution of the following boundary-value problems:

(a) $y'' = -f(x), \qquad y(0) = 0, \qquad y'(1) = 0.$

(b) $y'' = -f(x), \qquad y(-1) = 0, \qquad y(1) = 0.$

4. Find the solution of the following boundary-value problems:

(a) $y'' - y = -f(x), \qquad y(0) = y(1) = 0.$

(b) $y'' - y = -f(x), \qquad y'(0) = y'(1) = 0.$

5. If the boundary condition at $x = 0$ is replaced by a finiteness condition, explain why the discussion for some boundary-value problems with homogeneous boundary conditions and with $p(x) = x$ is still valid.

6. Determine the Green's function for the boundary-value problem

$$xy'' + y' = -f(x),$$

$$y(1) = 0,$$

$$\lim_{x \to 0} |y(x)| < \infty.$$

7. Determine the Green's function for the boundary-value problem

$$xy'' + y' - \frac{n^2}{x} y = -f(x),$$

$$y(1) = 0,$$

$$\lim_{x \to 0} |y(x)| < \infty$$

8. Determine the Green's function for the boundary-value problem

$$\left[(1 - x^2) y' \right]' - \frac{h^2}{1 - x^2} y = -f(x), \quad h = 1, 2, 3 \cdots$$

$$\lim_{x \to \pm 1} |y(x)| < \infty.$$

9. Prove the uniqueness of the Green's function for the boundary-value problem (6.2.1–6.2.3)

$$L[\,y\,] = -f(x),$$

$$a_1\,y(a) + a_2\,y'(a) = 0,$$

$$b_1\,y(b) + b_2\,y'(b) = 0.$$

10. Find the Green's function for the boundary-value problem

$$L[\,y\,] = y^{iv} = -f(x),$$

$$y(0) = y(1) = y'(0) = y'(1) = 0.$$

11. Find the generalized Green's function for the boundary-value problem

$$xy'' + y' = -f(x),$$

$$y(1) = 0, \qquad \lim_{x \to 0} |\,y(x)\,| < \infty.$$

12. Determine the generalized Green's function for the boundary-value problem

$$\left[(1 - x^2)\,y'\right]' = -f(x),$$

$$\lim_{x \to \pm 1} |\,y(x)\,| < \infty$$

13. Consider the nonhomogeneous boundary-value problem with continuous coefficients.

$$L[\,y\,] = y'' + p(x)\,y' + q(x)\,y = g(x),$$

$$U_1[\,y\,] = a_1\,y(a) + a_2\,y'(a) + b_1\,y(b) + b_2\,y'(b) = \alpha,$$

$$U_2[\,y\,] = a_3\,y(a) + a_4\,y'(a) + b_3\,y(b) + b_4\,y'(b) = \beta.$$

If the associated homogeneous boundary-value problem

$$L[\,y\,] = 0,$$

$$U_i[\,y\,] = 0$$

has a trivial solution only, prove that the nonhomogeneous problem has a unique solution.

14. Determine the Green's function for the boundary-value problem

$$y'' = -f(x),$$
$$y(-1) = y(1),$$
$$y'(-1) = y'(1).$$

15. Consider the non-self-adjoint boundary-value problem

$$L[y] = y'' + 3y' + 2y = -f(x),$$
$$2y(0) - y(1) = 0,$$
$$y'(1) = 2.$$

By direct integration of $GL[y]$ from 0 to 1 show that

$$\phi(x) = -2G(1,x) - \int_0^1 G(x,\xi) f(\xi) d\xi$$

is the solution of the boundary-value problem if G satisfies

$$G_{\xi\xi} - 3G_\xi + 2G = 0, \xi \neq x$$
$$G(0,x) = 0,$$
$$6G(1,x) - 2G_\xi(1,x) + G_\xi(0,x) = 0.$$

Find G.

16. Show that

$$\frac{dG(x,\xi)}{dx}\bigg|_{\xi=x-}^{\xi=x+} = \frac{1}{p(x)}$$

is equivalent to

$$\frac{dG(x,\xi)}{dx}\bigg|_{x=\xi-}^{x=\xi+} = -\frac{1}{p(\xi)}.$$

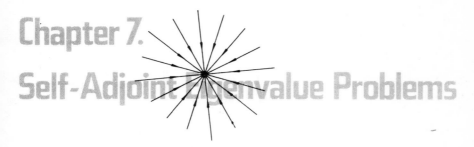

Chapter 7.
Self-Adjoint Eigenvalue Problems

7.1 Sturm-Liouville Systems

Eigenvalue problems associated with ordinary differential equations arise in considering physical problems, such as determining the displacement of a vibrating string or determining the temperature distribution of a heat-conducting rod by the method of separation of variables [28]. The typical equation that often occurs in problems is of the form

$$a_1(x)\frac{d^2y}{dx^2} + a_2(x)\frac{dy}{dx} + \left[a_3(x)+\lambda\right]y = 0. \tag{7.1.1}$$

If we introduce

$$p(x) = \exp\left[\int^x \frac{a_2(t)}{a_1(t)}\,dt\right], \qquad q(x) = \frac{a_3(x)}{a_1(x)}\,p(x), \qquad s(x) = \frac{p(x)}{a_1(x)} \tag{7.1.2}$$

into Eq. (7.1.1), we obtain

$$\frac{d}{dx}\left(p\frac{dy}{dx}\right) + (q+\lambda s)\,y = 0, \tag{7.1.3}$$

which is known as the *Sturm-Liouville equation*. In terms of the self-adjoint operator

$$L = \frac{d}{dx}\left(p\frac{d}{dx}\right) + q,$$

Eq. (7.1.3) can be written as

$$L[y] + \lambda s(x)y = 0, \qquad (7.1.4)$$

where λ is a parameter independent of x, and p, q and s are real-valued functions of x. To ensure the existence of solutions, we let q and s be continuous and p be continuously differentiable in a closed finite interval $[a,b]$.

The Sturm-Liouville equation is called *regular* in the interval $[a,b]$ if the functions $p(x)$ and $s(x)$ are positive in the interval $[a,b]$. Thus for a given λ there exist two linearly independent solutions of a regular Sturm-Liouville equation in the interval $[a,b]$.

DEFINITION 7.1.1 The Sturm-Liouville equation

$$L[y] + \lambda s(x)y = 0, \qquad a \leqslant x \leqslant b,$$

together with the separated end conditions

$$a_1 y(a) + a_2 y'(a) = 0,$$
$$b_1 y(b) + b_2 y'(b) = 0, \qquad (7.1.5)$$

where the constants a_1 and a_2, and likewise b_1 and b_2, are not both zero and are given real numbers, is called a regular *Sturm-Liouville system*.

The values of λ for which the Sturm-Liouville system has a nontrivial solution are called the *eigenvalues*, and the corresponding solutions are called the *eigenfunctions*.

Example 7.1.1 Consider the Sturm-Liouville system

$$y'' + \lambda y = 0, \qquad 0 \leqslant x \leqslant \pi,$$
$$y(0) = 0,$$
$$y'(\pi) = 0.$$

When $\lambda \leqslant 0$, it can be readily shown that λ is not an eigenvalue. However, when $\lambda > 0$, the solution of the Sturm-Liouville equation is

$$\phi(x) = A \cos\sqrt{\lambda}\, x + B \sin\sqrt{\lambda}\, x$$

Applying the condition $y(0) = 0$, we obtain $A = 0$. The condition $y'(\pi) = 0$ yields

$$B\sqrt{\lambda} \cos\sqrt{\lambda}\, \pi = 0.$$

Since $\lambda \neq 0$ and $B = 0$ yields a trivial solution, we must have

$$\cos\sqrt{\lambda}\, \pi = 0, \qquad B \neq 0.$$

This equation is satisfied if

$$\sqrt{\lambda} = \frac{2n-1}{2}, \qquad n = 1, 2, 3, \ldots,$$

and hence the eigenvalues are $\lambda_n = (2n-1)^2/4$, and the corresponding eigenfunctions are

$$\sin\left(\frac{2n-1}{2}\right)x, \qquad n = 1, 2, 3, \ldots.$$

Example 7.1.2 Consider the Euler equation

$$x^2 y'' + xy' + \lambda y = 0, \qquad 1 \leqslant x \leqslant e,$$

with the end conditions

$$y(1) = 0, \qquad y(e) = 0.$$

By using the transformation (7.1.2) the Euler equation can be put into Sturm-Liouville form:

$$\frac{d}{dx}\left(x\frac{dy}{dx}\right) + \frac{1}{x}\lambda y = 0.$$

The solution of the Euler equation is

$$\phi(x) = c_1 x^{i\sqrt{\lambda}} + c_2 x^{-i\sqrt{\lambda}}.$$

Noting that $x^{ia} = e^{ia\ln x} = \cos(a\ln x) + i\sin(a\ln x)$, $\phi(x)$ becomes

$$\phi(x) = A\cos(\sqrt{\lambda}\,\ln x) + B\sin(\sqrt{\lambda}\,\ln x),$$

where A and B are constants related to c_1 and c_2. The end condition $y(1)=0$ gives $A=0$, and the end condition $y(e)=0$ gives

$$\sin\sqrt{\lambda} = 0, \qquad B\neq 0,$$

which in turn yields the eigenvalues

$$\lambda_n = n^2\pi^2, \qquad n=1,2,3,\dots$$

and the corresponding eigenfunctions

$$\sin(n\pi\ln x), \qquad n=1,2,3,\dots$$

Another type of problem that often occurs in practice is the periodic Sturm-Liouville system.

DEFINITION 7.1.2   The Sturm-Liouville equation

$$\frac{d}{dx}\left(p(x)\frac{dy}{dx}\right) + \left[q(x) + \lambda s(x)\right]y = 0, \qquad a\leqslant x\leqslant b,$$

in which $p(a)=p(b)$, together with the periodic end conditions

$$y(a) = y(b),$$

$$y'(a) = y'(b),$$

is called a *periodic Sturm-Liouville system.*

Example 7.1.3   Consider the periodic Sturm-Liouville system

$$y'' + \lambda y = 0, \qquad -\pi \leqslant x \leqslant \pi,$$

$$y(-\pi) = y(\pi),$$

$$y'(-\pi) = y'(\pi).$$

Here we note that $p(x)=1$ and hence $p(-\pi)=p(\pi)$. When $\lambda>0$, we see that the solution of the Sturm-Liouville equation is

$$\phi(x) = A\cos\sqrt{\lambda}\,x + B\sin\sqrt{\lambda}\,x.$$

Application of the periodic end conditions yields

$$(2\sin\sqrt{\lambda}\,\pi)B=0,$$

$$(2\sqrt{\lambda}\,\sin\sqrt{\lambda}\,\pi)A=0.$$

Thus to obtain a nontrivial solution we must have

$$\sin\sqrt{\lambda}\,\pi=0, \qquad A\neq0, \quad B\neq0.$$

Consequently,

$$\lambda_n=n^2, \qquad n=1,2,3,\ldots.$$

Since $\sin\sqrt{\lambda}\,\pi=0$ is satisfied for arbitrary A and B, we obtain two linearly independent eigenfunctions $\cos nx, \sin nx$ corresponding to the same eigenvalue n^2.

It can be readily shown that if $\lambda<0$, the solution of the Sturm-Liouville equation does not satisfy the periodic end conditions. However, when $\lambda=0$ the corresponding eigenfunction is 1. Thus the eigenvalues of the periodic Sturm-Liouville system are $0,\{n^2\}$, and the corresponding eigenfunctions are $1,\{\cos nx\},\{\sin nx\}$, where n is a positive integer.

7.2 Eigenvalues and Eigenfunctions

In Examples 7.1.1 and 7.1.2 of regular Sturm-Liouville systems in the preceding section, we see that there exists only one linearly independent eigenfunction corresponding to the eigenvalue λ, which is called an eigenvalue of multiplicity one (or a simple eigenvalue). An eigenvalue is said to be of multiplicity k if there exist k linearly independent eigenfunctions corresponding to the same eigenvalue. In Example 7.1.3 of a periodic Sturm-Liouville system, the eigenfunctions $\cos nx, \sin nx$ correspond to the same eigenvalue n^2. Thus this eigenvalue is of multiplicity two.

In the preceding examples we see that the eigenfunctions are $\cos nx$ and $\sin nx$ for $n=1,2,3,\ldots.$ It can be easily shown by using trigonometric identities that

$$\int_{-\pi}^{\pi}\cos mx\cos nx\,dx=0, \qquad m\neq n,$$

$$\int_{-\pi}^{\pi}\cos mx\sin nx\,dx=0, \qquad \text{for all integers } m,n,$$

$$\int_{-\pi}^{\pi}\sin mx\sin nx\,dx=0, \qquad m\neq n.$$

We say that these functions are orthogonal to each other in the interval $[-\pi, \pi]$. The orthogonality relation holds in general for the eigenfunctions of Sturm-Liouville systems.

DEFINITION 7.2   Let $\phi(x)$ and $\psi(x)$ be any real-valued integrable functions on an interval I. Then ϕ and ψ are said to be *orthogonal* on I with respect to a weight function $\rho(x) > 0$ if and only if

$$(\phi, \psi) = \int_I \phi(x)\psi(x)\rho(x)\,dx = 0. \tag{7.2.1}$$

The interval I may be of infinite extent, or it may be either open or closed at one or both ends of the finite interval.

When $\phi = \psi$ in (7.2.1) we have the *norm* of ϕ

$$\|\phi\| = \left[\int_I \phi^2(x)\rho(x)\,dx\right]^{1/2}. \tag{7.2.2}$$

THEOREM 7.2.1   *Let the coefficients p, q and s in the Sturm-Liouville system be continuous in $[a,b]$. Let the eigenfunctions ϕ_j and ϕ_k, corresponding to λ_j and λ_k, be continuously differentiable. Then ϕ_j and ϕ_k are orthogonal with respect to the weight function s in $[a,b]$.*

Proof   Since ϕ_j corresponding to λ_j satisfies the Sturm-Liouville equation, we have

$$\frac{d}{dx}(p\phi_j') + (q + \lambda_j s)\phi_j = 0, \tag{7.2.3}$$

and for the same reason

$$\frac{d}{dx}(p\phi_k') + (q + \lambda_k s)\phi_k = 0. \tag{7.2.4}$$

Multiplying Eq. (7.2.3) by ϕ_k and Eq. (7.2.4) by ϕ_j, and subtracting, we obtain

$$(\lambda_j - \lambda_k)s\phi_j\phi_k = \phi_k \frac{d}{dx}(p\phi_j') - \phi_j \frac{d}{dx}(r\phi_k')$$

$$= \frac{d}{dx}\left[(p\phi_j')\phi_k - (p\phi_k')\phi_j\right],$$

and integration yields

$$(\lambda_j - \lambda_k) \int_a^b s\phi_j\phi_k \, dx = \left[p(\phi_j'\phi_k - \phi_j\phi_k') \right]_a^b$$

$$= p(b) \left[\phi_j'(b)\phi_k(b) - \phi_j(b)\phi_k'(b) \right]$$

$$- p(a) \left[\phi_j'(a)\phi_k(a) - \phi_j(a)\phi_k'(a) \right], \qquad (7.2.5)$$

the right side of which is called the boundary term of the Sturm-Liouville system. The end conditions for the eigenfunctions ϕ_j and ϕ_k are

$$b_1\phi_j(b) + b_2\phi_j'(b) = 0,$$

$$b_1\phi_k(b) + b_2\phi_k'(b) = 0.$$

If $b_2 \neq 0$, we multiply the first condition by $\phi_k(b)$ and the second condition by $\phi_j(b)$, and subtract to obtain

$$\left[\phi_j'(b)\phi_k(b) - \phi_j(b)\phi_k'(b) \right] = 0. \qquad (7.2.6)$$

In a similar manner, if $a_2 \neq 0$, we obtain

$$\left[\phi_j'(a)\phi_k(a) - \phi_j(a)\phi_k'(a) \right] = 0. \qquad (7.2.7)$$

We see by virtue of (7.2.6) and (7.2.7) that

$$(\lambda_j - \lambda_k) \int_a^b s\phi_j\phi_k \, dx = 0. \qquad (7.2.8)$$

If λ_j and λ_k are distinct eigenvalues, then

$$\int_a^b s\phi_j\phi_k \, dx = 0. \qquad (7.2.9)$$

∎

THEOREM 7.2.2 *The eigenfunctions of a periodic Sturm-Liouville system in $[a,b]$ are orthogonal with respect to the weight function s in $[a,b]$.*

Proof The periodic conditions for the eigenfunctions ϕ_j and ϕ_k are

$$\phi_j(a) = \phi_j(b), \qquad \phi_j'(a) = \phi_j'(b),$$

$$\phi_k(a) = \phi_k(b), \qquad \phi_k'(a) = \phi_k'(b).$$

Substitution of these into Eq. (7.2.5) yields

$$(\lambda_j - \lambda_k) \int_a^b s\phi_j\phi_k \, dx = \left[p(b) - p(a) \right]\left[\phi_j'(a)\phi_k(a) - \phi_j(a)\phi_k'(a) \right].$$

Since $p(a) = p(b)$, we have

$$(\lambda_j - \lambda_k) \int_a^b s\phi_j\phi_k \, dx = 0. \tag{7.2.10}$$

For distinct eigenvalues $\lambda_j \neq \lambda_k$, and thus

$$\int_a^b s\phi_j\phi_k \, dx = 0. \tag{7.2.11}$$

∎

THEOREM 7.2.3   *All the eigenvalues of a regular Sturm-Liouville system with $s(x) > 0$ are real.*

Proof   Suppose that there is a complex eigenvalue $\lambda_j = \alpha + i\beta$ with eigenfunction $\phi_j = u + iv$. Then, because the coefficients of the equation are real, the complex conjugate of the eigenvalue is also an eigenvalue. Thus, there exists an eigenfunction $\phi_k = u - iv$ corresponding to the eigenvalue $\lambda_k = \alpha - i\beta$.

By using the relation (7.2.8) we have

$$2\beta \int_a^b s(u^2 + v^2) \, dx = 0.$$

This implies that β must vanish for $s > 0$, and hence the eigenvalues are real.

∎

THEOREM 7.2.4   *If $\phi_1(x)$ and $\phi_2(x)$ are any two solutions of $L[y] + \lambda sy = 0$ on $[a, b]$, then $p(x)W(x; \phi_1, \phi_2) = constant$, where W is the Wronskian.*

Proof   Since ϕ_1 and ϕ_2 are solutions of $L[y] + \lambda sy = 0$, we have

$$\frac{d}{dx}\left(p\frac{d\phi_1}{dx} \right) + (q + \lambda s)\phi_1 = 0,$$

$$\frac{d}{dx}\left(p\frac{d\phi_2}{dx} \right) + (q + \lambda s)\phi_2 = 0.$$

Multiplying the first equation by ϕ_2 and the second by ϕ_1, and subtracting, we obtain

$$\phi_1 \frac{d}{dx}\left(p\frac{d\phi_2}{dx}\right) - \phi_2 \frac{d}{dx}\left(p\frac{d\phi_1}{dx}\right) = 0.$$

Integrating this equation from a to x, we obtain

$$p(x)\left[\phi_1(x)\phi_2'(x) - \phi_1'(x)\phi_2(x)\right] = p(a)\left[\phi_1(a)\phi_2'(a) - \phi_1'(a)\phi_2(a)\right]$$

$$= \text{constant}, \tag{7.2.12}$$

which is called *Abel's formula*. ∎

THEOREM 7.2.5 *An eigenfunction of a regular Sturm-Liouville system is unique except for a constant factor.*

Proof Let $\phi_1(x)$ and $\phi_2(x)$ be eigenfunctions corresponding to an eigenvalue λ. Then according to Abel's formula (7.2.12) we have

$$p(x)W(x;\phi_1,\phi_2) = \text{constant}, \qquad p(x) > 0,$$

where W is the Wronskian. Thus if W vanishes at a point in $[a,b]$, it must vanish for all $x \in [a,b]$.

Since ϕ_1 and ϕ_2 satisfy the end condition at $x = a$, we have

$$a_1\phi_1(a) + b_2\phi_1'(a) = 0,$$

$$b_1\phi_2(a) + a_2\phi_2'(a) = 0.$$

Since a_1 and a_2 are not both zero, we have

$$\begin{vmatrix} \phi_1(a) & \phi_1'(a) \\ \phi_2(a) & \phi_2'(a) \end{vmatrix} = + W(a;\phi_1,\phi_2) = 0.$$

Therefore $W(x;\phi_1,\phi_2) = 0$ for all $x \in [a,b]$, which is a sufficient condition for the linear dependence of ϕ_1 and ϕ_2. Hence $\phi_1(x)$ differs from $\phi_2(x)$ only by a constant factor. ∎

Theorem 7.2.3 states that all eigenvalues of a regular Sturm-Liouville system are real, but it does not guarantee that any eigenvalue exists. However, it can be proved that a self-adjoint regular Sturm-Liouville system has a denumerably infinite number of eigenvalues. Before we prove this, let us consider the following example:

Example 7.2.1   Consider the Sturm-Liouville system

$$y'' + \lambda y = 0, \qquad 0 \leqslant x \leqslant 1,$$

$$y(0) = 0,$$

$$y(1) + hy'(1) = 0, \qquad h > 0 \quad \text{a constant.}$$

Here $p = 1$, $q = 0$, $s = 1$. The solution of the Sturm-Liouville equation is

$$\phi(x) = A \cos \sqrt{\lambda}\, x + B \sin \sqrt{\lambda}\, x.$$

Since $y(0) = 0$ gives $A = 0$, we have

$$\phi(x) = B \sin \sqrt{\lambda}\, x.$$

Applying the second end condition, we have

$$\sin \sqrt{\lambda} + h \sqrt{\lambda} \cos \sqrt{\lambda} = 0 \qquad \text{for} \quad B \neq 0,$$

which can be rewritten as

$$\tan \sqrt{\lambda} = - h \sqrt{\lambda}$$

If $\alpha = \sqrt{\lambda}$ is introduced in this equation, we have

$$\tan \alpha = - h\alpha$$

This equation does not possess an explicit solution. Thus we determine the solution graphically by plotting the functions $\xi = \tan \alpha$ and $\xi = - h\alpha$ against α, as shown in Fig. 7.2-1. The roots are given by the intersection of two curves, and as is evident from the graph, there are infinitely many roots α_n for $n = 1, 2, 3, \ldots$. To each root α_n, there corresponds an eigenvalue

$$\lambda_n = \alpha_n^2, \qquad n = 1, 2, 3, \ldots.$$

Thus there exists a sequence of eigenvalues

$$\lambda_1 < \lambda_2 < \lambda_3 < \cdots$$

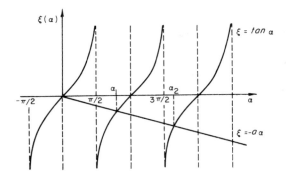

Figure 7.2-1

with

$$\lim_{n \to \infty} \lambda_n = \infty.$$

The corresponding eigenfunctions are $\sin \sqrt{\lambda_n}\, x$.

THEOREM 7.2.6 *A self-adjoint regular Sturm-Liouville system has an infinite sequence of real eigenvalues*

$$\lambda_0 < \lambda_1 < \lambda_2 < \lambda_3 < \cdots$$

with

$$\lim_{n \to \infty} \lambda_n = \infty.$$

For each n the corresponding eigenfunction $\phi_n(x)$, uniquely determined up to a constant factor, has exactly n zeros in the interval (a,b).

Proof By taking appropriate real numbers α and β in the interval $[0, \pi)$ we can rewrite (7.1.5) in the form

$$\cos \alpha\, y(a) - p(a) \sin \alpha\, y'(a) = 0, \tag{7.2.13}$$

$$\cos \beta\, y(b) - p(b) \sin \beta\, y'(b) = 0, \tag{7.2.14}$$

where α and β can be expressed in terms of a_1, a_2, b_1, b_2. It is obvious by the Prüfer substitution that the condition (7.2.13) is equivalent to the condition

$$\theta(a) = \alpha. \tag{7.2.15}$$

Let $\phi(x,\lambda)$ be a solution of the regular Sturm-Liouville equation (7.1.4). Then the Prüfer phase function of the solution $\theta(x,\lambda)$ satisfying $\theta(a,\lambda)=\alpha$ can be determined.

By Theorem 3.7.2, $\theta(x,\lambda)$ is a monotonic increasing function of λ for fixed x. Moreover, from the equation

$$\theta'(x)=\frac{1}{p(x)}\cos^2\theta(x)+\left[q(x)+\lambda s(x)\right]\sin^2\theta(x)$$

we see that $\theta'(x)>0$ when $\theta=0$ (mod π). Since $\theta(a)=\alpha\geqslant0$, we must have $\theta(x,\lambda)\geqslant0$. Thus if x_n denotes the location of the nth zero of $\phi(x,\lambda)$ on (a,b), then $\theta(x_n,\lambda)=n\pi$ for $n=0,1,2,\ldots$. Since $\theta(a,\lambda)=\alpha<\pi$, the first zero of $\phi(x,\lambda)$ in (a,b) occurs where $\theta=\pi$, and the nth zero where $\theta=n\pi$.

$\theta(x_n,\lambda)$ being a continuous function in $x_n(\lambda)$ and λ, we have

$$\frac{\partial\theta}{\partial x_n}\frac{dx_n}{d\lambda}+\frac{\partial\theta}{\partial\lambda}=0. \qquad (7.2.16)$$

Since $\partial\theta/\partial\lambda\geqslant0$ and $\partial\theta/\partial x_n>0$ when $\theta=0$ (mod π), it is evident from (7.2.16) that $x_n(\lambda)$ is a continuous and monotone decreasing function of λ.

To prove that $\lim_{\lambda\to\infty}\theta(x,\lambda)=\infty$, let P, Q and S be constants such that $p(x)\leqslant P$, $q(x)\geqslant Q$, $s(x)\geqslant S>0$. Then the equation

$$\frac{d}{dx}\left(P\frac{dy}{dx}\right)+(Q+\lambda S)\,y=0$$

with $(Q+\lambda S)>0$ has a solution

$$\tilde{\phi}(x)=\sin kx,$$

where $k^2=(Q+\lambda S)/P$. The successive zeros of $\tilde{\phi}(x)$ are spaced at a distance $\pi[(Q+\lambda S)/P]^{-1/2}$ apart. This tends to zero as $\lambda\to\infty$. By the Sturm comparison theorem (Theorem 3.7.3), $\phi(x)$ has a zero between any pair of consecutive zeros of $\tilde{\phi}(x)$. As we know ϕ has n zeros on (a,b) when λ is sufficiently large, it follows that $\phi(x)$ must have n zeros on (a,b). Thus $\theta(x,\lambda)=n\pi$ for sufficiently large λ. It is obvious then that $\theta(x,\lambda)$ approaches infinity as λ tends to zero.

To prove $\lim_{\lambda\to-\infty}\theta(x,\lambda)=0$, choose numbers ξ and δ such that $\alpha<\xi<\pi$ and $0<\delta<\pi$. Then the slope of the line segment in the x-θ plane connecting (a,ξ) and (c,δ) for some $c\in(a,b)$ is $(\delta-\xi)/(c-a)$.

Now choose $\lambda < \Lambda$ for some Λ such that

$$\theta' = \frac{\cos^2\theta}{p(x)} + \left[q(x) + \lambda s(x) \right] \sin^2\theta < \frac{\delta - \xi}{c - a}$$

for all (x, θ) on the segment. This can be done by choosing sufficiently large negative λ. Thus we conclude that $\theta(c, \lambda) < \delta$ for sufficiently large negative λ. Since $\theta(c, \lambda) > 0$, we must have $|\theta(c, \lambda)| < \delta$. Since c and δ are arbitrary, it follows that

$$\lim_{\lambda \to -\infty} \theta(x, \lambda) = 0.$$

We see from the above that $\theta(b, \lambda) \to 0$ as $\lambda \to -\infty$. Since $\beta > 0$ and since $\theta(b, \lambda)$ is an increasing function of λ, there is a λ_0 for which $\theta(b, \lambda_0) = \beta$. As λ increases there is an infinite sequence of λ_n for which $\theta(b, \lambda_n) = \beta + n\pi$. The eigenfunction that corresponds to the eigenvalue λ_n is given by

$$\phi_n(x) = r(x) \sin \theta(x, \lambda_n).$$

By the uniqueness theorem, any two solutions of the regular Sturm-Liouville equation satisfying the same initial condition are linearly dependent. Hence the eigenfunction $\phi_n(x)$ is uniquely determined up to a constant factor. ∎

For the periodic Sturm-Liouville system we shall state without proof the following theorem:

THEOREM 7.2.7 *The eigenvalues for a periodic Sturm-Liouville system form a sequence*

$$-\infty < \lambda_0 < \lambda_1 \leqslant \lambda_2 < \lambda_3 \leqslant \lambda_4 < \cdots.$$

There exists a unique eigenfunction ϕ_0 for λ_0. If $\lambda_{2j+1} < \lambda_{2j+2}$ for $j \geqslant 0$, then there exist unique corresponding eigenfunctions ϕ_{2j+1} and ϕ_{2j+2}. However, if $\lambda_{2j+1} = \lambda_{2j+2}$, there are two linearly independent eigenfunctions ϕ_{2j+1} and ϕ_{2j+2}.

A proof is given by Coddington and Levinson [8].

7.3 Eigenfunction Expansions

DEFINITION 7.3.1 A real-valued function $\phi(x)$ is said to be *square-integrable* with respect to a weight function $\rho(x) > 0$ if on an interval I

$$\int_I \phi^2(x) \rho(x) \, dx < +\infty. \qquad (7.3.1)$$

An immediate consequence of the definition is the *Schwarz inequality*

$$\left| \int_I \phi(x)\psi(x)\rho(x)\,dx \right|^2 \leqslant \int_I \phi^2(x)\rho(x)\,dx \int_I \psi^2(x)\rho(x)\,dx \qquad (7.3.2)$$

for square-integrable functions $\phi(x)$ and $\psi(x)$ (see Exercise 12).

Let $\{\phi_n(x)\}$, for a positive integer n, be an orthogonal set of square-integrable functions with a positive weight function $\rho(x)$ on an interval I. Let $f(x)$ be a given function that can be represented by a uniformly convergent series of the form

$$f(x) = \sum_{n=1}^{\infty} c_n\phi_n(x), \qquad (7.3.3)$$

where the coefficients c_n are constants. Now multiplying both sides of (7.3.3) by $\phi_m(x)\rho(x)$ and integrating term by term over the interval I (uniform convergence of the series is a sufficient condition for this), we obtain

$$\int_I f(x)\phi_m(x)\rho(x)\,dx = \sum_{n=1}^{\infty} \int_I c_n\phi_n(x)\phi_m(x)\rho(x)\,dx,$$

and hence

$$\int_I f(x)\phi_n(x)\rho(x)\,dx = c_n \int_I \phi_n^2(x)\rho(x)\,dx.$$

Thus

$$c_n = \frac{\displaystyle\int_I f\phi_n\rho\,dx}{\displaystyle\int_I \phi_n^2\rho\,dx}. \qquad (7.3.4)$$

Hence we have the following theorem:

THEOREM 7.3.1 *If f is represented by a uniformly convergent series*

$$f(x) = \sum_{n=1}^{\infty} c_n\phi_n(x)$$

on an interval I, where ϕ_n are square-integrable functions orthogonal with *respect to a positive weight function $\rho(x)$, then c_n are determined by*

$$c_n = \frac{\int_I f\phi_n \rho \, dx}{\int_I \phi_n^2 \rho \, dx}.$$

Example 7.3.1 The Legendre polynomials $P_n(x)$ are orthogonal with respect to the weight function $\rho(x) = 1$ on $(-1, 1)$. If we assume that $f(x)$ can be represented by the *Fourier-Legendre series*

$$f(x) = \sum_{n=1}^{\infty} c_n P_n(x),$$

then c_n are given by

$$c_n = \frac{\int_{-1}^{1} f(x) P_n(x) \, dx}{\int_{-1}^{1} P_n^2(x) \, dx}$$

$$= \frac{2n+1}{2} \int_{-1}^{1} f(x) P_n(x) \, dx.$$

In the above discussion we assumed that the given function $f(x)$ is represented by a uniformly convergent series. This is rather restrictive, and we will show in the following section that $f(x)$ can be represented by a mean-square convergent series.

7.4   Convergence in the Mean

Let $\{\phi_n\}$ be the set of square-integrable functions orthogonal with respect to the weight function $\rho(x)$ on $[a, b]$. Let

$$s_n(x) = \sum_{k=1}^{n} c_k \phi_k(x)$$

be the nth partial sum of the series $\sum_{k=1}^{\infty} c_k \phi_k(x)$.

DEFINITION 7.4.1   Let f be a square-integrable function. The sequence $\{s_n\}$ is said to *converge in the mean* to $f(x)$ on the interval I with respect to the weight function $\rho(x)$ if

$$\lim_{n \to \infty} \int_I [f(x) - s_n(x)]^2 \rho(x)\, dx = 0. \tag{7.4.1}$$

We shall now seek the coefficients c_k such that $s_n(x)$ represents the best approximation to $f(x)$ in the sense of least squares, that is, we seek to minimize the integral

$$E(c_k) = \int_I [f(x) - s_n(x)]^2 \rho(x)\, dx$$

$$= \int_I f^2 \rho\, dx - 2 \sum_{k=1}^{n} c_k \int_I f\phi_k \rho\, dx + \sum_{k=1}^{n} c_k^2 \int_I \phi_k^2 \rho\, dx. \tag{7.4.2}$$

This is an extremal problem. A necessary condition on the c_k for E to be a minimum is that the first partial derivatives of E with respect to these coefficients vanish. Thus differentiating (7.4.2) with respect to c_k, we obtain

$$\frac{\partial E}{\partial c_k} = -2 \int_I f\phi_k \rho\, dx + 2c_k \int_I \phi_k^2 \rho\, dx = 0, \tag{7.4.3}$$

and hence

$$c_k = \frac{\int_I f\phi_k \rho\, dx}{\int_I \phi_k^2 \rho\, dx}. \tag{7.4.4}$$

Now if we complete the square, the right side of (7.4.2) becomes

$$E = \int_I f^2 \rho\, dx + \sum_{k=1}^{n} \int_I \phi_k^2 \rho\, dx \left[c_k - \frac{\int_I f\phi_k \rho\, dx}{\int_I \phi_k^2 \rho\, dx} \right]^2 - \sum_{k=1}^{n} \frac{\left[\int_I f\phi_k \rho\, dx \right]^2}{\int_I \phi_k^2 \rho\, dx}.$$

The right side shows that E is a minimum if and only if c_k is given by (7.4.4). Therefore this choice of c_k yields the best approximation to $f(x)$ in the sense of least squares.

For series convergent in the mean to $f(x)$ we conventionally write

$$f(x) \sim \sum_{k=1}^{\infty} c_k \phi_k(x),$$

where the coefficients c_k are called the *Fourier coefficients* and the series is called the *Fourier series*. This series may or may not be pointwise or uniformly convergent.

7.5 Completeness and Parseval's Equality

Substituting the Fourier coefficients (7.4.4) into (7.4.2), we obtain

$$\int_I \left[f(x) - \sum_{k=1}^{n} c_k \phi_k(x) \right]^2 \rho(x)\, dx = \int_I f^2 \rho\, dx - \sum_{k=1}^{n} c_k^2 \int_I \phi_k^2 \rho\, dx.$$

Since the left side is nonnegative, we have

$$\sum_{k=1}^{n} c_k^2 \int_I \phi_k^2 \rho\, dx \leqslant \int_I f^2 \rho\, dx. \tag{7.5.1}$$

The integral on the right side is finite, and hence the series on the left side is bounded above for any n. Thus as $n \to \infty$, the inequality (7.5.1) may be written as

$$\sum_{k=1}^{\infty} c_k^2 \int_I \phi_k^2 \rho\, dx \leqslant \int_I f^2 \rho\, dx. \tag{7.5.2}$$

This is called *Bessel's inequality.*

If the series converges in the mean to $f(x)$, that is,

$$\lim_{n \to \infty} \int_I \left[f(x) - \sum_{k=1}^{n} c_k \phi_k(x) \right]^2 \rho(x)\, dx = 0,$$

then it follows from the above derivation that

$$\sum_{k=1}^{\infty} c_k^2 \int_I \phi_k^2 \rho\, dx = \int_I f^2 \rho\, dx,$$

which is called *Parseval's equality*. Sometimes it is known as the complete-ness relation. Thus when every continuous square-integrable function $f(x)$ can be expanded into an infinite series

$$f(x) = \sum_{k=1}^{\infty} c_k \phi_k(x),$$

the sequence of continuous square-integrable functions $\{\phi_k\}$ orthogonal with respect to the weight function ρ is said to be *complete*.

Example 7.5.1 One of the most important examples is the set of trigono-metric functions $\{1, \cos kx, \sin kx\}$ on the interval $[-\pi, \pi]$. These functions are orthogonal with respect to the weight function $\rho = 1$. Since

$$\int_{-\pi}^{\pi} \cos^2 kx\, dx = \int_{-\pi}^{\pi} \sin^2 kx\, dx = \pi,$$

we find

$$a_k = \frac{1}{\pi} \int_{-\pi}^{\pi} f(x) \cos kx\, dx, \qquad k = 0, 1, 2, \ldots,$$

$$b_k = \frac{1}{\pi} \int_{-\pi}^{\pi} f(x) \sin kx\, dx, \qquad k = 1, 2, 3, \ldots.$$

If f is a continuously differentiable function periodic with period 2π, then the Fourier series of $f(x)$ is given by

$$f(x) = \frac{a_0}{2} + \sum_{k=1}^{\infty} a_k \cos kx + b_k \sin kx,$$

which converges uniformly on $[-\pi, \pi]$.

Next we state without proof the following theorem:

THEOREM 7.5.1 *The eigenfunctions of any regular Sturm-Liouville sys-tem are complete in the space of functions that are piecewise continuous on the interval $[a, b]$ with respect to the weight function $s(x)$. Moreover, any piecewise smooth function on $[a, b]$ that satisfies the end conditions of the regular Sturm-Liouville system can be expanded in an absolutely and uniformly convergent series*

$$f(x) = \sum_{k=1}^{\infty} c_k \phi_k(x),$$

where c_k are given by

$$c_k = \frac{\int_a^b f \phi_k s \, dx}{\int_a^b \phi_k^2 s \, dx} .$$

A proof of a more general theorem is given by Coddington and Levinson [8].

7.6 Singular Sturm-Liouville Systems

A Sturm-Liouville equation is called singular when it is given on a semiin-
finite or infinite interval, or when the coefficient $p(x)$ or $s(x)$ vanishes, or
when one of the coefficients becomes infinite at one end or both ends of a
finite interval. A singular Sturm-Liouville equation together with appropriate
linear homogeneous end conditions is called a *singular Sturm-Liouville
system*. The conditions imposed in this case are not like the separated end
conditions in the regular Sturm-Liouville system. The condition that it is
often necessary to prescribe is the boundedness of the function $y(x)$ at the
singular end point. To exhibit this, let us consider a problem with a
singularity at the end point $x = a$. By the relation (3.6.12), for any twice
continuously differentiable functions $y(x)$ and $z(x)$, we have on $(a,b]$

$$\int_{a+\varepsilon}^b \{ zL[\,y\,] - yL[\,z\,] \} \, dx = p(b) \big[\, y'(b)z(b) - y(b)z'(b) \, \big]$$

$$- p(a+\varepsilon) \big[\, y'(a+\varepsilon)z(a+\varepsilon) - y(a+\varepsilon)z'(a+\varepsilon) \, \big],$$

where ε is a small positive number. If the conditions

$$\lim_{x \to a+} p(x) \big[\, y'(x)z(x) - y(x)z'(x) \, \big] = 0, \tag{7.6.1}$$

$$p(b) \big[\, y'(b)z(b) - y(b)z'(b) \, \big] = 0 \tag{7.6.2}$$

are imposed on y and z, it follows that

$$\int_a^b \{ zL[\,y\,] - yL[\,z\,] \} \, dx = 0. \tag{7.6.3}$$

For example, when $p(a) = 0$ the relations (7.6.1) and (7.6.2) are replaced by
the conditions

1. $y(x)$ and $y'(x)$ are finite as $x \to a$.
2. $b_1 y(b) + b_2 y'(b) = 0$.

Thus we say that the singular Sturm-Liouville system is *self-adjoint* if any functions $y(x)$ and $z(x)$ that satisfy the end conditions

$$\int_a^b \{ zL[\,y\,] - yL[\,z\,] \}\, dx = 0.$$

Example 7.6.1   Consider the singular Sturm-Liouville system involving Legendre's equation

$$\frac{d}{dx}\left[(1 - x^2)\frac{dy}{dx} \right] + \lambda y = 0, \qquad -1 < x < 1,$$

with the conditions that y and y' are finite as $x \to \pm 1$.

In this case $p(x) = 1 - x^2$ and $s(x) = 1$, and $p(x)$ vanishes at $x = \pm 1$. The Legendre functions of the first kind, $P_n(x)$, $n = 0, 1, 2, \ldots$, are the eigenfunctions which are finite as $x \to \pm 1$. The corresponding eigenvalues are $\lambda_n = n(n + 1)$ for $n = 0, 1, 2, \ldots$. We observe here that the singular Sturm-Liouville system has infinitely many real eigenvalues, and the eigenfunctions $P_n(x)$ are orthogonal to each other.

Example 7.6.2   Another example of a singular Sturm-Liouville system is the Bessel equation for fixed ν,

$$\frac{d}{dx}\left(x\frac{dy}{dx} \right) + \left(\lambda x - \frac{\nu^2}{x} \right) y = 0, \qquad 0 < x \leqslant a,$$

with the end conditions that $y(a) = 0$ and y, y' are finite as $x \to 0+$.

Here $p(x) = x$, $q(x) = -\nu^2/x$, $s(x) = x$. Now $p(0) = 0$, $q(x)$ becomes infinite as $x \to 0+$, and $s(0) = 0$; therefore the system is singular. If $\lambda = k^2$, the eigenfunctions of the system are Bessel functions of the first kind and of order ν, namely $J_\nu(k_n x)$, $n = 1, 2, 3, \ldots$, where $k_n a$ is the nth zero of J_ν. The Bessel function J_ν and its derivative are both finite as $x \to 0+$. The eigenvalues are $\lambda_n = k_n^2$. Thus the system has infinitely many eigenvalues, and the eigenfunctions are orthogonal with respect to the weight function x.

In the preceding examples we see that the eigenfunctions are orthogonal with respect to the weight function $s(x)$. In general the eigenfunctions of a singular Sturm-Liouville system are orthogonal if they are square-integrable with respect to the weight function $s(x)$.

THEOREM 7.6.1 *The square-integrable eigenfunctions corresponding to distinct eigenvalues of a singular Sturm-Liouville system are orthogonal with respect to a weight function $s(x)$.*

Proof Proceeding as in Theorem 7.2.1, we arrive at

$$(\lambda_j - \lambda_k) \int_a^b s\phi_j\phi_k \, dx = p(b)\left[\phi_j'(b)\phi_k(b) - \phi_j(b)\phi_k'(b)\right]$$
$$- p(a)\left[\phi_j'(a)\phi_k(a) - \phi_j(a)\phi_k'(a)\right].$$

Suppose the boundary term vanishes, as in the case mentioned earlier, where $p(a)=0$, y and y' are finite as $x \to a$, and at the other end $b_1 y(b) + b_2 y'(b) = 0$. Then we have

$$(\lambda_j - \lambda_k) \int_a^b s\phi_j\phi_k \, dx = 0.$$

This integral exists by virtue of (7.3.2). Thus for distinct eigenvalues $\lambda_j \neq \lambda_k$, the square-integrable functions ϕ_j and ϕ_k are orthogonal with respect to the weight function $s(x)$. ∎

Example 7.6.3 Consider the singular Sturm-Liouville system involving the *Hermite equation*

$$u'' - 2xu' + \lambda u = 0, \qquad -\infty < x < \infty, \tag{7.6.4}$$

which is not self-adjoint.

If we let $y(x) = e^{-x^2/2}u(x)$, the Hermite equation takes the self-adjoint form

$$y'' + \left[(1 - x^2) + \lambda\right]y = 0, \qquad -\infty < x < \infty.$$

Here $p = 1$, $q(x) = 1 - x^2$, $s = 1$. The eigenvalues are $\lambda_n = 2n$ for nonnegative integer n, and the corresponding eigenfunctions are $\phi_n(x) = e^{-x^2/2}H_n(x)$, where $H_n(x)$ are the Hermite polynomials of Eq. (7.6.4). (See Magnus and Oberhettinger [26].)

Now we impose the end condition that y tends to zero as $x \to \pm\infty$. This is satisfied because $H_n(x)$ are polynomials in x and in fact $x^n e^{-x^2/2} \to 0$ as $x \to \pm\infty$. Since $\phi_n(x)$ are square-integrable, we have

$$\int_{-\infty}^{\infty} H_m(x)H_n(x)e^{-x^2} \, dx = 0, \qquad m \neq n.$$

EXERCISES

1. Determine the eigenvalues and eigenfunctions of the following regular Sturm-Liouville systems:

   (a) $y'' + \lambda y = 0$,
   $$y(0) = 0, \qquad y(\pi) = 0.$$

   (b) $y'' + \lambda y = 0$,
   $$y(0) = 0, \qquad y'(1) = 0.$$

   (c) $y'' + \lambda y = 0$,
   $$y'(0) = 0, \qquad y'(\pi) = 0.$$

   (d) $y'' + \lambda y = 0$,
   $$y(1) = 0, \qquad y(0) + y'(0) = 0.$$

2. Find the eigenvalues and eigenfunctions of the following periodic Sturm-Liouville systems:

   (a) $y'' + \lambda y = 0$,
   $$y(-1) = y(1), \qquad y'(-1) = y'(1).$$

   (b) $y'' + \lambda y = 0$,
   $$y(0) = y(2\pi), \qquad y'(0) = y'(2\pi).$$

   (c) $y'' + \lambda y = 0$,
   $$y(0) = y(\pi), \qquad y'(0) = y'(\pi).$$

3. Obtain the eigenvalues and eigenfunctions of the following Sturm-Liouville systems:

   (a) $y'' + y' + (1 + \lambda)\, y = 0$,
   $$y(0) = 0, \qquad y(1) = 0.$$

   (b) $y'' + 2y' + (1 - \lambda)\, y = 0$,
   $$y(0) = 0, \qquad y'(1) = 0.$$

   (c) $y'' - 3y' + 3(1 + \lambda)y = 0$,
   $$y'(0) = 0, \qquad y'(\pi) = 0.$$

4. Show that if ϕ_1 and ϕ_2 are two linearly independent solutions of the Sturm-Liouville system

$$\frac{d}{dx}\left[p(x)\, y' \right] + \left[q(x) + \lambda s(x) \right] y = 0,$$

$$a_1\, y(a) + a_2\, y(b) + a_3\, y'(a) + a_4\, y'(b) = 0,$$

$$b_1\, y(a) + b_2\, y(b) + b_3\, y'(a) + b_4\, y'(b) = 0,$$

then they are orthogonal with respect to the weight function $s(x)$ in $[a, b]$.

5. Find the eigenvalues and eigenfunctions of the following regular Sturm-Liouville systems:

   (a) $x^2 y'' + 3xy' + \lambda y = 0$, $1 \leqslant x \leqslant e$,
   $y(1) = 0$, $y(e) = 0$.

   (b) $\dfrac{d}{dx}[(2 + x)^2 y'] + \lambda y = 0$, $-1 \leqslant x \leqslant 1$,
   $y(-1) = 0$, $y(1) = 0$.

   (c) $(1 + x)^2 y'' + 2(1 + x) y' + 3\lambda y = 0$, $0 \leqslant x \leqslant 1$,
   $y(0) = 0$, $y(1) = 0$.

6. Determine all eigenvalues and eigenfunctions of the singular Sturm-Liouville systems

   (a) $x^2 y'' + xy' + \lambda y = 0$,
   $y(1) = 0$, y, y' bounded at $x = 0$.

   (b) $y'' + \lambda y = 0$,
   $y(0) = 0$, y, y' bounded at infinity.

7. Expand the function

$$f(x) = \sin x, \qquad 0 \leqslant x \leqslant \pi,$$

   in terms of the eigenfunctions of the Sturm-Liouville problem

$$y'' + \lambda y = 0,$$
$$y(0) = 0, \qquad y(\pi) + y'(\pi) = 0.$$

8. Find the expansion of

$$f(x) = x, \qquad 0 \leqslant x \leqslant \pi,$$

   in a series of eigenfunctions of the Sturm-Liouville system

$$y'' + \lambda y = 0,$$
$$y'(0) = 0, \qquad y'(\pi) = 0.$$

9. Transform each of the following equations into the equivalent self-adjoint form:

   (a) The Laguerre equation

$$xy'' + (1 - x) y' + ny = 0, \qquad n = 0, 1, 2, \dots .$$

(b)   The Hermite equation

$$y'' - 2xy' + 2ny = 0, \qquad n = 0, 1, 2, \dots \, .$$

(c)   The Tchebycheff equation

$$(1 - x^2)\, y'' - xy' + n^2 y = 0, \qquad n = 0, 1, 2, \dots \, .$$

10.   If $q(x)$ and $s(x)$ are continuous and $p(x)$ is twice continuously differentiable in $[a, b]$, then the solutions of the fourth-order Sturm-Liouville system

$$\big[\, p(x)\, y''\,\big]'' + \big[\, q(x) + \lambda s(x)\,\big]\, y = 0,$$

$$\big[\, a_1\, y + a_2 (py'')' \,\big]_{x=a} = 0, \qquad \big[\, b_1\, y + b_2 (py'')' \,\big]_{x=b} = 0,$$

$$\big[\, c_1\, y' + c_2 (py'') \,\big]_{x=a} = 0, \qquad \big[\, d_1\, y' + d_2 (py'') \,\big]_{x=b} = 0,$$

with $a_1^2 + a_2^2 \neq 0$, $b_1^2 + b_2^2 \neq 0$, $c_1^2 + c_2^2 \neq 0$, $d_1^2 + d_2^2 \neq 0$, are orthogonal with respect to $s(x)$ in $[a, b]$.

11.   If the eigenfunctions of the problem

$$\frac{1}{r} \frac{d}{dr} (ry') + \lambda y = 0, \qquad 0 < r < a,$$

$$c_1\, y(a) + c_2\, y'(a) = 0,$$

$$\lim_{r \to 0+}\, y(r) < \infty$$

satisfy

$$\lim_{r \to 0+}\, ry'(r) = 0,$$

show that all the eigenvalues are real for real c_1 and c_2.

12.   Prove the Schwarz inequality for square-integrable functions $\phi(x)$ and $\psi(x)$:

$$\left| \int_I \phi(x)\psi(x)\rho(x)\, dx \right|^2 \leqslant \int_I \phi^2(x)\rho(x)\, dx \int_I \psi^2(x)\rho(x)\, dx.$$

Chapter 8. Stability

8.1 Autonomous Systems

We have seen earlier that when $F(t, X)$ is continuous and satisfies a Lipschitz condition in some domain D of $(n + 1)$-dimensional (t, X) space, the initial-value problem

$$\frac{dX}{dt} = F(t, X),$$

$$X(t_0) = X_0$$

has a unique solution in D which depends continuously on the initial data t_0, X_0. That is, if we perturb the initial value X_0 by a small amount, the solution $X(t)$ changes by a small amount in a short interval about t_0. The question now is whether a small change in the initial data leads to a small change in the solution for large values of t. This is the field of study known as *stability theory*, which has been applied successfully in such areas as automatic controls.

Stability theory has been related historically to nonlinear differential equations, the explicit solutions of which are extremely difficult to attain, so that the qualitative behavior of solutions must be studied without actually solving the equations.

We will be concerned here with *autonomous systems*, that is, systems with F independent of time. They have the form

$$\dot{X} = F(X), \tag{8.1.1}$$

199

where the dot, as usual, denotes differentiation with respect to time. Such a system defines a time-independent vector field in a region of n-space. A steady fluid flow in three-dimensional space is a good example. $F(X)$ represents the velocity of the fluid at the point X. The solution $X(t,c)$ describes a streamline of a moving fluid particle.

We have a special interest in the case where F vanishes at some value C. In this case the function $X(t) = C$ is the solution of Eq. (8.1.1), and the streamline becomes a point at C where the velocity F vanishes. This point is called a *stagnation point*.

DEFINITION 8.1.1   A point C in R^n at which $F(C) = 0$ is called an *equilibrium point* or *critical point* of the autonomous system $\dot{X} = F(X)$.

If we confine our attention to the two dimensional system

$$\frac{dx}{dt} = f(x,y),$$

$$\frac{dy}{dt} = g(x,y),$$

(8.1.2)

we see that every solution $x = x(t)$, $y = y(t)$ of the system (8.1.2) defines a curve in the xy plane. This curve is called the *orbit* or *trajectory* of the system and the xy plane is called the *phase plane* of the system.

Before we define stability of an equilibrium point consider the motion of a simple pendulum which consists of a concentrated mass m suspended by a weightless rod of length l.

The tangential component of the gravitational force is $(-mg\sin\theta)$ where θ is the angle of swing measured from the vertical axis through the point of suspension. If s is the arc length subtended by θ, then by Newton's second law of motion the equation of motion is

$$m\frac{d^2s}{dt^2} = -mg\sin\theta.$$

Since $s = l\theta$, we have

$$\frac{d^2\theta}{dt^2} = -\frac{g}{l}\sin\theta,$$

or

$$\frac{d^2\theta}{dt^2} + k\sin\theta = 0,$$

(8.1.3)

where $k = g/l$. If we let $\omega = \dot{\theta}$, Eq. (8.1.3) becomes

$$\dot{\omega} + k\sin\theta = 0.$$

Thus we have an autonomous system

$$\dot{\theta} = \omega,$$
$$\dot{\omega} = -k\sin\theta.$$

Noting that

$$\frac{d\omega}{dt} = \frac{d\omega}{d\theta}\frac{d\theta}{dt} = \omega\frac{d\omega}{d\theta},$$

the preceding equation may be written as

$$\omega\frac{d\omega}{d\theta} + k\sin\theta = 0,$$

the solution of which is

$$\omega^2 = 2k\cos\theta + h, \qquad (8.1.4)$$

where the constant $h \geqslant -2k$. These curves in the phase plane are shown in Fig. 8.1-1.

It is evident from the figure that there are infinitely many critical points at $\omega = 0$ and $\theta = n\pi$, $n = 0, \pm 1, \pm 2, \ldots$. The pendulum is in stable equilibrium when n is even, (that is, when the pendulum is in a vertically downward position), and is in unstable equilibrium when n is odd (that is, when the pendulum is in a vertically upward position).

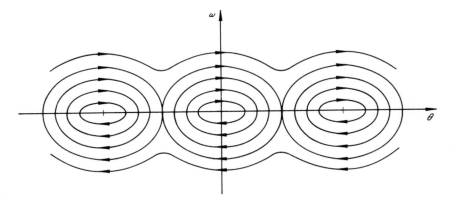

Figure 8.1-1

We observe that for $|h| < 2k$ the curves (8.1.4) are closed curves surrounding the points $\omega = 0$ and $\theta = 2n\pi$, and for $h > 2k$ the curves are open curves as shown in Fig. 8.1-1. The transition occurs when $h = 2k$, that is when $\omega^2 = 4k \cos^2(\theta/2)$. Physically speaking, if $\omega^2 < 4k \cos^2(\theta/2)$, the pendulum oscillates about its equilibrium position $(\theta = 2n\pi)$. If the initial velocity is such that $\omega^2 > 4k \cos^2(\theta/2)$, then the pendulum always turns in the same direction about the point of suspension.

Now we can present formal definitions concerning the stability of a critical point.

DEFINITION 8.1.2 Let C be a critical point for the system

$$\dot{X} = F(X).$$

The point C is said to be

(i) *stable* if, for given $\varepsilon > 0$, there exists a $\delta > 0$ such that whenever $\|X(0) - C\| < \delta$, $\|X(t) - C\| < \varepsilon$ for all $t > 0$;
(ii) *asymptotically stable* if there exists a $\delta > 0$ such that whenever $\|X(0) - C\| < \delta$, $\lim_{t \to \infty} \|X(t) - C\| = 0$;
(iii) *strictly stable* if it is stable and asymptotically stable;
(iv) *unstable* if it is not stable.

To interpret stability geometrically, let R_δ be a spherical region of radius δ and R_ε a spherical region of radius ε, as shown in Fig. 8.1-2. The equilibrium point C is stable if every trajectory in R_δ at time $t = 0$ remains inside R_ε for

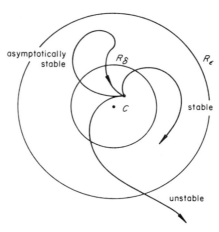

Figure 8.1-2

all $t>0$. The equilibrium point C is asymptotically stable if every trajectory sufficiently near C at time $t=0$ approaches C as t tends to infinity. The equilibrium point C is unstable if every trajectory in R_δ at time $t=0$ escapes from the region R_ε.

We should remark that asymptotic stability does not imply strict stability. In fact, one can construct an asymptotically stable autonomous system which is unstable (See Birkhoff and Rota [3], p. 130.).

8.2 Stability for Linear Systems with Constant Coefficients

We consider the linear autonomous system with constant coefficients

$$\dot{X} = AX, \qquad (8.2.1)$$

where A is a nonsingular real $n \times n$ matrix. Let the origin be a critical point for this system.

THEOREM 8.2.1 *Let $\dot{X} = AX$ be a linear autonomous system with $n \times n$ real nonsingular constant coefficient matrix A. Let the critical point be .at the origin in R^n. Then the critical point is*

(i) *strictly stable if the real parts of the eigenvalues of A are negative;*
(ii) *stable if A has at least one pair of pure imaginary eigenvalues of multiplicity one;*
(iii) *unstable otherwise.*

Proof For linear systems fundamental solutions can be expressed in terms of the eigenvalues. The fundamental solutions are of the form

$$Pt^k e^{\alpha t} \cos \beta t, \qquad Qt^k e^{\alpha t} \sin \beta t,$$

where P and Q are constant vectors, α and β are the real and imaginary parts of the complex eigenvalues of A, and k is a nonnegative integer depending on the multiplicity of the eigenvalues.

(i) Noting that the origin is the critical point, we have

$$|Pt^k e^{\alpha t} \cos \beta t| \leqslant |P| t^k e^{\alpha t}.$$

Now k is finite, α is negative, and P depends on the initial condition in such a way that $|P| < \delta$. Therefore we have

$$|Pt^k e^{\alpha t} \cos \beta t| < \varepsilon \qquad \text{whenever} \quad |P| < \delta.$$

Similarly we can show that

$$|Qt^k e^{\alpha t} \sin \beta t| < \varepsilon \qquad \text{whenever} \quad |Q| < \delta.$$

This proves the stability. For the asymptotic stability, we see that if $\alpha < 0$,

$$\lim_{t \to \infty} |Pt^k e^{\alpha t} \cos \beta t| = 0.$$

Similarly,

$$\lim_{t \to \infty} |Qt^k e^{\alpha t} \sin \beta t| = 0.$$

Thus if $\alpha < 0$, the origin is strictly stable.

(ii) Let the eigenvalues of A be $\pm i\beta$. Then the fundamental solutions are $P \cos \beta t$ and $Q \sin \beta t$. Whenever $|P| < \delta$ and $|Q| < \delta$, we have $|P \cos \beta t| < \delta$ and $|Q \sin \beta t| < \delta$. Hence the origin is stable, but it is not asymptotically stable, as is evident from the fact that $\cos \beta t$ and $\sin \beta t$ do not approach zero as t tends to infinity.

Other pairs of pure imaginary eigenvalues of multiplicity one can be treated in a similar manner.

(iii) If $\alpha \geqslant 0$, $|Pt^k e^{\alpha t} \cos \beta t|$ and $|Qt^k e^{\alpha t} \sin \beta t|$ are unbounded, and hence the origin is unstable. ∎

Example 8.2.1 Consider the damped harmonic motion represented by the equation

$$\ddot{x} + 2\dot{x} + 2x = 0.$$

The corresponding system in the phase plane is

$$\dot{x} = y,$$
$$\dot{y} = -2x - 2y. \tag{8.2.2}$$

The characteristic equation is given by

$$\begin{vmatrix} -\lambda & 1 \\ -2 & -2-\lambda \end{vmatrix} = 0,$$

from which we obtain $\lambda = -1 \pm i$. According to the above theorem, the origin is strictly stable.

The solution of Eq. (8.2.2) is

$$x = e^{-t}(a\cos t + b\sin t),$$

$$x + y = e^{-t}(-a\sin t + b\cos t).$$

The trajectories associated with (8.2.2) can be obtained by introducing the polar coordinates. Thus the system (8.2.2) takes the form

$$x = r\cos\theta = ce^{-t}\cos(t - \alpha), \qquad c = (a^2 + b^2)^{1/2}$$

$$x + y = r\sin\theta = ce^{-t}\sin(t - \alpha), \qquad \alpha = \tan^{-1}\left(\frac{b}{a}\right)$$

The elimination of t yields

$$r = ce^{-(\theta + \alpha)},$$

which describes a family of spirals.

8.3 Linear Plane Autonomous Systems

We will now consider in detail the linear plane autonomous system

$$\dot{X} = AX, \tag{8.3.1}$$

where

$$A = \begin{pmatrix} a & b \\ c & d \end{pmatrix}$$

is a nonsingular constant matrix.

The characteristic equation for this system is

$$|A - \lambda I| = 0$$

or

$$\lambda^2 - (a + d)\lambda + (ad - bc) = 0. \tag{8.3.2}$$

If we introduce

$$p = a + d,$$

$$q = ad - bc,$$

then Eq. (8.3.2) takes the form

$$\lambda^2 - p\lambda + q = 0.$$

Thus if λ_1 and λ_2 are the roots of this equation, we have

$$\lambda_{1,2} = \tfrac{1}{2}\left[p \pm \sqrt{p^2 - 4q} \right]. \tag{8.3.3}$$

It is obvious that the stability of the system depends on the discriminant $\Delta = p^2 - 4q$.

1. If $\Delta > 0$ and $q > 0$, then λ_1, λ_2 have the same sign and are both positive or negative according as $p > 0$ or $p < 0$. If $\Delta > 0$ and $q < 0$, then λ_1, λ_2 have different signs.
2. If $\Delta = 0$, then λ_1, λ_2 are equal, and positive or negative according as $p > 0$ or $p < 0$.
3. If $\Delta < 0$, then λ_1, λ_2 are complex, and the real part is positive, zero or negative according as $p > 0$, $p = 0$ or $p < 0$.

Then by Theorem 8.2.1, the origin for the system is

1. strictly stable if

$$\begin{aligned}
\Delta &> 0, \quad q > 0 \quad \text{and} \quad p < 0, \\
\Delta &= 0, \quad p < 0, \\
\Delta &< 0, \quad p < 0;
\end{aligned}$$

2. stable if $\Delta < 0$, $p = 0$;
3. unstable if

$$\begin{aligned}
\Delta &> 0, \quad q > 0 \quad \text{and} \quad p > 0, \\
\Delta &= 0, \quad p > 0, \\
\Delta &< 0, \quad p > 0.
\end{aligned}$$

In order to describe the behavior of trajectories near a critical point, we apply a linear transformation

$$Y = BX, \qquad |B| \neq 0, \tag{8.3.4}$$

so that the essential behavior near the critical point remains unchanged.

1. *Real and distinct roots.* If we apply the transformation with B given by

$$B = \begin{pmatrix} c & \lambda_1 - a \\ c & \lambda_2 - a \end{pmatrix},$$

the system (8.3.1) transforms into the system

$$\dot{x} = \lambda_1 x,$$
$$\dot{y} = \lambda_2 y, \tag{8.3.5}$$

where for simplicity x and y are again used as the new coordinates. The solutions are

$$x(t) = c_1 e^{\lambda_1 t},$$
$$y(t) = c_2 e^{\lambda_2 t}, \tag{8.3.6}$$

where c_1 and c_2 are arbitrary real constants. The elimination of t yields

$$y = c x^{\lambda_2 / \lambda_1}, \tag{8.3.7}$$

where c is an arbitrary constant. When λ_1 and λ_2 have the same sign, Eq. (8.3.7) represents parabolic curves tangent at the origin as shown in Fig. 8.3-1(a). The critical point is called a *proper node* for this system.

If λ_1 and λ_2 are negative, the origin is stable and is called a *stable node*. It is also asymptotically stable.

If λ_1 and λ_2 are positive, the origin is unstable and is called an *unstable node*.

When λ_1 and λ_2 have opposite signs, Eq. (8.3.7) represents hyperbolic curves as shown in Fig. 8.3-1(b). The origin in this case is called a *saddle point* and is unstable.

2. *Real and equal roots.* In this case $\Delta = (a - d)^2 + 4bc = 0$ and hence $\lambda_1 = \lambda_2 = (a + d)/2 = \lambda$ (say).

The first simpler case arises when b or $c = 0$ and $a = d$. Then the system (8.3.1) becomes

$$\dot{x} = \lambda x,$$
$$\dot{y} = \lambda y,$$

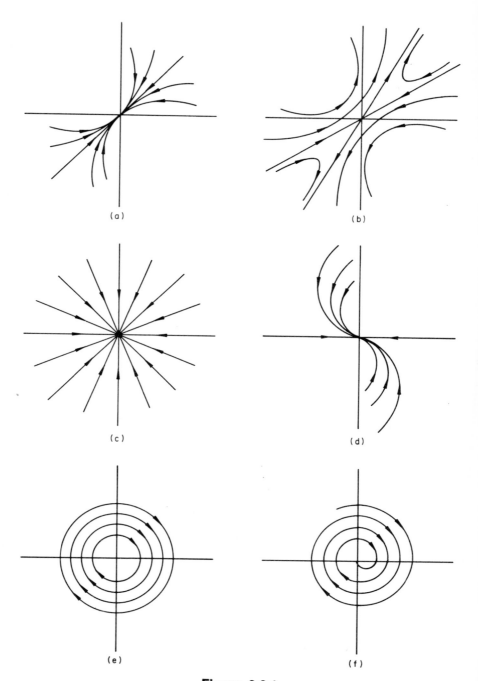

Figure 8.3-1

the solution of which is

$$x = c_1 e^{\lambda t},$$

$$y = c_2 e^{\lambda t},$$

where c_1 and c_2 are arbitrary constants. The elimination of t yields the trajectories, which are the straight lines

$$y = \frac{c_2}{c_1} x.$$

If $\lambda < 0$, the origin is asymptotically stable and is a proper node, as shown in Fig. 8.3-1(c). If $\lambda > 0$, it is unstable.

Now we consider other possibilities which are more complicated. In the general case we choose

$$B = \begin{bmatrix} \dfrac{a-d}{2b} & 1 \\ \dfrac{1}{b} & 0 \end{bmatrix}, \qquad b \neq 0,$$

so that the system (8.3.1) transforms into

$$\dot{x} = \lambda x,$$

$$\dot{y} = x + \lambda y,$$

the general solution of which is

$$x = c_1 e^{\lambda t},$$

$$y = (c_1 t + c_2) e^{\lambda t}.$$

The trajectories are shown in Fig. 8.3-1(d). The critical point is an improper node, asymptotically stable when $\lambda < 0$ and unstable when $\lambda > 0$.

3. *Complex conjugate roots.* Let $\lambda_1 = \alpha + i\beta$ and $\lambda_2 = \alpha - i\beta$ with $\beta > 0$. In this case we choose

$$B = \begin{pmatrix} c & \alpha - a \\ 0 & \beta \end{pmatrix},$$

so that the system (8.3.1) transforms into

$$\dot{x} = \alpha x - \beta y,$$
$$\dot{y} = \beta x + \alpha y. \tag{8.3.8}$$

(a)   When $\alpha = 0$, the system (8.3.8) becomes

$$\dot{x} = -\beta y,$$
$$\dot{y} = \beta x,$$

the general solution of which is

$$x = c_1 \cos \beta t + c_2 \sin \beta t,$$
$$y = c_1 \sin \beta t - c_2 \cos \beta t,$$

where c_1 and c_2 are arbitrary constants. Since

$$x^2 + y^2 = c_1^2 + c_2^2,$$

the trajectories are circles as shown in Fig. 8.3-1(e). The critical point is a center which is clearly stable. However, it is not asymptotically stable.

(b)   When $\alpha \neq 0$, the solution of the system (8.3.8) is

$$x = e^{\alpha t}(c_1 \cos \beta t + c_2 \sin \beta t),$$
$$y = e^{\alpha t}(c_1 \sin \beta t - c_2 \cos \beta t).$$

The trajectories are a family of spirals

$$x^2 + y^2 = (c_1^2 + c_2^2)e^{2\alpha t}.$$

The critical point is a focal point, as shown in Fig. 8.3-1(f), which is asymptotically stable if $\alpha < 0$ and unstable if $\alpha > 0$.

8.4   Perturbed Systems

Consider the autonomous nonlinear system

$$\dot{x} = f(x, y),$$
$$\dot{y} = g(x, y), \tag{8.4.1}$$

with $f(0,0) = g(0,0) = 0$, so that the origin is a critical point. Let f and g be real analytic functions of x and y. Expanding in Taylor series, we obtain

$$f(x,y) = f(0,0) + f_x(0,0)x + f_y(0,0)y + f_{xx}(0,0)\frac{x^2}{2}$$

$$+ f_{xy}(0,0)xy + f_{yy}(0,0)\frac{y^2}{2} + \cdots,$$

$$g(x,y) = g(0,0) + g_x(0,0)x + g_y(0,0)y + g_{xx}(0,0)\frac{x^2}{2}$$

$$+ g_{xy}(0,0)xy + g_{yy}(0,0)\frac{y^2}{2} + \cdots.$$

Noting that $f(0,0) = g(0,0) = 0$, and denoting $f_x(0,0) = a$, $f_y(0,0) = b$, $g_x(0,0) = c$, $g_y(0,0) = d$ and the remaining higher-order terms by $f_1(x,y)$ and $g_1(x,y)$, we have

$$\begin{aligned}\dot{x} &= ax + by + f_1(x,y),\\\dot{y} &= cx + dy + g_1(x,y).\end{aligned} \qquad (8.4.2)$$

We assume that $ad - bc \neq 0$. The functions f_1 and g_1 are called the *perturbations* and they satisfy[†]

$$f_1 = o(r), \qquad r = \sqrt{x^2 + y^2},$$

$$g_1 = o(r).$$

This condition insures that f_1 and g_1 tend to zero faster than the linear terms in Eqs. (8.4.2). Thus it would seem that the nature of the critical point of the nonlinear system (8.4.2) is similar to that of the associated linear system

$$\begin{aligned}\dot{x} &= ax + by,\\\dot{y} &= cx + dy.\end{aligned} \qquad (8.4.3)$$

The nature of the critical point of the nonlinear system is, in general, the same as that of the associated linear system. However, there are exceptional cases.

When the roots of (8.4.3) are pure imaginary, the origin is a center of the linear system, whereas it may be a center or a spiral point of the nonlinear

---

[†] $\phi(\tau) = o(\psi(\tau))$ as $\tau \to \tau_0$ if for given $\delta > 0$, there exists a neighborhood N_δ of τ_0 such that $|\phi| < \delta|\psi|$ for $\tau \in N_\delta$. More simply, $\phi = o(\psi)$ if $\phi/\psi \to 0$ as $\tau \to \tau_0$.

system. When the roots are real and equal and $b = c = 0$ and $a = d$, the origin is a node of the linear system, whereas it may be a node or a spiral point of the nonlinear system.

The proof of this statement and the following theorem can be found in Hale [15].

THEOREM 8.4.1 *If the critical point $(0,0)$ of the associated linear system is strictly stable, then the critical point of the nonlinear system*

$$\dot{x} = ax + by + f_1(x, y),$$

$$\dot{y} = cx + dy + g_1(x, y)$$

is also strictly stable provided that $f_1 = o(r)$ and $g_1 = o(r)$.

8.5 Method of Lyapunov for Nonlinear Systems

The investigation of the stability of nonlinear autonomous systems of differential equations without actually determining the solutions was first devised by A. A. Lyapunov, and is known as *Lyapunov's direct (or second) method*. It is based on the concept that the potential energy of a conservative dynamical system has a relative minimum at a stable equilibrium point.

Let $V(X)$ be a potential function. If on a trajectory, $V(X(t))$ decreases to zero, then any trajectory of the system which crosses the surface $V(X(t)) = $ constant surrounding the origin remains in that region. This implies that the origin is stable and indeed asymptotically stable.

Now we will present a formal definition of the function $V(X)$.

DEFINITION 8.5.1 Let $V(X)$ be a real-valued function of class C^1 in some open region Ω about the origin. Then the function $V(X)$ is said to be *positive definite* if

   (i) $V(X) > 0$ for all $X \neq 0$ in Ω.
  (ii) $V(X) = 0$ if and only if $X = 0$.

DEFINITION 8.5.2 If the function $V(X)$ is positive definite and satisfies

$$\dot{V}(t) = \frac{d}{dt} V(X(t)) = \nabla V(X) \cdot \dot{X} = \nabla V(X) \cdot F(X) \leqslant 0$$

in Ω, where ∇ is the vector operator $\nabla = (\partial/\partial x, \partial/\partial y, \ldots)$; then V is called a *Lyapunov function* for the autonomous nonlinear system $\dot{X} = F(X)$.

THEOREM 8.5.1 *If there exists a Lyapunov function $V(X)$ in Ω, then the origin is stable.*

Proof Let S_ε be a sphere of radius ε centered at the origin in Ω. Since V is continuous on the compact set S_ε, it assumes its minimum value m on S_ε. Because of its positive definiteness, V assumes a positive minimum on S_ε.

Since $V(0) = 0$ and is continuous at the origin, there exists $\delta < \varepsilon$ such that $V(X) < m$ for $|X| \leqslant \delta$. Let this sphere be S_δ.

Let $X(t, X_0)$ be a trajectory of the system initially at X_0 in S_δ. Then $V(X_0) < m$. By hypothesis $\dot{V} \leqslant 0$ for X in Ω. Thus

$$V(X(t)) \leqslant V(X(0)) < m.$$

But $V(X(t)) \geqslant m$ on S_ε. We conclude that $X(t)$ must remain in S_δ for all $t > 0$. Hence the origin is stable. ∎

THEOREM 8.5.2 *If V is a Lyapunov function such that $-\nabla V(X) \cdot F(X)$ is positive definite in Ω, then the origin is asymptotically stable.*

Proof Since the origin is stable by the previous theorem, $V(X)$ decreases along a trajectory of the system to V_0 as $t \to \infty$. We will now show that $V_0 = 0$.

Suppose that $V_0 > 0$. Then there exists $\alpha < \varepsilon$ such that $V(X) < V_0$ for all X in S_α. Now let $-\dot{V}$ assume a minimum value m in the region $\alpha \leqslant |X| \leqslant \varepsilon$. Since $-\dot{V} > 0$, we have $\dot{V} \leqslant -m$ for all $t \geqslant 0$. Thus

$$V(X(t, X_0)) - V(X_0) = \int_0^t \frac{\partial V}{\partial t} dt \leqslant -mt.$$

Consequently, as $t \to \infty$, $V(X(t, X_0))$ tends to negative infinity. This contradicts the assumption that V is positive definite in Ω and equals V_0 as $t \to \infty$. Hence V_0 must vanish, and the origin is then asymptotically stable. ∎

THEOREM 8.5.3 *Let V be a real-valued function of class C^1 in Ω with $V(0) = 0$, and let $V(X_0) > 0$ for all X in $|X| < \delta$. If $\nabla V(X) \cdot F(X)$ is positive definite in Ω, then the origin is unstable.*

Proof Let X_0 be the initial point in S_δ of the trajectory of the system. By hypothesis $V(0) = 0$ and $V(X_0) > 0$ for all X in S_δ.

Since $\dot{V} > 0$, V is increasing, and thus along the trajectory we have

$$\dot{V} \geqslant m > 0,$$

where m is the positive minimum value of $\dot{V}$ in the region $0<|X|\leqslant\delta$. Thus

$$V(X(t,X_0))-V(X_0)=\int_0^t \frac{\partial V}{\partial t}\,dt \geqslant mt$$

Consequently, as $t\to\infty$, $V(X(t,X_0))$ approaches infinity. Hence the origin is unstable. ∎

If we can construct Lyapunov functions, we can determine by the application of the preceding theorems the stability or instability of critical points for autonomous systems. With the exception of few methods applicable to certain classes of systems, there is no general method of constructing a Lyapunov function. For a brief description of some methods, one may refer to Barnett and Storey [1].

Example 8.5.1   Consider the system

$$\dot{x}=-y+xy,$$

$$\dot{y}=x-x^2,$$

which has a critical point at the origin.
   Let the Lyapunov function be

$$V=\tfrac{1}{2}(x^2+y^2).$$

Then

$$\dot{V}=x(-y+xy)+y(x-x^2)=0.$$

Since V is positive definite and $\dot{V}=0$, the Lyapunov function V exists. Hence by Theorem 8.5.1, the origin is stable.

Example 8.5.2   Consider the system

$$\dot{x}=y,$$

$$\dot{y}=-x-y-x^3,$$

which has a critical point at the origin.
   Let $V=\tfrac{1}{4}(2x^2+2y^2+x^4)$. Then

$$\dot{V}=(x+x^3)y+y(-x-y-x^3)=-y^2.$$

Since V is positive definite and $\dot{V} < 0$ ($y = 0$ is not a trajectory of the system), the Lyapunov function V exists, and by Theorem 8.5.2 the origin is asymptotically stable.

8.6 Limit Cycles of Poincaré

We have seen earlier that an autonomous system sometimes possesses periodic solutions whose trajectories are represented by closed curves in the phase plane.

Autonomous systems, such as a negatively damped nonlinear oscillator, admit solutions which commonly tend to a limiting finite periodic solution. This limiting closed curve in the phase plane is called a *limit cycle*.

A limit cycle is a closed curve. No other solution that is a closed curve exists in its neighborhood. It is an isolated closed curve. Every neighboring trajectory spirals and approaches the limit cycle from the inside or from the outside as $t \to +\infty$ or as $t \to -\infty$. If all neighboring trajectories approach a limit cycle as $t \to +\infty$ or as $t \to -\infty$, then the limit cycle is said to be stable.

We should note that limit cycles arise physically only in nonlinear, nonconservative systems. We will now illustrate a limit cycle with a well-known example.

Example 8.6.1 Consider the system

$$\dot{x} = y + \frac{x(1 - x^2 - y^2)}{\sqrt{x^2 + y^2}},$$

$$\dot{y} = -x + \frac{y(1 - x^2 - y^2)}{\sqrt{x^2 + y^2}}. \tag{8.6.1}$$

In terms of polar coordinates (r, θ) the system becomes

$$\dot{x} = y + \frac{x}{r}(1 - r^2),$$

$$\dot{y} = -x + \frac{y}{r}(1 - r^2). \tag{8.6.2}$$

Since

$$x\dot{x} + y\dot{y} = \frac{1}{2}\frac{dr^2}{dt},$$

$$y\dot{x} - x\dot{y} = -r^2\frac{d\theta}{dt},$$

we obtain from (8.6.2)

$$\dot{r} = 1 - r^2,$$

$$\dot{\theta} = -1.$$

From the second equation we find that

$$\theta = -t + a,$$

where a is an arbitrary constant. The first equation can easily be solved by separating the variables. The solution is

$$r = \frac{ce^{2t} - 1}{ce^{2t} + 1},$$

where c is an arbitrary constant.

Let $\theta(0) = 0$, so that $a = 0$ and hence $\theta = -t$. Thus the solution of the system may be written as

$$x = \left(\frac{ce^{2t} - 1}{ce^{2t} + 1} \right) \cos t,$$

$$y = -\left(\frac{ce^{2t} - 1}{ce^{2t} + 1} \right) \sin t.$$

(8.6.3)

If $c = 0$, the solution is represented by the circle $x^2 + y^2 = 1$. If $c > 0$, the trajectories are spirals inside the circle $x^2 + y^2 = 1$ approaching the circle as $t \to +\infty$, and if $c < 0$, the trajectories approach the circle spirally from outside as $t \to +\infty$. Thus we conclude that this circle is a limit cycle of the system (8.6.1).

In the preceding example we have shown how a limit cycle was determined. In general, it is very difficult, if not impossible, to find a limit cycle of a system. We will now state a theorem on the nonexistence of closed trajectories of the system

$$\dot{x} = f(x, y),$$

$$\dot{y} = g(x, y).$$

(8.6.4)

THEOREM 8.6.1 *Let* $f(x, y)$ *and* $g(x, y)$ *have continuous first partial derivatives in a simply connected domain* D *in* R^2. *If* $f_x + g_y$ *has the same sign in* D, *then the system* (8.6.4) *has no closed trajectory in* D.

Proof Let C be a closed curve in D. Then by Green's theorem, we have

$$\int_C f(x, y)\, dy - g(x, y)\, dx = \int\int_R (f_x + g_y)\, dx\, dy, \tag{8.6.5}$$

where R is the region bounded by C. But if C is represented parametrically by $x = x(t)$, $y = y(t)$, then

$$\int_C f(x, y)\, dy - g(x, y)\, dx = \int_0^\tau \left(f \frac{dy}{dt} - g \frac{dx}{dt} \right) dt,$$

where τ is the period of C. Now using (8.6.4) we obtain

$$\int_C f(x, y)\, dy - g(x, y)\, dx = \int_0^\tau (fg - gf)\, dt = 0.$$

Thus from (8.6.5) we have

$$\int\int_R (f_x + g_y)\, dx\, dy = 0.$$

This relation holds true only if $f_x + g_y$ changes sign. This is a contradiction, and hence C is not a closed trajectory in D. ∎

Although the theorem on the nonexistence of closed trajectories was not difficult to prove, the proof of the existence theorem of Poincaré and Bendixson is rather involved, and it would take us far afield. So we will state the theorem without proof.

THEOREM 8.6.2 (Poincaré-Bendixson Theorem) *Let* $f(x, y)$ *and* $g(x, y)$ *have continuous first partial derivatives in a domain* D *in* R^2. *Let* H *be a bounded subdomain of* D, *and let* R *be the region consisting of* H *and its boundary. Suppose that* R *contains no critical point of the system* (8.6.4).

If there exists a solution $x = \alpha(t)$, $y = \beta(t)$ *of the system* (8.6.4) *which remains in* R *for* $t \geq t_0$, *then either* $x = \alpha(t)$, $y = \beta(t)$ *is a closed trajectory or it approaches a closed trajectory as* $t \to \infty$.

Proof of this theorem and detailed analysis of the subject can be found in Coddington and Levinson [8].

EXERCISES

1. Describe the nature of the critical point of each system and sketch the trajectories.

   (a) $\dot{x} = x,$
         $\dot{y} = 2x + 2y.$

   (b) $\dot{x} = -x + 2y,$
         $\dot{y} = x - y.$

   (c) $\dot{x} = 2x - 8y,$
         $\dot{y} = x - 2y.$

   (d) $\dot{x} = -x,$
         $\dot{y} = x - y.$

   (e) $\dot{x} = -x + y,$
         $\dot{y} = 2x.$

   (f) $\dot{x} = -3x + 2y,$
         $\dot{y} = -2x.$

2. Determine the asymptotic behavior of the solution of each system near the critical point. Sketch the trajectories of the associated linear system.

   (a) $\dot{x} = 2\sin x + y,$
         $\dot{y} = \sin x - 3y.$

   (b) $\dot{x} = -x - x^2 + xy,$
         $\dot{y} = -y + xy - y^2.$

   (c) $\dot{x} = x + e^{-y} - 1,$
         $\dot{y} = -y - e^{-y} + 1.$

3. The equation of motion of a mass-spring system with damping is given by

$$m\ddot{x} + c\dot{x} + kx = 0,$$

   where m, c and k are positive constants. By changing this equation into a system, discuss the nature and stability of the critical point.

4. Show that the critical points of the system

$$\dot{x} = 8x - y^2,$$

$$\dot{y} = -y + x^2$$

   are $(0,0)$ and $(2,4)$. Determine the type and stability of the origin from its associated linear system. Using the transformation $\xi = x - 2$, $\eta = y - 4$, describe the nature of the critical point $(2,4)$.

5. Determine the type of the critical point $(0,0)$ depending on a real parameter μ of the nonlinear system

$$\dot{x} = -2x - y + x^2,$$

$$\dot{y} = 4x + \mu y - y^2,$$

   where $\mu \neq 2$.

6.   Let (α, β) be a singular point of the system

$$\frac{dx}{dt} = f(x, y),$$

$$\frac{dy}{dt} = g(x, y).$$

If $f^2 + g^2 \neq 0$ in the neighborhood of (α, β), show that the system

$$\frac{dx}{d\tau} = \frac{rf}{\sqrt{f^2 + g^2}},$$

$$\frac{dy}{d\tau} = \frac{rg}{\sqrt{f^2 + g^2}},$$

where $r = [(x - \alpha)^2 + (y - \beta)^2]^{1/2}$, has a critical point at (α, β). Apply this result to

$$\frac{dx}{dt} = \frac{1 + x^2}{x^2 + xy + y^2},$$

$$\frac{dy}{dt} = \frac{1 + y^2}{x^2 + xy + y^2}.$$

7.   Let $x(t)$ and $y(t)$ denote the populations of two species the interaction of which is described by the *Lotka-Volterra equations*

$$\dot{x} = ax - \alpha x^2 - \beta xy,$$

$$\dot{y} = cy - \gamma xy - \delta y^2.$$

Show that if a and c are negative, the system is asymptotically stable. That is, both populations will become extinct if the initial populations are small. Study the remaining possible cases.

8.   Prove that if $x(t), y(t), t_1 < t < t_2$, is a solution of $\dot{x} = f(x, y), \dot{y} = g(x, y)$, then $x(t + c), y(t + c)$ for any real constant c is also a solution. This property does not hold in general for nonautonomous systems. Illustrate with the example $\dot{x} = x, \dot{y} = tx$.

9.   The motion of a pendulum in a resisting medium is governed by

$$\ddot{\theta} + 2k\dot{\theta} + q \sin \theta = 0, \qquad k > 0, \quad q > 0.$$

Describe the nature of the critical points and sketch the trajectories. Let $\theta = \phi + \pi$. Then the preceding equation becomes

$$\ddot{\phi} + 2k\dot{\phi} - q\phi = 0.$$

Make a detailed analysis.

10. Using the Lyapunov function $V(x,y) = \frac{1}{2}(x^2 + y^2)$, determine the stability of the critical point $(0,0)$ for each system.

   (a) $\dot{x} = -x - \dfrac{x^3}{3} - x \cos y,$

   $\dot{y} = -y - y^3.$

   (b) $\dot{x} = -y - x \sin^2 x,$

   $\dot{y} = x - y \sin^2 x.$

   (c) $\dot{x} = x - y^2,$

   $\dot{y} = y + xy.$

11. Consider the system

$$\dot{x} = y - xf(x,y),$$

$$\dot{y} = -x - yf(x,y),$$

where $f(x,y)$ is analytic at the origin and $f(0,0) = 0$. Describe the relation between $f(x,y)$ and the type of stability.

12. Consider the *Liénard equation*

$$\ddot{x} + f(x)\dot{x} + g(x) = 0,$$

where $xg(x) > 0$ for $x \neq 0$, $f(x) > 0$ for $x \neq 0$, and

$$G(x) = \int_0^x g(x)\, dx$$

approaches infinity as $|x| \to \infty$. Prove that the origin is stable. [Use $V = \frac{1}{2}y^2 + G(x)$.]

13. Consider the *Van der Pol equation*

$$\ddot{x} + \mu(x^2 - 1)\dot{x} + x = 0.$$

For $\mu < 0$, determine the region of asymptotic stability in the phase plane. Also show that if $\mu > 0$ a limit cycle exists.

14. Show that

$$\dot{x} = y + x(1 - x^2 - y^2),$$

$$\dot{y} = -x + y(1 - x^2 - y^2)$$

has a limit cycle.

15. Consider the *Hamiltonian equation*

$$\dot{q} = \frac{\partial H}{\partial p}, \qquad \dot{p} = -\frac{\partial H}{\partial q}.$$

Let $H(p,q) = T(p) + W(q)$, where T is the kinetic energy and W is the potential energy. If H is analytic in p and q and $H(0,0) = 0$, prove the *Lagrange theorem*: a position of stable equilibrium is a point at which the potential energy is a relative minimum.

Chapter 9.
The Laplace Transform
Applications

9.1 The Laplace Transform

Because of its simplicity, the Laplace transform is frequently used in determining solutions of a class of ordinary differential equations. The method consists of transforming an ordinary differential equation into an algebraic equation with the use of initial conditions. The Laplace transform is thus best suited for application to initial-value problems, although one may sometimes be able to manipulate the method to find solutions for boundary-value problems.

The Laplace transform of the function $f(t)$, which will be denoted by either of the symbols $F(s)$ or $\mathcal{L}[f(t)]$, is defined by the equation

$$\mathcal{L}[f(t)] = F(s) = \int_0^\infty e^{-st} f(t)\, dt, \qquad s > 0, \tag{5.1.1}$$

provided the improper integral converges. s is the transform variable.

The inverse of the Laplace transform will be denoted by

$$\mathcal{L}^{-1}[F(s)] = f(t).$$

Let us now find the Laplace transforms of some elementary functions.

1. Given $f(t) = c$, a constant,

$$\mathcal{L}[c] = \int_0^\infty e^{-st} c \, dt$$

$$= \left[-\frac{ce^{-st}}{s} \right]_0^{\infty\dagger}$$

$$= \frac{c}{s}.$$

2. Given $f(t) = e^{at}$, a a constant,

$$\mathcal{L}[e^{at}] = \int_0^\infty e^{-st} e^{at} \, dt$$

$$= \left[-\frac{e^{-(s-a)t}}{s-a} \right]_0^\infty$$

$$= \frac{1}{s-a}, \qquad s > a.$$

3. Given $f(t) = t^2$,

$$\mathcal{L}[t^2] = \int_0^\infty e^{-st} t^2 \, dt.$$

Integration by parts yields

$$\mathcal{L}[t^2] = \left[-\frac{t^2 e^{-st}}{s} \right]_0^\infty + \int_0^\infty 2t \frac{e^{-st}}{s} \, dt.$$

Since $t^2 e^{-st} \to 0$ as $t \to \infty$, we have

$$\mathcal{L}[t^2] = \frac{2}{s} \left[-\frac{e^{-st}}{s} t \right]_0^\infty + \frac{2}{s} \int_0^\infty \frac{e^{-st}}{s} \, dt$$

$$= \frac{2}{s^3}.$$

$\dagger$For abbreviation $[\quad]_0^\infty$ will denote $\lim\limits_{b \to \infty} [\quad]_0^b$.

4.   Given $f(t) = \sin \omega t$,

$$F(s) = \mathcal{L}[\sin \omega t] = \int_0^\infty e^{-st} \sin \omega t \, dt$$

$$= \left[-\frac{e^{-st}}{s} \sin \omega t \right]_0^\infty + \int_0^\infty \frac{e^{-st}}{s} \omega \cos \omega t \, dt$$

$$= \frac{\omega}{s} \left[-\frac{e^{-st}}{s} \cos \omega t \right]_0^\infty - \frac{\omega}{s} \int_0^\infty \frac{e^{-st}}{s} \omega \sin \omega t \, dt,$$

$$F(s) = \frac{\omega}{s^2} - \frac{\omega^2}{s^2} F(s).$$

Thus solving for $F(s)$, we obtain

$$\mathcal{L}[\sin \omega t] = \frac{\omega}{s^2 + \omega^2}.$$

DEFINITION 9.1.1 A function $f(t)$ is said to be *of exponential order* as $t \to \infty$ if there exists a constant $a > 0$ such that $e^{-at}|f(t)|$ is bounded for all $t > T$; that is, for some constant $M > 0$,

$$|f(t)| \leqslant M e^{at}.$$

Functions such as $t^k e^{at} \sin bt$, $t^k e^{at} \cos bt$ are of exponential order.

THEOREM 9.1.1 *Let f be piecewise continuous in the interval $[0, T]$ for every positive T, and let f be of exponential order, that is, $f(t) = O(e^{at})$ as $t \to \infty$ for some $a > 0$. Then the Laplace transform of f exists for $s > a$.*

Proof Since f is piecewise continuous and of exponential order, we have

$$|\mathcal{L}[f(t)]| = \left| \int_0^\infty e^{-st} f(t) \, dt \right|$$

$$\leqslant \int_0^\infty e^{-st} |f(t)| \, dt$$

$$\leqslant \int_0^\infty e^{-st} M e^{at} \, dt$$

$$= M \int_0^\infty e^{-(s-a)t} \, dt$$

$$= \frac{M}{s-a}, \qquad s > a.$$

Thus

$$\int_0^\infty e^{-st} f(t)\, dt$$

exists for $s > a$.   ∎

9.2 Properties of the Laplace Transform

THEOREM 9.2.1 (Linearity)   *If $\mathcal{L}[f(t)]$ and $\mathcal{L}[g(t)]$ are the Laplace transforms of f and g respectively, then*

$$\mathcal{L}[af(t) + bg(t)] = a\mathcal{L}[f(t)] + b\mathcal{L}[g(t)],$$

where a and b are constants.

Proof

$$\mathcal{L}[af(t) + bg(t)] = \int_0^\infty [af(t) + bg(t)]e^{-st}\, dt$$

$$= a\int_0^\infty f(t)e^{-st}\, dt + b\int_0^\infty g(t)e^{-st}\, dt$$

$$= a\mathcal{L}[f(t)] + b\mathcal{L}[g(t)].$$ ∎

THEOREM 9.2.2 (Shifting)   *If the Laplace transform of $f(t)$ is $F(s)$, then the Laplace transform of $e^{at}f(t)$ is $F(s-a)$.*

Proof

$$\mathcal{L}[e^{at}f(t)] = \int_0^\infty e^{-st}e^{at}f(t)\, dt$$

$$= \int_0^\infty e^{-(s-a)t}f(t)\, dt$$

$$= F(s-a).$$ ∎

Example 9.2.1

1. If $\mathcal{L}[t^2] = 2/s^3$, then $\mathcal{L}[t^2 e^t] = 2/(s-1)^3$.
2. If

$$\mathcal{L}[\sin \omega t] = \frac{\omega}{s^2 + \omega^2},$$

then

$$\mathcal{L}[(\sin \omega t)e^t] = \frac{\omega}{(s-1)^2 + \omega^2}.$$

THEOREM 9.2.3 (Scaling) *If the Laplace transform of $f(t)$ is $F(s)$, then the Laplace transform of $f(ct)$ with $c > 0$ is $(1/c)F(s/c)$.*

Proof

$$\mathcal{L}[f(ct)] = \int_0^\infty e^{-st} f(ct)\, dt$$

$$= \int_0^\infty \frac{1}{c} e^{-s\xi/c} f(\xi)\, d\xi \qquad \text{(by substituting } \xi = ct)$$

$$= \frac{1}{c} F\left[\frac{s}{c}\right]. \qquad\qquad\qquad \blacksquare$$

Example 9.2.2

1. If

$$\frac{s}{s^2 + 1} = \mathcal{L}[\cos t],$$

then

$$\frac{1}{\omega} \frac{s/\omega}{(s/\omega)^2 + 1} = \frac{s}{s^2 + \omega^2} = \mathcal{L}[\cos \omega t].$$

2. If

$$\frac{1}{s-1} = \mathcal{L}[e^t],$$

then

$$\frac{1}{a}\frac{1}{(s/a)-1} = \mathcal{L}\left[e^{at}\right],$$

$$\frac{1}{s-a} = \mathcal{L}\left[e^{at}\right].$$

THEOREM 9.2.4 (Differentiation) *Let f be continuous and f' piecewise continuous in $0 \leqslant t \leqslant T$ for all $T > 0$. Let f also be of exponential order as $t \to \infty$. Then the Laplace transform of f' exists and is given by*

$$\mathcal{L}\left[f'(t)\right] = s\mathcal{L}\left[f(t)\right] - f(0).$$

Proof   Consider the integral

$$\int_0^T e^{-st}f'(t)\,dt = e^{-st}f(t)\Big|_0^T + \int_0^T se^{-st}f(t)\,dt$$

$$= e^{-sT}f(T) - f(0) + s\int_0^T e^{-st}f(t)\,dt.$$

Since $|f(t)| \leqslant Me^{at}$ for large t, with $a > 0$ and $M > 0$,

$$\left|e^{-sT}f(T)\right| \leqslant Me^{-(s-a)T}.$$

In the limit as $T \to \infty$, $e^{-sT}f(T) \to 0$ whenever $s > a$. Hence

$$\mathcal{L}\left[f'(t)\right] = s\mathcal{L}\left[f(t)\right] - f(0). \qquad\blacksquare$$

If f' and f'' satisfy the same conditions imposed on f and f' respectively, then the Laplace transform of $f''(t)$ can be immediately obtained by applying the preceding theorem; that is,

$$\mathcal{L}\left[f''(t)\right] = s\mathcal{L}\left[f'(t)\right] - f'(0)$$

$$= s\left\{s\mathcal{L}\left[f(t)\right] - f(0)\right\} - f'(0)$$

$$= s^2\mathcal{L}\left[f(t)\right] - sf(0) - f'(0).$$

Clearly, the Laplace transform of $f^{(n)}(t)$ can be obtained in a similar manner by successive application of the theorem. The result may be written as

$$\mathcal{L}\left[f^{(n)}(t) \right] = s^n \mathcal{L}\left[f(t) \right] - s^{n-1} f(0) - \cdots - s f^{(n-2)}(0) - f^{(n-1)}(0).$$

THEOREM 9.2.5 (Integration)   *If $F(s)$ is the Laplace transform of $f(t)$, then*

$$\mathcal{L}\left[\int_0^t f(\tau)\, d\tau \right] = \frac{F(s)}{s}.$$

Proof

$$\mathcal{L}\left[\int_0^t f(\tau)\, d\tau \right] = \int_0^\infty \left[\int_0^t f(\tau)\, d\tau \right] e^{-st}\, dt$$

$$= \left[-\frac{e^{-st}}{s} \int_0^t f(\tau)\, d\tau \right]_0^\infty + \frac{1}{s} \int_0^\infty f(t) e^{-st}\, dt$$

$$= \frac{F(s)}{s},$$

since $\int_0^t f(\tau)\, d\tau$ is of exponential order (See Exercise 6).   ∎

In solving problems by this method the difficulty arises in finding inverse transforms. Although an inversion formula exists, its use requires a knowledge of complex variables (see Section 9.5). However, for a certain class of problems of mathematical physics we need not use this inversion formula. We can avoid its use by expanding a given transform by the method of partial fractions in terms of simple fractions in the transform variables. With these simple functions one refers to the table of Laplace transforms and obtains the corresponding functions. Here we should note that we use the assumption that there is essentially a one-to-one correspondence between functions and their Laplace transforms. This may be stated as follows:

THEOREM 9.2.6 (Lerch)   *Let f and g be piecewise continuous functions of exponential order. If there exists a constant s_0 such that $\mathcal{L}[f] = \mathcal{L}[g]$ for all $s > s_0$, then $f(t) = g(t)$ for all $t > 0$ except possibly at the points of discontinuity.*

For a proof the reader is referred to Kreider et al. [23].

Example 9.2.3   Solve the initial-value problem

$$y'' - 3y' + 2y = e^{3t},$$
$$y(0) = 0,$$
$$y'(0) = 0.$$

Let $\phi(t)$ be the solution. Applying the Laplace transform, the given equation becomes

$$\mathcal{L}\left[\phi''(t) - 3\phi'(t) + 2\phi(t)\right] = \mathcal{L}\left[e^{3t}\right].$$

By Theorems 9.2.1 and 9.2.4 we obtain

$$\left\{s^2\mathcal{L}\left[\phi(t)\right] - s\phi(0) - \phi'(0)\right\} - 3\left\{s\mathcal{L}\left[\phi(t)\right] - \phi(0)\right\} + 2\mathcal{L}\left[\phi(t)\right] = \mathcal{L}\left[e^{3t}\right].$$

Since $\phi(0) = 0$ and $\phi'(0) = 0$,

$$\mathcal{L}\left[\phi(t)\right] = \frac{1}{(s-1)(s-2)(s-3)}.$$

Resolving into partial fractions, we arrive at

$$\mathcal{L}\left[\phi(t)\right] = \frac{1}{2(s-1)} - \frac{1}{s-2} + \frac{1}{2(s-3)}.$$

Hence we have

$$\phi(t) = \mathcal{L}^{-1}\left[\frac{1}{2(s-1)} - \frac{1}{s-2} + \frac{1}{2(s-3)}\right]$$

$$= \tfrac{1}{2}e^t - e^{2t} + \tfrac{1}{2}e^{3t}.$$

Example 9.2.4   Consider the boundary-value problem

$$y'' + 2y' + y = 0,$$
$$y(0) = 0,$$
$$y(1) = 2.$$

Let $\phi(t)$ be the solution. Transforming the equation, we obtain

$$\mathcal{L}\left[\phi''(t)+2\phi'(t)+\phi(t)\right]=0.$$

By Theorems 9.2.1 and 9.2.4 we have

$$\left\{s^2\mathcal{L}\left[\phi(t)\right]-s\phi(0)-\phi'(0)\right\}+2\left\{s\mathcal{L}\left[\phi(t)\right]-\phi(0)\right\}+\mathcal{L}\left[\phi(t)\right]=0.$$

In this case $\phi(0)=0$. But $\phi'(0)$ is not known. Hence we assume that

$$\phi'(0)=c.$$

Thus the transformed equation is

$$\mathcal{L}\left[\phi(t)\right]=\frac{c}{(s+1)^2},$$

and hence

$$\phi(t)=ct\,e^{-t}.$$

Now applying the boundary condition $\phi(1)=2$, we obtain

$$\phi(t)=2et\,e^{-t}.$$

We shall illustrate in the next example that the method of Laplace transforms can be applied to find the general solution of a differential equation.

Example 9.2.5 Determine the general solution of

$$y''+4y=0.$$

Since supplementary conditions are not prescribed, we arbitrarily choose the initial conditions

$$y(0)=A,$$

$$y'(0)=B.$$

Let $\phi(t)$ be the solution. Applying the initial conditions, the transformed equation takes the form

$$s^2\mathcal{L}\left[\phi(t)\right]-As-B+4\mathcal{L}\left[\phi(t)\right]=0.$$

Thus

$$\mathcal{L}[\phi(t)] = \frac{As + B}{s^2 + 4},$$

and hence the general solution is

$$\phi(t) = A\cos 2t + B\sin 2t,$$

where A and B are arbitrary constants.

9.3 Convolution Theorem

One of the important theorems of the Laplace transform is the *convolution theorem*. It is used in constructing inverses especially for linear differential equations with constant coefficients.

The function

$$(f*g)(t) = \int_0^t f(t-\xi)\,g(\xi)\,d\xi \tag{9.3.1}$$

is called the *convolution* of the functions f and g.

THEOREM 9.3.1 (Convolution theorem) *If $F(s)$ and $G(s)$ are the Laplace transforms of $f(t)$ and $g(t)$ respectively, then the Laplace transform of the convolution $f*g$ is the product $F(s)G(s)$.*

Proof

$$\mathcal{L}[f*g] = \int_0^\infty e^{-st} \int_0^t f(t-\xi)\,g(\xi)\,d\xi\,dt$$

$$= \int_0^\infty \int_0^t e^{-st} f(t-\xi)\,g(\xi)\,d\xi\,dt.$$

The region of integration is shown in Figure 9.3-1. By reversing the order of integration we have

$$\mathcal{L}[f*g] = \int_0^\infty \int_\xi^\infty e^{-st} f(t-\xi)\,g(\xi)\,dt\,d\xi$$

$$= \int_0^\infty g(\xi) \int_\xi^\infty e^{-st} f(t-\xi)\,dt\,d\xi.$$

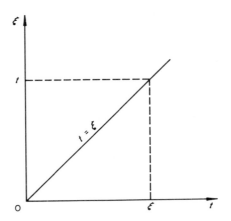

Figure 9.3-1

If we introduce the new variable $\eta = t - \xi$ in the inner integral, we obtain

$$\mathcal{L}[f*g] = \int_0^\infty g(\xi) \int_0^\infty e^{-s(\xi+\eta)} f(\eta) \, d\eta \, d\xi$$

$$= \int_0^\infty g(\xi) e^{-s\xi} d\xi \int_0^\infty f(\eta) e^{-s\eta} d\eta$$

$$= F(s)G(s). \tag{9.3.2}$$

■

The convolution has the following properties:

1. $f*g = g*f$ (commutative).
2. $f*(g*h) = (f*g)*h$ (associative).   (9.3.3)
3. $f*(g+h) = f*g + f*h$ (distributive).

Example 9.3.1   Find the solution of the initial-value problem

$$y'' - 3y' + 2y = f(t),$$

$$y(0) = 0,$$

$$y'(0) = 0,$$

where $f(t)$ is a function of exponential order.

If $\phi(t)$ is the solution, then the transformed equation after applying the initial conditions is

$$\mathcal{L}[\phi(t)] = \frac{\mathcal{L}[f(t)]}{(s-1)(s-2)}.$$

Since

$$\mathcal{L}^{-1}\left[\frac{1}{(s-1)(s-2)}\right] = -e^t + e^{2t},$$

by the Convolution Theorem (Theorem 9.3.1) we obtain

$$\phi(t) = \int_0^t \left[-e^{t-\xi} + e^{2(t-\xi)}\right] f(\xi)\,d\xi.$$

9.4   Step Function

A unit step function is defined by

$$u_a(t) = \begin{cases} 0, & t < a, \\ 1, & t \geq a, \end{cases} \quad a \geq 0, \tag{9.4.1}$$

s shown in Figure 9.4-1.

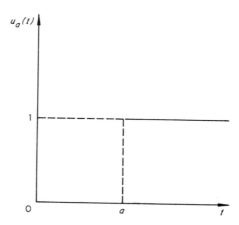

Figure 9.4-1

The Laplace transform of the unit step function can easily be determined. In fact

$$\mathcal{L}[u_a(t)] = \int_0^\infty e^{-st} u_a(t)\, dt$$

$$= \int_a^\infty e^{-st}\, dt$$

$$= \frac{e^{-as}}{s}, \qquad s > 0. \tag{9.4.2}$$

THEOREM 9.4.1 (Second shifting theorem) *If $F(s)$ is the Laplace transform of $f(t)$, then*

$$\mathcal{L}[u_a(t) f(t-a)] = e^{-as} F(s). \tag{9.4.3}$$

Proof

$$\mathcal{L}[u_a(t) f(t-a)] = \int_0^\infty e^{-st} u_a(t) f(t-a)\, dt$$

$$= \int_a^\infty e^{-st} f(t-a)\, dt.$$

Introducing the new variable $\xi = t - a$, we have

$$\mathcal{L}[u_a(t) f(t-a)] = \int_0^\infty e^{-(\xi + a)s} f(\xi)\, d\xi$$

$$= e^{-as} \int_0^\infty e^{-s\xi} f(\xi)\, d\xi$$

$$= e^{-as} F(s).$$

Example 9.4.1

1. Given that

$$f(t) = \begin{cases} 0, & t < 2, \\ t - 2, & t \geqslant 2, \end{cases}$$

find the Laplace transform of $f(t)$.

$$\mathcal{L}[f(t)] = \mathcal{L}[u_2(t)(t-2)]$$

$$= e^{-2s}\mathcal{L}[t]$$

$$= \frac{e^{-2s}}{s^2}.$$

2. Find the inverse transform of

$$F(s) = \frac{1+e^{-2s}}{s^2}.$$

$$\mathcal{L}^{-1}[F(s)] = \mathcal{L}^{-1}\left[\frac{1}{s^2} + \frac{e^{-2s}}{s^2}\right]$$

$$= \mathcal{L}^{-1}\left[\frac{1}{s^2}\right] + \mathcal{L}^{-1}\left[\frac{e^{-2s}}{s^2}\right]$$

$$= t + u_2(t)(t-2)$$

$$= \begin{cases} t, & 0 \leqslant t < 2, \\ 2(t-1), & t \geqslant 2. \end{cases}$$

Example 9.4.2   Solve the initial-value problem

$$y'' + y = g(t),$$

$$y(0) = 0, \qquad\qquad\qquad (9.4.4)$$

$$y'(0) = 1,$$

where

$$g(t) = \begin{cases} 1, & 1 \leqslant t < 2 \\ 0, & 0 \leqslant t < 1, \quad t \geqslant 2. \end{cases}$$

Let $\phi(t)$ be the solution. We express $g(t)$ as

$$g(t) = u_1(t) - u_2(t).$$

The Laplace transform of the initial-value problem (9.4.4) is

$$(s^2 + 1)\mathcal{L}[\phi(t)] - 1 = \mathcal{L}[u_1(t) - u_2(t)]$$

and hence

$$\mathcal{L}[\phi(t)] = \frac{1}{s^2+1} + \frac{e^{-s}}{s(s^2+1)} - \frac{e^{-2s}}{s(s^2+1)}.$$

Thus we have

$$\phi(t) = \mathcal{L}^{-1}\left[\frac{1}{s^2+1}\right] + \mathcal{L}^{-1}\left[\frac{e^{-s}}{s(s^2+1)}\right] - \mathcal{L}^{-1}\left[\frac{e^{-2s}}{s(s^2+1)}\right].$$

Since by partial fractions

$$\frac{1}{s(s^2+1)} = \frac{1}{s} - \frac{s}{s^2+1},$$

we obtain

$$\phi(t) = \sin t + u_1(t)\left[1 - \cos(t-1)\right] - u_2(t)\left[1 - \cos(t-2)\right].$$

9.5 Impulse Function

An *impulse function* is defined by

$$p(t) = \begin{cases} h, & a - \varepsilon < t < a + \varepsilon, \\ 0, & t \leqslant a - \varepsilon, \quad t \geqslant a + \varepsilon, \end{cases} \tag{9.5.1}$$

where a is positive, h is large and positive, and ε is a small positive constant, as shown in Figure 9.5-1. This type of impulse function appears in practical

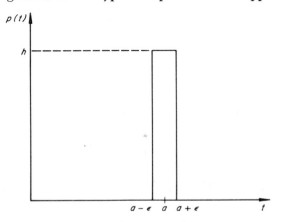

Figure 9.5-1

applications—for instance, a force of large magnitude may act over a very short period of time.

The Laplace transform of the impulse function $p(t)$ is given by

$$\mathcal{L}\big[\,p(t)\,\big] = \int_0^\infty e^{-st} p(t)\,dt$$

$$= \int_{a-\varepsilon}^{a+\varepsilon} h e^{-st}\,dt$$

$$= h\left[\,-\frac{e^{-st}}{s}\,\right]_{a-\varepsilon}^{a+\varepsilon}$$

$$= \frac{h e^{-as}}{s}\left(e^{\varepsilon s} - e^{-\varepsilon s}\right)$$

$$= 2\frac{h e^{-as}}{s}\sinh \varepsilon s. \tag{9.5.2}$$

If we choose the value of h to be $1/2\varepsilon$, then the impulse is given by

$$I(\varepsilon) = \int_{-\infty}^\infty p(t)\,dt$$

$$= \int_{a-\varepsilon}^{a+\varepsilon} \frac{1}{2\varepsilon}\,dt$$

$$= 1.$$

Thus in the limit this particular impulse function satisfies

$$\lim_{\varepsilon \to 0} p_\varepsilon(t) = 0, \qquad t \neq a,$$

$$\lim_{\varepsilon \to 0} I(\varepsilon) = 1.$$

From this result we obtain the *Dirac delta function* which satisfies

$$\delta(t-a) = 0, \qquad t \neq a,$$

$$\int_{-\infty}^\infty \delta(t-a)\,dt = 1. \tag{9.5.3}$$

Thus we may define the Laplace transform of δ as the limit of the transform of $p_\varepsilon(t)$.

$$\mathcal{L}\big[\delta(t-a)\big] = \lim_{\varepsilon \to 0} \mathcal{L}\big[p_\varepsilon(t)\big]$$

$$= \lim_{\varepsilon \to 0} e^{-as}\frac{\sinh \varepsilon s}{\varepsilon s}$$

$$= e^{-as}. \tag{9.5.4}$$

Hence if $a = 0$, we have

$$\mathcal{L}\big[\delta(t)\big] = 1. \tag{9.5.5}$$

One very useful result that can be derived is the integral of the product of the delta function and any continuous function $f(t)$.

$$\int_{-\infty}^{\infty} \delta(t-a)f(t)\,dt = \lim_{\varepsilon \to 0} \int_{-\infty}^{\infty} p_\varepsilon(t)f(t)\,dt$$

$$= \lim_{\varepsilon \to 0} \int_{a-\varepsilon}^{a+\varepsilon} \frac{f(t)}{2\varepsilon}\,dt$$

$$= \lim_{\varepsilon \to 0} \frac{1}{2\varepsilon}2\varepsilon f(t^*), \qquad a-\varepsilon < t^* < a+\varepsilon$$

$$= f(a). \tag{9.5.6}$$

Suppose that $f(t)$ is a periodic function with period T. Let f be piecewise continuous on $[0, T]$. Then the Laplace transform of f is

$$\mathcal{L}\big[f(t)\big] = \int_0^{\infty} e^{-st}f(t)\,dt$$

$$= \sum_{n=0}^{\infty} \int_{nT}^{(n+1)T} e^{-st}f(t)\,dt.$$

If we introduce the new variable $\xi = t - nT$, then

$$\mathcal{L}\big[f(t)\big] = \sum_{n=0}^{\infty} e^{-nTs}\int_0^{T} e^{-s\xi}f(\xi)\,d\xi$$

$$= \sum_{n=0}^{\infty} e^{-nTs}F_1(s),$$

where $F_1(s) = \int_0^T e^{-s\xi} f(\xi) d\xi$ is the transform of the function f over the first period. Since the series is the geometric series, we obtain for the transform of the periodic function

$$\mathcal{L}[f(t)] = \frac{F_1(s)}{1 - e^{-Ts}}. \tag{9.5.7}$$

Example 9.5.1 Find the Laplace transform of the function

$$f(t) = \begin{cases} h, & 0 < t < c, \\ -h, & c < t < 2c, \end{cases}$$

and

$$f(t + 2c) = f(t),$$

shown in Figure 9.5-2.

$$F_1(s) = \int_0^{2c} e^{-s\xi} f(\xi) d\xi$$

$$= \int_0^c e^{-s\xi} h \, d\xi + \int_c^{2c} e^{-s\xi} (-h) d\xi$$

$$= \frac{h}{s} (1 - e^{-cs})^2.$$

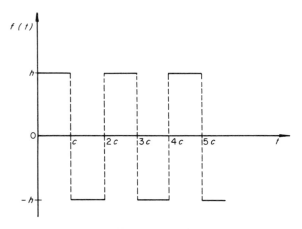

Figure 9.5-2

Thus the Laplace transform of $f(t)$ is

$$\mathcal{L}[f(t)] = \frac{F_1(s)}{1 - e^{-2cs}}$$

$$= \frac{h(1 - e^{-cs})^2}{s(1 - e^{-2cs})}$$

$$= \frac{h}{s} \frac{1 - e^{-sc}}{1 + e^{-cs}}$$

$$= \frac{h}{s} \tanh \frac{cs}{2}.$$

Example 9.5.2 Find the solution of the initial-value problem

$$y'' + 2y' + 5y = \delta(t-1),$$

$$y(0) = 0,$$

$$y'(0) = 0.$$

Let $\phi(t)$ be the solution. Taking the Laplace transform of the differential equation and applying the initial conditions, we obtain

$$(s^2 + 2s + 5)\mathcal{L}[\phi(t)] = e^{-s},$$

and hence

$$\mathcal{L}[\phi(t)] = \frac{e^{-s}}{(s+1)^2 + 4}.$$

Thus we have

$$\phi(t) = \tfrac{1}{2} u_1(t) e^{-(t-1)} \sin 2(t-1).$$

In the illustrations of the application of the Laplace transform, only problems that yielded simple transforms were considered. The transforms could be separated into partial fractions, and the inverses were determined by referring to the tables. In general, Laplace-transform problems require the use of the Laplace inversion formula. If $F(s)$ is the Laplace transform of a real function $f(t)$, with the transform variable s complex, the inversion formula is given by

$$f(t) = \frac{1}{2\pi i} \int_{\gamma - i\infty}^{\gamma + i\infty} F(s) e^{st} ds.$$

For readers who are interested in extended applications of the Laplace transform, some useful references are listed at the end of this book.

EXERCISES

1. Let f be piecewise continuous on $[0, \infty)$. If $\lim_{t \to \infty} f(t) e^{-\alpha t} = 0$ for some constant α, prove that f is of exponential order.

2. Show that each of the following functions is of exponential order:
    (a) $\sin \omega t$, ω a constant.
    (b) e^{at}, a a constant.
    (c) $\ln(1 + t)$.
    (d) t^n, n a positive integer.

3. Find the Laplace transform of each of the following functions:

    (a) t^n.   (g) $e^{at} \cos \omega t$.
    (b) $\cos \omega t$.   (h) $t \sinh kt$.
    (c) $\sinh kt$.   (i) $t \cosh kt$.
    (d) $\cosh kt$.   (j) $\sqrt{t^{-1}}$.
    (e) $t e^{at}$.   (k) $\sqrt{t}$.
    (f) $e^{at} \sin \omega t$.   (l) $(\sin at)/t$.

4. Find the inverse transform of each of the following functions:

    (a) $\dfrac{s}{(s^2 + 1)(s^2 + 2)}$.   (d) $\dfrac{1}{s(s + 1)^2}$.

    (b) $\dfrac{1}{(s^2 + 1)(s^2 + 2)}$.   (e) $\dfrac{1}{s(s + 1)}$.

    (c) $\dfrac{1}{(s - 1)(s - 2)}$.   (f) $\dfrac{s - 4}{(s^2 + 4)^2}$.

5. Find the Laplace transform of each of the following functions:

    (a) $f(t) = \begin{cases} t, & 0 < t < b \\ 2b - t, & b < t < 2b \end{cases},$ $f(t+2b) = f(t).$

    (b) $f(t) = \begin{cases} h, & 0 < t < b \\ 0, & b < t < 2b \end{cases},$ $f(t+2b) = f(t).$

    (c) $f(t) = \begin{cases} \sin t, & 0 < t < \pi \\ 0, & \pi < t < 2\pi \end{cases},$ $f(t+2\pi) = f(t).$

    (d) $f(t) = \dfrac{ht}{b},$ $0 < t < b,$ $f(t+b) = f(t).$

    (e) $f(t) = nhb,$ $nb < t < (n+1)b,$ $n = 0, 1, 2, \ldots.$

6. If f is of exponential order, prove that

    $$\int_{t_0}^{t} f(\tau) \, d\tau \qquad \text{for} \quad t_0 \geqslant 0$$

    is of exponential order.

7. If $f(t)$ is of exponential order, show that every solution of the equation $L[y] = f$ with constant coefficients is of exponential order.

8. Determine the solution of each of the following initial-value problems:
    (a) $y'' + 3y' + 2y = 0,\ y(0) = 1,\ y'(0) = 2.$
    (b) $y'' - y' - 6y = 2,\ y(0) = 1,\ y'(0) = 0.$
    (c) $y'' + y = t,\ y(0) = 0,\ y'(0) = 1.$
    (d) $y'' - 3y' + 2y = 4t + e^{3t},\ y(0) = 1,\ y'(0) = -1.$

9. Find the solution of each of the following initial-value problems:
    (a) $y'' + 4y' + 13y = 0,$
         $y(0) = 0, \qquad y'(0) = -1.$
    (b) $y'' + y = e^{-2t} \sin t,$
         $y(0) = 0, \qquad y'(0) = 0.$

10. Find the solution of the initial-value problem

    $$y'' + 2y' + 10y = h(t),$$

    $$y(0) = 0, \qquad y'(0) = 0,$$

    where

    $$h(t) = \begin{cases} 1, & 0 < t < 1, \\ 0, & 1 < t < 2. \end{cases}$$

11. Prove the following properties of convolution:
    (a) $f*g = g*f$.
    (b) $f*(g*h) = (f*g)*h$.
    (c) $f*(g+h) = f*g + f*h$.
    (d) $f*0 = 0*f$.

12. Compute the convolution and its Laplace transform of the following functions:
    (a) $e^t * e^{2t}$.
    (b) $\sin \omega t * \cos \omega t$.
    (c) $t * e^t$.

13. Obtain the solution of each of the *Volterra integral equations*
    (a) $y(t) = t + \int_0^t \cos(t-\tau)\, y(\tau)\, d\tau$.
    (b) $y(t) = e^t - \int_0^t (t-\tau)^2 y(\tau)\, d\tau$.

14. Solve the following boundary-value problems:
    (a) $y'' + 4y' + 4y = t$,
        $y(0) = 1, \qquad y(1) = 2$.
    (b) $y'' + y = e^t$,
        $y'(0) = 0, \qquad y(1) = 1$.

15. Let L be the linear differential operator with constant coefficients, and let

$$p(s) = s^n + a_{n-1}s^{n-1} + \cdots + a_0$$

be the auxiliary polynomial of L. If

$$\mathcal{L}[f(t)] = \frac{1}{p(s)},$$

show that the Green's function for L is given by $f(t-\tau)$ on $(-\infty, \infty)$.

16. Solve the initial-value problem

$$y'' - 2y' + y = t^2,$$

$$y(0) = 0, \qquad y'(0) = 0,$$

by using a Green's function.

17. Determine the solution of each of the following initial-value problems:

    (a) $y'' + 4y = \cos \omega t - \delta(t-1)$,

         $y(0) = 0, \qquad y'(0) = 0.$

    (b) $y''' + y' = \delta(t-2) + e^{-t}$,

         $y(0) = 1, \qquad y'(0) = 0, \qquad y''(0) = 0.$

18. Solve the initial-value problem

    $$y'' - y = f(t),$$

    $$y(0) = 0, \qquad y'(0) = 0,$$

    by

    (a) the method of the Laplace transform directly,
    (b) the Laplace transform using a Green's function,
    (c) the method of variation of parameters.

Chapter 10.
Numerical Methods

10.1 Introduction

Numerical methods are often most practical for determining solutions of ordinary differential equations. As we have seen, analytical methods are sometimes available. But for many equations encountered in practice, explicit analytical solutions either do not exist or are not well adapted for numerical computations.

For a higher-order equation or a system of first-order equations the labor of solving generally increases with the order or number of equations. For these reasons, the search for efficient and effective techniques for determining numerical solutions is becoming increasingly important.

Let us consider the initial-value problem

$$y' = f(x, y),$$

$$y(x_0) = y_0.$$

$$(10.1.1)$$

We shall assume that it is a well-posed problem. In addition, we shall assume that f is sufficiently differentiable in both x and y.

In numerical methods ordinary differential equations are approximated by so-called *difference equations*. It is therefore natural to require the approximate difference equations to possess a unique solution. The solution of the difference equation must be sufficiently close to the exact solution of the differential equation. The solution of the difference equation must be effective in that the solution must remain within reasonable limits in spite of roundoff errors in computations, and efficient in that the time of computation must be minimal.

We shall introduce in this chapter a brief description of a few of the methods used in finding numerical solutions of ordinary differential equations.

10.2 Euler Method

Let $\phi(x)$ be the exact solution of the initial-value problem (10.1.1) on a certain interval. We divide this interval at a finite number of points $x_0, x_1, x_2, \ldots, x_n$. For simplicity we consider the mesh points to be equally spaced with *step size* h, that is,

$$x_{k+1} = x_k + h, \qquad 0 \leqslant k < n.$$

Integrating $y' = f(x, y)$ from x_n to x_{n+1}, we obtain

$$y(x_{n+1}) - y(x_n) = \int_{x_k}^{x_{k+1}} f(x, y)\, dx. \tag{10.2.1}$$

If we approximate the integral in (10.2.1) by the product of the function f evaluated at the left end point x_n and the interval $x_{n+1} - x_n$, we have

$$y_{n+1} = y_n + hf(x_n, y_n), \tag{10.2.2}$$

which is known as the *Euler formula*.

The Euler formula may also be interpreted geometrically. From the given initial condition $y(x_0) = y_0$ we find $\phi'(x_0) = f(x_0, y_0)$, which is the slope of the tangent line to the solution curve at x_0. We then compute the approximate value of y_1 of $\phi(x_1)$ at x_1, namely,

$$y_1 = y_0 + \phi'(x_0)(x_1 - x_0)$$

$$= y_0 + hf(x_0, y_0).$$

Now that the value of y_1 at x_1 is known, we compute the approximate slope $y_1' = f(x_1, y_1)$ at x_1, and

$$y_2 = y_1 + y_1'(x_2 - x_1)$$

$$= y_1 + hf(x_1, y_1).$$

Thus in general we find the Euler formula (10.2.2).

The Euler formula may be obtained alternatively by expanding the solution in a Taylor series about the point x_n, namely,

$$y(x_n + h) = y(x_n) + hy'(x_n) + \frac{h^2}{2!} y''(x_n) + \cdots .$$

Truncating the series after the linear term, we obtain

$$y_{n+1} = y_n + hf(x_n, y_n).$$

A typical flow chart for implementing the method is shown in Figure 10.2-1.

The accuracy of the Euler method is poor, and it is, therefore, not suitable for practical applications. However, it is simple and displays the essential characteristics of more complicated methods.

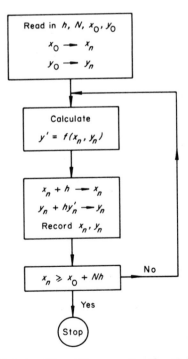

Figure 10.2-1 Flow Diagram for the Euler Method

Example 10.2.1 Consider the problem

$$y' = x + y,$$
$$y(0) = 1.$$

It can easily be determined that the solution is

$$\phi(x) = -1 - x + 2e^x.$$

Let the step size be $h = 0.1$. We then compute

$$y_0' = f(0, 1) = 1.$$

and

$$y_1 = y_0 + hf(0, 1)$$
$$= 1 + (0.1)1 = 1.1.$$

Next we compute

$$y_2 = y_1 + hf(x_1, y_1)$$
$$= 1.1 + (0.1) f(0.1, 1.1)$$
$$= 1.1 + (0.1)(0.1 + 1.1)$$
$$= 1.22.$$

The exact value is $\phi(0.2) = 1.2428$. The error is approximately $1.24 - 1.22 = 0.02$, which is about 1.6%. This percentage error is large. We can reduce it by taking a smaller step size. However, reducing the step size will not only increase the amount of work but will also introduce roundoff errors in added computations. There are more accurate methods which yield better results without using a very small step size.

The errors introduced in methods for solving differential equations arise from two sources. The first source is the error introduced by the approximation of formula in a method. This error is called the *truncation error* or *discretization error*.

The error that would be introduced in computing from the value y_n to the value y_{n+1} if y_n were exact is called the *local truncation error*. Thus the local truncation error at the nth step of the iteration is defined to be

$$e_n = \phi(x_{n+1}) - y_{n+1}. \tag{10.2.3}$$

The difference between the exact solution $\phi(x)$ and the approximate solution y_n,

$$E_n = \phi(x) - y_n,$$

is called the *accumulated truncation error*.

The *roundoff error* is another source of error introduced at each stage of computation. It can be reduced by keeping more decimal places. It is obvious that we have a *local roundoff error* and an *accumulated roundoff error* in computations. The accumulated roundoff error is defined to be

$$R_n = y_n - Y_n,$$

where Y_n is the actual computed value for y_n. The roundoff error in general is more difficult to analyze, since it depends on many factors, such as the type of computer used, the procedure of computation, the method of rounding off and so forth.

By using the triangle inequality we find the *total error* to be

$$|\phi(x) - Y_n| \leqslant |\phi(x) - y_n| + |y_n - Y_n| = |E_n| + |R_n|, \qquad (10.2.4)$$

which shows that the total error is bounded by the sum of the absolute values of the truncation and roundoff errors.

We shall now estimate the local truncation error generated by the Euler method.

THEOREM 10.2.1 *Let $f(x,y)$ and its first partial derivatives be continuous in $R : \{ a \leqslant x \leqslant b, \, |y| < \infty \}$. Let $\phi(x)$ be the exact solution and y_n be the approximate solution of the initial-value problem (10.1.1). Then for some constant M,*

$$|e_n| \leqslant \tfrac{1}{2} M h^2. \qquad (10.2.5)$$

Proof It is evident that

$$\phi(x_{n+1}) - \phi(x_n) = \int_{x_n}^{x_{n+1}} \phi'(x) \, dx = \int_{x_n}^{x_{n+1}} f(x, \phi(x)) \, dx.$$

Hence we have

$$\phi(x_{n+1}) = \phi(x_n) + \int_{x_n}^{x_{n+1}} f(x, \phi(x)) \, dx. \qquad (10.2.6)$$

But the approximate value according to the Euler formula is

$$y_{n+1} = y_n + (x_{n+1} - x_n) f(x_n, y_n). \qquad (10.2.7)$$

Subtracting (10.2.7) from (10.2.6) and assuming that $\phi(x_n) = y_n$, we obtain

$$|e_n| = \left| \int_{x_n}^{x_{n+1}} f(x, \phi(x)) \, dx - (x_{n+1} - x_n) f(x_n, y_n) \right|$$

By the mean-value theorem we have

$$f(x, \phi(x)) - f(x_n, \phi(x_n)) = (x - x_n) f'(c),$$

where c is some point between x_n and x. Thus it follows that

$$\int_{x_n}^{x_{n+1}} f(x, \phi(x)) \, dx = \int_{x_n}^{x_{n+1}} \left[f(x_n, \phi(x_n)) + (x - x_n) f'(c) \right] dx$$

$$= (x_{n+1} - x_n) f(x_n, \phi(x_n)) + \int_{x_n}^{x_{n+1}} (x - x_n) f'(c) \, dx.$$

Consequently,

$$|e_n| = \left| \int_{x_n}^{x_{n+1}} (x - x_n) f'(c) \, dx \right|.$$

We obviously have

$$f'(x, \phi(x)) = f_x(x, \phi(x)) + f_y(x, \phi(x)) \phi'(x)$$

$$= f_x(x, \phi(x)) + f_y(x, \phi(x)) f(x, \phi(t)).$$

Since f has continuous first derivatives, f' is bounded in some region $R : \{a \leqslant x \leqslant b, \, |y| < \infty \}$. Thus if we suppose

$$M = \max_{a \leqslant x \leqslant b} |f'(x)|,$$

then

$$|e_n| \leqslant \tfrac{1}{2} M h^2. \qquad (10.2.8)$$

∎

As far as the truncation error is concerned the Euler method evidently needs refinement. One way to improve this is by approximating the integral in (10.2.6).

10.3   Modified Euler Method

The Euler method can be modified by using the midpoint quadrature for the integral in (10.2.6). The resulting method is called the *modified Euler method*.

For the interval x_n to x_{n+2} we write, using (10.2.6),

$$\phi(x_{n+2}) = \phi(x_n) + \int_{x_n}^{x_{n+2}} f(x, \phi(x)) \, dx. \tag{10.3.1}$$

Now approximating the integral by $2hf(x_{n+1}, \phi(x_{n+1}))$, we obtain the *modified Euler formula*

$$y_{n+2} = y_n + 2hf(x_{n+1}, y_{n+1}). \tag{10.3.2}$$

This method requires y_n and y_{n+1} to compute y_{n+2}. For this reason it is called a *two-step method*, in contrast to the preceding *one-step method*. Here as a start one needs y_0 and y_1 to compute y_2. The initial condition provides y_0, and y_1 is to be determined. One method of determining y_1 is by the expansion of f, if analytic, about x_0. The other method is to use the Euler method.

Example 10.3.1   Consider the initial-value problem

$$y' = x + y,$$
$$y(0) = 1.$$

with the step size $h = 0.1$.

We expand f about the origin to obtain

$$y_1 = y(h) = y(0) + y'(0)h + y''(0)\frac{h^2}{2!} + \cdots$$

$$= 1 + h + h^2 + \cdots$$

$$= 1.11$$

to two decimal places. Thus from

$$y_{n+2} = y_n + 0.2(x_{n+1} + y_{n+1}),$$

we find

$$y_2 = y_0 + 0.2(x_1 + y_1)$$
$$= 1 + 0.2(0.1 + 1.11)$$
$$= 1.24,$$

which is very close to the exact value $\phi(0.2) = 1.2428$.

We shall now prove that the local truncation error of the modified Euler method is of the order of h^3.

THEOREM 10.3.1 *Let $f(x, y)$ and its first- and second-order partial derivatives be continuous in $R : \{a \leqslant x \leqslant b, |y| < \infty\}$. Then for some constant M,*

$$|e_n| \leqslant \tfrac{1}{3} M h^3. \tag{10.3.3}$$

Proof Subtracting (10.3.2) from (10.3.1), we obtain

$$\phi(x_{n+2}) - y_{n+2} = \phi(x_n) - y_n + \int_{x_n}^{x_{n+2}} f(x, \phi(x)) \, dx - 2hf(x_{n+1}, y_{n+1}).$$

Here the approximate values y_n and y_{n+1} are assumed to be exact, that is, $\phi(x_n) = y_n$ and $\phi(x_{n+1}) = y_{n+1}$. Thus

$$e_n = \int_{x_n}^{x_{n+2}} f(x, \phi(x)) \, dx - 2hf(x_{n+1}, \phi(x_{n+1}))$$

Since f is twice continuously differentiable, we have by Taylor's theorem

$$f(x, \phi(x)) = f(x_{n+1}, \phi(x_{n+1})) + f'(x_{n+1}, \phi(x_{n+1}))(x - x_{n+1})$$
$$+ f''(\xi)(x - x_{n+1})^2 / 2!, \tag{10.3.4}$$

where $x_n \leqslant x \leqslant x_{n+2}$ and $x_n < \xi < x_{n+2}$. Now integration yields

$$\int_{x_n}^{x_{n+2}} f(x, \phi(x)) \, dx - 2hf(x_{n+1}, \phi(x_{n+1})) = \int_{x_n}^{x_{n+2}} \frac{(x - x_{n+1})^2}{2!} f''(\xi) \, dx$$

where the integration of the second term on the right in (10.3.4) vanishes. Hence we find

$$e_n = \int_{x_n}^{x_{n+2}} \frac{(x - x_{n+1})^2}{2!} f''(\xi)\, dx$$

and

$$|e_n| \leqslant \frac{M}{2} \int_{x_n}^{x_{n+2}} (x - x_{n+1})^2\, dx = \tfrac{1}{3} M h^3,$$

where

$$M = \max_{a \leqslant x \leqslant b} |f''(x, \phi(x))|. \qquad \blacksquare$$

There are other improved Euler methods. In fact, one of them is conventionally called the *improved Euler method* or the *Heun method*. The *Heun formula* is given by

$$y_{n+1} = y_n + \frac{h}{2} \left[f(x_n, y_n) + f(x_{n+1}, y_{n+1}) \right], \qquad (10.3.5)$$

which is obtained by approximating the integral in (10.2.6) by the trapezoidal rule.

Another such method is the *Milne method*; the *Milne formula* is given by

$$y_{n+2} = y_n + \frac{h}{3} \left[f(x_n, y_n) + 4f(x_{n+1}, y_{n+1}) + f(x_{n+2}, y_{n+2}) \right], \quad (10.3.6)$$

which is obtained by approximating the integral in (10.2.6) by Simpson's rule.

Both methods are implicit in that the respective iterative formula has the unknown y_{n+i} appearing as one of the arguments of f. The usual technique is to compute y_{n+1} in the Heun formula or y_{n+2} in the Milne formula by some explicit method such as the Euler method. The respective value is called the *predictor*. Then the *corrector* y_{n+1} in the Heun formula or y_{n+2} in the Milne formula is calculated from the respective *predictor-corrector formula* (10.3.5) or (10.3.6).

10.4   Accumulated Truncation Error

We shall consider a general method of determining the estimate of accumulated truncation error for one-step methods. This method can also be extended to two-step methods.

THEOREM 10.4.1   *Let $f(x, y)$ and its first partial derivatives be continuous in $R: \{a \leqslant x \leqslant b, |y| < \infty\}$. If the local truncation error $|e_n| \leqslant \varepsilon$, then the accumulated truncation error $|E_n| \leqslant \varepsilon/h$.*

Proof   Let y_n be the approximate solution corresponding to the exact solution $\phi(x)$ of the initial-value problem (10.1.1). For convenience let us define ϕ_n to be the exact solution such that

$$\phi_n(x_n) = y_n,$$

$$\phi_0(x_0) = y_0 = \phi(x_0),$$

for $n = 0, 1, 2, \ldots, N-1$, as shown in Figure 10.4-1.

Thus the local truncation error is

$$|e_n| = |y_{n+1} - \phi_n(x_{n+1})|$$

$$= |\phi_{n+1}(x_{n+1}) - \phi_n(x_{n+1})|,$$

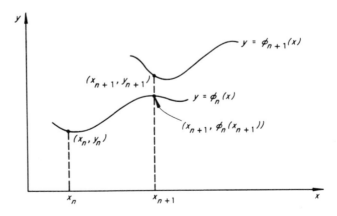

Figure 10.4-1

and the accumulated truncation error is

$$|E_N| = |y_N - \phi(x_N)| = |\phi_N(x_N) - \phi_0(x_N)| \leqslant \sum_{n=1}^{N} |\phi_n(x_N) - \phi_{n-1}(x_N)|. \quad (10.4.1)$$

As in (10.2.6), we write

$$\phi_n(x_N) = \phi_n(x_n) + \int_{x_n}^{x_N} f(x, \phi_n(x)) \, dx,$$

$$\phi_{n-1}(x_N) = \phi_{n-1}(x_n) + \int_{x_n}^{x_N} f(x, \phi_{n-1}(x)) \, dx,$$

for $n = 1, 2, \ldots, N$. Now subtracting $\phi_{n-1}(x_N)$ from $\phi_n(x_N)$ we obtain

$$|\phi_n(x_N) - \phi_{n-1}(x_N)| \leqslant |\phi_n(x_n) - \phi_{n-1}(x_n)|$$

$$+ \int_{x_n}^{x_N} |f(x, \phi_n(x)) - f(x, \phi_{n-1}(x))| \, dx. \quad (10.4.2)$$

Since f and $\partial f / \partial y$ are continuous in $R = \{x, y \,|\, a \leqslant x \leqslant b, \, |y| \geqslant 0\}$, f satisfies a Lipschitz condition (see Appendix I) with a Lipschitz constant L

$$|f(x, \phi_n(x)) - f(x, \phi_{n-1}(x))| \leqslant L |\phi_n(x) - \phi_{n-1}(x)|$$

Consequently (10.4.2) becomes

$$|\phi_n(x_N) - \phi_{n-1}(x_N)| \leqslant |e_n| + L \int_{x_n}^{x_N} |\phi_n(x) - \phi_{n-1}(x)| \, dx.$$

Now applying the Gronwall inequality (Exercise 18), we obtain

$$|\phi_n(x_N) - \phi_{n-1}(x_N)| \leqslant \varepsilon e^{L(x_N - x_n)} = \varepsilon e^{L(N-n)h}.$$

Thus from (10.4.1) we have

$$|E_N| \leqslant \varepsilon \sum_{n=1}^{N} e^{L(N-n)h} = \varepsilon e^{LNh} \sum_{n=1}^{N} e^{-Lhn}.$$

The series is the geometric series, the sum of which is

$$\sum_{n=1}^{N} e^{-Lhn} = e^{-Lh} \left(\frac{1 - e^{-LhN}}{1 - e^{-Lh}} \right) = \frac{1 - e^{-LhN}}{e^{Lh} - 1}.$$

Hence

$$|E_N| \leqslant \varepsilon \left(\frac{e^{LhN} - 1}{e^{Lh} - 1} \right)$$

Since

$$e^{Lh} - 1 \geqslant Lh,$$

we obtain

$$|E_N| \leqslant \frac{\varepsilon M}{h},$$

where $M = [e^{L(x_N - x_0)} - 1]/L = [e^{L(b - a)} - 1]/L$.   ■

Thus the theorem alternatively states that if the local truncation error of a one-step method is $O(h^p)$, then the accumulated truncation error is $O(h^{p-1})$. For instance, the accumulated truncation error of the Euler method is $O(h)$.

It is evident that the truncation error can be made smaller by taking a smaller step size. However, in that case more computations will be required, thereby increasing roundoff errors. Hence for an effective procedure an optimal step size is necessary. This is true provided, of course, the constant factor M for a method is not too large.

In general roundoff errors can be minimized by taking more decimal places. A numerical method is said to be *stable* if the approximate solution of a differential equation is insensitive to roundoff errors in computations. That is, a small change in roundoff errors produces only a small change in the solution.

If the solution of a differential equation satisfies the difference equation, the approximation method is said to be *consistent*. If the approximate solution approaches the exact solution as the step size tends to zero, then the method of approximation is said to be *convergent*.

The theory of roundoff errors and the analysis of the consistency, convergence and stability of difference methods are specialized subjects. We refer the reader to such books as those of Henrici [17] and Isaacson and Keller [20].

10.5   Runge-Kutta Method

Due to its simple programming and its accuracy, the Runge-Kutta method is one of the most frequently applied methods in determining numerical solutions of initial-value problems.

We shall first consider the Taylor series expansion:

$$y_{n+1} = y_n + y_n' h + y_n'' \frac{h^2}{2!} + y_n''' \frac{h^3}{3!} + \cdots . \qquad (10.5.1)$$

Since $y' = f(x, y)$, we find

$$y' = f(x, y),$$

$$y'' = f_x + f_y y' = f_x + f f_y,$$

$$y''' = f_{xx} + 2 f f_{xy} + f^2 f_{yy} + f_y (f_x + f f_y),$$

etc., where the subscripts denote differentiations. Now substituting these values in (10.5.1), we obtain

$$y_{n+1} = y_n + f_n h + \left[f_x + f f_y \right]_n \frac{h^2}{2!}$$

$$+ \left[f_{xx} + 2 f f_{xy} + f^2 f_{yy} + f_y (f_x + f f_y) \right]_n \frac{h^3}{3!} + \cdots, \qquad (10.5.2)$$

in which the subscript n denotes that the functions are to be evaluated at the point (x_n, y_n).

In order to avoid using many derivatives, we arbitrarily take

$$y_{n+1} = y_n + \alpha_0 k_0 + \alpha_1 k_1 + \alpha_2 k_2 + \alpha_3 k_3 + \cdots + \alpha_m k_m, \qquad (10.5.3)$$

where

$$k_0 = f(x_n, y_n) h,$$

$$k_1 = f(x_n + a_1 h, y_n + b_{10} k_0) h,$$

$$k_2 = f(x_n + a_2 h, y_n + b_{20} k_0 + b_{21} k_1) h, \qquad (10.5.4)$$

$$\vdots$$

$$k_m = f(x_n + a_m h, y_n + b_{m0} k_0 + b_{m1} k_1 + \cdots) h.$$

Here α_j, a_j and b_{ji} are the unknown constants. The Taylor series for two variables about the point (x, y) is given by

$$f(x + p, y + q) = f(x, y) + f_x(x, y) p + f_y(x, y) q$$

$$+ \frac{1}{2!} \left[f_{xx}(x, y) p^2 + 2 f_{xy}(x, y) pq + f_{yy}(x, y) q^2 \right] + \cdots,$$

which can also be written in the form

$$f(x+p,y+q)=f(x,y)+\left(p\frac{\partial}{\partial x}+q\frac{\partial}{\partial y}\right)f(x,y)$$

$$+\frac{1}{2!}\left(p\frac{\partial}{\partial x}+q\frac{\partial}{\partial y}\right)^{2}f(x,y)$$

$$+\frac{1}{3!}\left(p\frac{\partial}{\partial x}+q\frac{\partial}{\partial y}\right)^{3}f(x,y)+\cdots. \qquad (10.5.5)$$

Now if we use (10.5.5) in expanding the right sides of (10.5.4), we obtain for $m=3$,

$$k_0=f_n h,$$

$$k_1=\left[f_n+\left(a_1h\frac{\partial}{\partial x}+b_{10}k_0\frac{\partial}{\partial y}\right)f_n+\frac{1}{2!}\left(a_1h\frac{\partial}{\partial x}+b_{10}k_0\frac{\partial}{\partial y}\right)^{2}f_n\right.$$

$$\left.+\frac{1}{3!}\left(a_1h\frac{\partial}{\partial x}+b_{10}k_0\frac{\partial}{\partial y}\right)^{3}f_n+\cdots\right]h,$$

$$k_2=\left[f_n+\left(a_2h\frac{\partial}{\partial x}+(b_{20}k_0+b_{21}k_1)\frac{\partial}{\partial y}\right)f_n\right.$$

$$+\frac{1}{2!}\left(a_2h\frac{\partial}{\partial x}+(b_{20}k_0+b_{21}k_1)\frac{\partial}{\partial y}\right)^{2}f_n$$

$$\left.+\frac{1}{3!}\left(a_2h\frac{\partial}{\partial x}+(b_{20}k_0+b_{21}k_1)\frac{\partial}{\partial y}\right)^{3}f_n+\cdots\right]h, \qquad (10.5.6)$$

$$k_3=\left[f_n+\left(a_3h\frac{\partial}{\partial x}+(b_{30}k_0+b_{31}k_1+b_{32}k_2)\frac{\partial}{\partial y}\right)f_n\right.$$

$$+\frac{1}{2!}\left(a_3h\frac{\partial}{\partial x}+(b_{30}k_0+b_{31}k_1+b_{32}k_2)\frac{\partial}{\partial y}\right)^{2}f_n$$

$$\left.+\frac{1}{3!}\left(a_3h\frac{\partial}{\partial x}+(b_{30}k_0+b_{31}k_1+b_{32}k_2)\frac{\partial}{\partial y}\right)^{3}f_n+\cdots\right]h.$$

Equating the coefficients of the corresponding terms in (10.5.2) and (10.5.3), we obtain

$$a_1 = b_{10},$$

$$a_2 = b_{20} + b_{21},$$

$$a_3 = b_{30} + b_{31} + b_{32},$$

$$\alpha_0 + \alpha_1 + \alpha_2 + \alpha_3 = 1,$$

$$\alpha_1 a_1 + \alpha_2 a_2 + \alpha_3 a_3 = \tfrac{1}{2},$$

$$\alpha_1 a_1^2 + \alpha_2 a_2^2 + \alpha_3 a_3^2 = \tfrac{1}{3}, \qquad (10.5.7)$$

$$\alpha_1 a_1^3 + \alpha_2 a_2^3 + \alpha_3 a_3^3 = \tfrac{1}{4}$$

$$\alpha_2 a_1 b_{21} + \alpha_3 (a_1 b_{31} + a_2 b_{32}) = \tfrac{1}{6}$$

$$\alpha_2 a_1^2 b_{21} + \alpha_3 (a_1^2 b_{31} + a_2^2 b_{32}) = \tfrac{1}{12}$$

$$\alpha_2 a_1 a_2 b_{21} + \alpha_3 a_3 (a_1 b_{31} + a_2 b_{32}) = \tfrac{1}{8}$$

$$\alpha_3 a_1 b_{21} b_{32} = \tfrac{1}{24}$$

Since there are 13 unknowns and only 11 equations, we arbitrarily take $\alpha_1 = \alpha_2 = \tfrac{1}{3}$. With these values of α, the set

$$\alpha_0 = \tfrac{1}{6}, \quad a_1 = \tfrac{1}{2}, \quad b_{10} = \tfrac{1}{2},$$

$$\alpha_1 = \tfrac{1}{3}, \quad a_2 = \tfrac{1}{2}, \quad b_{20} = 0, \quad b_{21} = \tfrac{1}{2},$$

$$\alpha_2 = \tfrac{1}{3}, \quad a_3 = 1, \quad b_{30} = 0, \quad b_{31} = 0, \quad b_{32} = 1,$$

$$\alpha_3 = \tfrac{1}{6} \qquad (10.5.8)$$

is a solution of the equations (10.5.7), as can be easily verified. Substituting these constants into (10.5.3), we obtain the *Runge-Kutta formula* with *Runge's coefficients*

$$y_{n+1} = y_n + \frac{h}{6} (k_{n0} + 2k_{n1} + 2k_{n2} + k_{n3}), \qquad (10.5.9)$$

where $k_{nj} = k_j/h$ are given by

$$k_{n0} = f(x_n, y_n),$$

$$k_{n1} = f\left(x_n + \frac{h}{2}, y_n + \frac{k_{n0}}{2} h\right),$$

$$k_{n2} = f\left(x_n + \frac{h}{2}, y_n + \frac{k_{n1}}{2} h\right),$$

$$k_{n3} = f(x_n + h, y_n + k_{n2} h).$$

Another set of constants which satisfies the equations (10.5.7) is

$$\alpha_0 = \tfrac{1}{8}, \quad a_1 = \tfrac{1}{3}, \quad b_{10} = \tfrac{1}{3},$$

$$\alpha_1 = \tfrac{3}{8}, \quad a_2 = \tfrac{2}{3}, \quad b_{20} = -\tfrac{1}{3}, \quad b_{21} = 1,$$

$$\alpha_2 = \tfrac{3}{8}, \quad a_3 = 1, \quad b_{30} = 1, \quad b_{31} = -1, \quad b_{32} = 1,$$

$$\alpha_3 = \tfrac{1}{8}.$$

Using these constants in (10.5.3), we have the Runge-Kutta formula with *Kutta's coefficients*

$$y_{n+1} = y_n + \frac{h}{8}(k_{n0} + 3k_{n1} + 3k_{n2} + k_{n3}),$$

where

$$k_{n0} = f(x_n, y_n),$$

$$k_{n1} = f\left(x_n + \frac{h}{3}, y_n + \frac{k_{n0}}{3} h\right),$$

$$k_{n2} = f\left[x_n + \tfrac{2}{3} h, y_n + (k_{n1} - k_{n0}) \frac{h}{3}\right],$$

$$k_{n3} = f\left[x_n + h, y_n + (k_{n0} - k_{n1} + k_{n2}) h\right].$$

In addition to Runge's and Kutta's coefficients there are others which give different orders of accuracy in determining solutions of initial-value problems.

It is interesting to observe that when f is independent of y, the Runge-Kutta formula becomes the well-known *Simpson's rule*:

$$y_{n+1} = y_n + \frac{h}{6}(k_{n0} + 2k_{n1} + 2k_{n2} + k_{n3}),$$

where

$$k_{n0} = f(x_n),$$

$$k_{n1} = f\left(x_n + \frac{h}{2}\right),$$

$$k_{n2} = f\left(x_n + \frac{h}{2}\right),$$

$$k_{n3} = f(x_n + h),$$

or in more familiar form,

$$y_{n+1} = y_n + \frac{h}{6}\left[f(x_n) + 4f\left(x_n + \frac{h}{2}\right) + f(x_n + h)\right].$$

The Runge-Kutta formula with Runge's coefficients, may be interpreted geometrically. All the coefficients k_{nj} represent the slopes at different points. k_{n0} is the slope at the left starting point of the interval $[x_n, x_{n+1}]$, k_{n1} is the slope at the midpoint with the ordinate $y_n + (k_{n0}/2)h$, k_{n2} is also the slope at the midpoint but with the ordinate $y_n + (k_{n1}/2)h$, and k_{n3} is the slope at the right end point, the ordinate of which is $y_n + k_{n2}h$. The sum $(k_{n0} + 2k_{n1} + 2k_{n2} + k_{n3})/6$ can be interpreted as a weighted average slope with the center slopes weighing twice as much as the slopes at the ends.

Example 10.5.1 Consider the initial-value problem

$$y' = x + y,$$

$$y(0) = 1,$$

with $h = 0.2$. We compute

$$k_{00} = f(0, 1) = 1,$$

$$k_{01} = f(0 + 0.1, 1 + 0.1) = 0.1 + 1.1 = 1.2,$$

$$k_{02} = f(0 + 0.1, 1 + 0.1 \times 1.2) = 0.1 + 1.12 = 1.22,$$

$$k_{03} = f(0 + 0.2, 1 + 0.2 \times 1.22) = 0.2 + 1.244 = 1.444.$$

Thus

$$y_1 = 1 + \frac{0.2}{6}\left[1 + 2(1.2) + 2(1.22) + 1.444\right]$$

$$= 1.2428.$$

The exact solution $\phi(0.2)$ is 1.2428. Thus the numerical solution by the Runge-Kutta method with $h = 0.2$ agrees with the exact solution to four decimal places. It gives better results than the Euler or the modified Euler method even with $h = 0.1$.

We should remark that the main disadvantage of the Runge-Kutta method is the time required in evaluating the coefficients, especially for complicated functions $f(x, y)$. But for a class of initial-value problems the Runge-Kutta method simplifies programming and yields an accuracy with the local truncation error $O(h^5)$. Since the error analysis of the Runge-Kutta method is more involved than the preceding numerical methods, we will omit the treatment here. It can be found in Ralston [34].

Remark The approximation methods mentioned in this chapter can also be applied to systems of first-order equations. If, for example, we wish to find the solution of

$$x' = f(t, x, y),$$

$$y' = g(t, x, y)$$

with the initial conditions $x(t_0) = x_0$ and $y(t_0) = y_0$, we may for simple illustrative purpose choose the Euler method. Thus we write the difference equations as

$$x_{n+1} = x_n + hf(t_n, x_n, y_n) = x_n + hx'_n,$$

$$y_{n+1} = y_n + hg(t_n, x_n, y_n) = y_n + hy'_n.$$

These two equations can then be solved simultaneously.

Numerical analysis is an important field of study in itself. Those wishing to study further the numerical aspects of ordinary differential equations should consult the books listed in the bibliography.

EXERCISES

1. By the Euler method determine an approximate solution of the initial-value problem

   (a) $y' = 3x + y$, $y(0) = 1$;

   (b) $y' = x^2 + y$, $y(0) = 2$,

   at $x = 0.2$ using $h = 0.1$, and compare with the exact solution. Repeat the computations for $h = 0.05$ and $h = 0.2$.

2. By the Euler method obtain an approximate solution of the initial-value problem

$$y' = x - y,$$

$$y(0) = 1$$

   at $x = 0.2$ using $h = 0.1$. Show that the exact solution is

$$\phi(x) = x - 1 + 2e^{-x}.$$

   By the Taylor expansion show that

$$e_n = \tfrac{1}{2}\phi''(\bar{x}_n)h^2, \qquad x_n < \bar{x}_n < x_n + h,$$

   and hence

$$e_n = e^{-\bar{x}_n}h^2,$$

   which implies

$$|e_n| \leqslant h^2.$$

   Compute e_1 and e_2.

3. Consider the initial-value problem

$$y' = y,$$

$$y(0) = 1.$$

   From the Euler formula show that

$$y_{n+1} = (1+h)\, y_n, \qquad n = 0, 1, 2, \ldots .$$

With the initial condition it reduces to

$$y_n = (1+h)^n, \qquad n = 1, 2, 3, \ldots .$$

Using $x = nh$, show that the approximate solution at $x = x_n$ as $h \to 0$ converges to the exact solution $\phi(x) = e^x$.

4. Consider the initial-value problem

$$y' = y,$$

$$y(0) = 1,$$

the exact solution of which is $\phi(x) = e^x$.
From the Euler formula show that

$$\phi(x_{n+1}) - (1+h)\phi(x_n) = e^{nh}(e^h - h - 1) \leqslant kh^2$$

for some constant $k > 0$. Show that the Euler method is consistent.

5. Show that the modified Euler method for $y' = y$, $y(0) = 1$ is consistent and convergent.

6. Using the Euler and the modified Euler methods, obtain approximate solutions of the initial-value problem

$$y' = x^2 + y^2,$$

$$y(0) = 1$$

at $x = 0.2$ with the step size $h = 0.1$.

7. Estimate the value of e by the modified Euler method from the initial-value problem

$$y' = y,$$

$$y(0) = 1.$$

Choose proper h and determine the results up to three decimal places.

8. Show that the Euler method fails to determine an approximate solution of the initial-value problem

$$y' = y^\alpha, \qquad \alpha < 1,$$

$$y(0) = 0,$$

although the exact solution exists.

9. Consider the initial-value problem

$$y' = x^3 + y^3,$$
$$y(0) = 1.$$

Find an approximate solution by the Taylor series expansion through terms in h^3 at $x = 0.2$. Estimate the truncation error.

10. Prove that

$$y' = -2ax$$

can be solved exactly by the modified Euler method (Henrici [17]).

11. Obtain the Milne formula. Using the Milne method with $h = 0.1$ and the Euler method as predictor, find an approximate value at $x = 0.2$ of the initial-value problem

$$y' = x^2 + y^2,$$
$$y(0) = 1.$$

Compare the results with that of the Euler and modified Euler methods in No. 6.

12. If $f(x, y)$ is sufficiently differentiable in x and y, show that the local truncation error of the Milne method satisfies

$$|e_n| \leqslant kMh^5$$

for some constants k and M, assuming that the local truncation error of the method used to calculate the predictor is $O(h^5)$ or lower.

13. Obtain the Heun formula. Using the Heun method with $h = 0.1$ and the Euler method as predictor, determine an approximate solution at $x = 0.2$ of the initial-value problem

$$y' = x^2 + y^2,$$
$$y(0) = 1.$$

Compare the results with that in No. 11.

14. By the Runge-Kutta method obtain the solution of the initial-value problems:

    (a) $y' = 1 + x + y$, $y(0) = 1$,

    (b) $y' = 1 + y^2$, $y(0) = 0$,

    (c) $y' = x^2 + y^2$, $y(0) = 1$,

    at $x = 0.2$, using $h = 0.2$.

15. Consider the initial-value problem

$$y' = 1 + x + 2y,$$
$$y(0) = 1,$$

    with $h = 0.1$. Using the Runge-Kutta method for starting values and predictor-corrector formulae, find the solution by the Milne method at $x = 0.4$ and $x = 0.5$.

16. Determine an approximate value of $\phi(0.2)$, by the Euler method and the Runge-Kutta method, for the initial-value problem

$$x' = x + 4y, \quad x(0) = 1,$$
$$y' = x - y, \quad y(0) = 0.$$

17. Consider the motion of a simple pendulum governed by the equation

$$\frac{d\omega}{d\theta} = -\frac{g}{l}\frac{\sin\theta}{\omega},$$

    where ω is the angular velocity in radians per second, θ is the angle of swing in degrees, $g = 32.2014$ feet per second per second, and $l = 2$ feet. If the initial condition is $\omega(\pi/3) = \frac{1}{2}$, find $\omega(70°)$ by applying the Runge-Kutta method with Runge's coefficients. Use $\Delta\theta = 0.5°$.

18. (Gronwall's inequality). Let f and g be continuous and nonnegative in an interval I. Let $C \geqslant 0$ and let $x_0 \in I$. If

$$f(x) \leqslant C + \int_{x_0}^{x} f(s)\, g(s)\, ds,$$

    on I, then

$$f(x) \leqslant C \exp\left[\int_{x_0}^{x} g(s)\, ds\right]$$

    on I.

Appendixes

I Lipschitz Condition

Let $f(x,y)$ be a function defined in a domain D. Then f is said to satisfy a *Lipschitz condition* (with respect to y) in D if there exists a constant $K > 0$ such that

$$|f(x,y_1) - f(x,y_2)| \leqslant K|y_1 - y_2|$$

for every $(x,y_1), (x,y_2) \in D$. The constant K is called a *Lipschitz constant*.

An immediate consequence of the definition of Lipschitz condition is the following theorem.

THEOREM I.1 *Let f be continuous in a convex[†] domain D. If $\partial f/\partial y$ exists and is bounded on D, then f satisfies a Lipschitz condition in D.*

Proof By the Mean Value Theorem

$$f(x,y_1) - f(x,y_2) = \frac{\partial f}{\partial y}(x,y^*)(y_1 - y_2),$$

where y^* is some point between y_1 and y_2. Since $\partial f/\partial y$ is bounded, we have

[†]A region R is said to be *convex* if it contains the line joining any two points in R.

$|\partial f/\partial y| \leqslant K$. Thus

$$|f(x,y_1)-f(x,y_2)| \leqslant K(y_1-y_2). \qquad \blacksquare$$

It should be noted that the continuity of f does not imply that f satisfies a Lipschitz condition.

Example I.1 We consider a continuous function $f(x,y)=y^{\frac{2}{3}}$ in a domain D containing the origin. We see that

$$|f(x,0)-f(x,y)|=|0-y^{\frac{2}{3}}| \leqslant K|0-y|$$

This shows that f does not satisfy a Lipschitz condition in any domain D. However, if we choose $K=\varepsilon^{-\frac{1}{3}}$ with $\varepsilon>0$, then f satisfies a Lipschitz condition in any strip $|y| \geqslant \varepsilon$.

II Gamma Function

The Gamma function is defined by the improper integral

$$\Gamma(x)= \int_0^\infty t^{x-1}e^{-t}dt. \qquad (\text{II.1})$$

This integral is continuous and converges for all $x>0$ [10: p. 336].

From the definition it follows immediately that

$$\Gamma(x+1)= \int_0^\infty t^x e^{-t}dt$$

$$= \lim_{b \to \infty} \left[-t^x e^{-t} \right]_0^b + x \int_0^\infty t^{x-1}e^{-t}dt$$

$$= x\Gamma(x) \qquad (\text{II.2})$$

since the first term on the right vanishes.

We note that

$$\Gamma(1)= \int_0^\infty e^{-t}dt=1, \qquad (\text{II.3})$$

and consequently we obtain, using relation (II.2),

$$\Gamma(2) = 1 \cdot \Gamma(1) = 1 \cdot 1 = 1!,$$
$$\Gamma(3) = 2 \cdot \Gamma(2) = 2 \cdot 1 = 2!,$$
$$\Gamma(4) = 3 \cdot \Gamma(3) = 3 \cdot 2 \cdot 1 = 3!.$$

In general,

$$\Gamma(n+1) = n! \quad \text{for} \quad n = 0, 1, 2, \dots. \tag{II.4}$$

From Eqs. (II.3) and (II.4) we obtain the value of 0!

$$\Gamma(1) = 0! = 1. \tag{II.5}$$

If we write Eq. (II.2) in the form

$$\Gamma(x) = (1/x)\Gamma(x+1), \tag{II.6}$$

we obtain by repeated application of (II.6)

$$\Gamma(x) = \frac{\Gamma(x+k)}{x(x+1)(x+2)\cdots(x+k-1)}, \tag{II.7}$$

for $k = 1, 2, 3, \dots$. We see that $\Gamma(x)$ is infinite for all negative integers.

The values of $\Gamma(x)$ are tabulated for $1 < x < 2$.[†] From these values one can find, for example,

$$\Gamma(3.5) = (2.5)(1.5)\Gamma(1.5)$$

and

$$\Gamma(-1.4) = \frac{\Gamma(1.6)}{(-1.4)(-.4)(.6)}$$

where $\Gamma(1.5) = 0.88623$ and $\Gamma(1.6) = 0.89352$.

[†]For the table of Gamma functions, see H. B. Dwight [11].

III The Exponential Matrix

DEFINITION III.1   Let A be any $n \times n$ matrix. Then the *exponential matrix* e^A is defined by the series

$$e^A = I + \sum_{k=1}^{\infty} \frac{A^k}{k!},$$

where A^k represents the kth power of A, and I is the $n \times n$ identity matrix.

THEOREM III.1   *If A is a square matrix, then the series defining e^A converges.*

Proof   Let $A = (a_{ij})$ and let $h = \max_{ij} |a_{ij}|$. Now if we let $A^2 = (\alpha_{ij})$, then

$$|\alpha_{ij}| = \left| \sum_{k=1}^{n} a_{ik} a_{kj} \right| \leqslant \sum_{k=1}^{n} |a_{ik}| |a_{kj}| \leqslant \sum_{k=1}^{n} h^2 = nh^2$$

Thus every element of A^2 is bounded by nh^2. It can be easily proved by induction that A^k is bounded by $n^{k-1} h^k$, for $k = 1, 2, 3, \ldots$.

If ξ_{ij} is the ijth element of $A^k / k!$, then

$$\sum_{k=0}^{s} |\xi_{ij}| \leqslant 1 + h + \frac{nh^2}{2!} + \cdots + \frac{n^{s-1} h^s}{s!}$$

$$\leqslant 1 + nh + \frac{n^2 h^2}{2!} + \cdots + \frac{n^s h^s}{s!}$$

Since the terms on the right side represent a partial sum for e^{nh}, which converges for any h and n, the series for e^A converges.   ∎

We will state without proof some of the useful properties of the exponential matrix in the following theorem.

THEOREM III.2   *Let A be any $n \times n$ matrix and let 0 be an $n \times n$ zero matrix. Then*

(a) $e^0 = I$

(b) $(e^A)^{-1} = e^{-A}$

(c) $(e^A)^k = e^{Ak}$, k is an integer

(d) $e^{A+B} = e^A \cdot e^B$, if $AB = BA$

(e) $\dfrac{d}{dt} e^{tA} = A e^{tA}$, t is a scalar

IV Table of Laplace Transforms

$f(t)$	$\mathcal{L}[f(t)]$
c, a constant	$\dfrac{c}{s}$
$t^n, n = 1, 2, 3, \ldots$	$n!/s^{n+1}$
e^{at}	$1/(s-a)$
te^{at}	$1/(s-a)^2$
$\sin \omega t$	$\omega/(s^2 + \omega^2)$
$\cos \omega t$	$s/(s^2 + \omega^2)$
$\sinh \kappa t$	$\kappa/(s^2 - \kappa^2)$
$\cosh \kappa t$	$s/(s^2 - \kappa^2)$
$\sqrt{t}$	$\sqrt{\pi}/2\sqrt{s^3}$
$1/\sqrt{t}$	$\sqrt{\pi}/\sqrt{s}$
$e^{at} \sin \omega t$	$\omega/\left[(s-a)^2 + \omega^2\right]$
$e^{at} \cos \omega t$	$(s-a)/\left[(s-a)^2 + \omega^2\right]$
$\mathrm{erf}(a\sqrt{t})$	$a/s\sqrt{s + a^2}$
$\mathrm{erfc}(a/2\sqrt{t})$	$e^{-a\sqrt{s}}/s$
$t^{\kappa-1}, \kappa > 0$	$\Gamma(\kappa)/s^\kappa$
$J_0(at)$	$1/\sqrt{s^2 + a^2}$
$I_0(at)$	$1/\sqrt{s^2 - a^2}$
$(\sin \omega t)/t$	$\tan^{-1}(\omega/s)$
$t \sinh \kappa t$	$2\kappa s/(s^2 - \kappa^2)^2$
$t \cosh \kappa t$	$(s^2 + \kappa^2)/(s^2 - \kappa^2)^2$

V Mathematical model for the motion of a low-altitude artificial satellite

Consider the motion of a low-altitude artificial satellite around the earth. The motion is perturbed substantially by the earth's oblateness and atmospheric resistance. Other comparatively small forces such as lunisolar attraction and radiation pressure are neglected. It is also assumed that the lift on the satellite is small. The earth is considered to be axially symmetric about its polar axis. The atmosphere is assumed to be rotating with the same angular velocity as the earth.

The equations of motion in terms of Cartesian coordinates centered at the earth and in the equatorial plane, in accordance with Newton's second law of motion, are

$$\frac{d^2 x_k}{dt^2} = -\frac{\partial U}{\partial x_k} + F_k, \qquad k = 1, 2, 3, \tag{V.1}$$

where $U(x_1, x_2, x_3)$ is the gravitational potential of the earth and $F_k(x_1, x_2, x_3)$ are the other perturbing forces acting on the satellite.

If the center of mass is assumed to be at the origin, the gravitational potential, taking into account only the major harmonic, is given by

$$U = -\frac{\mu}{r^*} \left[1 - \frac{J_2 R^2}{2 r^{*2}} \left(\frac{3 x_3^2}{r^{*2}} - 1 \right) \right], \tag{V.2}$$

where r^* is the distance of the satellite from the origin, R the equatorial radius, μ the gravitational constant and J_2 the coefficient of the second zonal harmonic.

The atmospheric drag is represented by

$$F_k = -\frac{C_D A}{2m} \rho v \frac{d x_k}{dt}, \tag{V.3}$$

where ρ is the atmospheric density, v the satellite speed, C_D the drag coefficient, A the effective cross sectional area and m the mass of the satellite.

If one denotes $J = \frac{3}{2} J_2$, then the equations (V.1) may be written in the form

$$\frac{d^2 x_k}{dt^2} = -\mu \left[1 - \frac{J R^2}{r^{*2}} \left\{ \frac{5 x_3^2}{r^{*2}} - (k^2 - 3k + 3) \right\} \right] \frac{x_k}{r^{*3}} - B \rho v \frac{d x_k}{dt} \tag{V.4}$$

for $k = 1, 2, 3$.

By using the transformation

$$\begin{bmatrix} x_1 \\ x_2 \\ x_3 \end{bmatrix} = \begin{bmatrix} r \cos \theta \\ r \sin \theta \\ z \end{bmatrix}, \tag{V.5}$$

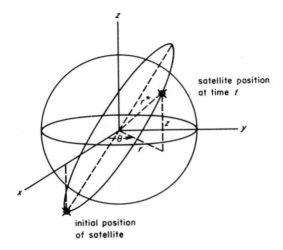

satellite position
at time t

initial position
of satellite

Figure V–1

as shown in Fig. V–1, the equations (V.4) can be transformed into

$$\ddot{r} - r\dot{\theta}^2 = -B\rho v\dot{r} - \mu\left[\frac{r}{(r^2+z^2)^{3/2}} + \frac{JR^2r}{(r^2+z^2)^{5/2}} - \frac{5JR^2rz^2}{(r^2+z^2)^{7/2}}\right],$$

$$r\ddot{\theta} + 2\dot{r}\dot{\theta} = -B\rho v r\dot{\theta}, \qquad\qquad\qquad\qquad\qquad (\text{V.6})$$

$$\ddot{z} = -B\rho v\dot{z} - \mu\left[\frac{z}{(r^2+z^2)^{3/2}} + \frac{3JR^2z}{(r^2+z^2)^{5/2}} - \frac{5JR^2z^3}{(r^2+z^2)^{7/2}}\right],$$

where the dot denotes differentiation with respect to time t.
Introducing the dimensionless variables by the transformation

$$\begin{bmatrix} X \\ Y \\ Z \end{bmatrix} = \begin{bmatrix} R/r \\ \mu R/r^4\dot{\theta}^2 \\ z/r \end{bmatrix}, \qquad\qquad (\text{V.7})$$

the satellite speed

$$v = \sqrt{\dot{r}^2 + r^2\dot{\theta}^2 + \dot{z}^2}$$

becomes

$$v = \sqrt{\frac{\mu}{RY}} \left[X^2 + X'^2 + (XZ' - X'Z)^2 \right]^{1/2}, \tag{V.8}$$

where the prime denotes differentiation with respect to θ.

The atmospheric density may be expressed as

$$\rho = \rho_0 e^{-k(r^* - r_0^*)}, \tag{V.9}$$

where k is the reciprocal of the scale height and ρ_0 the density referred to the initial perigee r_0^*. In terms of the new variables, the density becomes

$$\rho = \rho_0 e^{\gamma - \delta X^{-1}(1 + Z^2)^{1/2}}, \tag{V.10}$$

where $\gamma = kr_0^*$ and $\delta = kR$.

By using Eqs. (V.7)–(V.10), the equations (V.6) can be transformed into

$$X'' + X = Y \left[\frac{1}{(1 + Z^2)^{3/2}} + \frac{JX^2}{(1 + Z^2)^{5/2}} - \frac{5JX^2Z^2}{(1 + Z^2)^{7/2}} \right],$$

$$Y' = DX^{-2}Ye^{\gamma - \delta X^{-1}(1 + Z^2)^{1/2}} \left[X^2 + X'^2 + (XZ' - X'Z)^2 \right]^{1/2}, \tag{V.11}$$

$$Z'' + Z = -\frac{2JXYZ}{(1 + Z^2)^{5/2}},$$

where $D = C_D AR\rho_0/m$. This is a system of nonlinear equations with two small parameters J and D. The system represents a suitable model for the motion of a low-altitude artificial satellite.

For the motion in the equatorial plane where $Z = 0$, the preceding system (V.11) becomes

$$X'' + X = Y(1 + JX^2),$$

$$Y' = DX^{-2}Y(X^2 + X'^2)^{1/2}e^{\gamma - \delta X^{-1}}. \tag{V.12}$$

If one neglects the effect of both the oblateness and the drag (that is, if $J = D = 0$), the system (V.12) simplifies to

$$X'' + X = Y,$$
$$Y' = 0,$$

(V.13)

which are the classical equations representing, as a model, the motion of a particle subject to a central force inversely proportional to the square of the distance from a Newtonian center.

For further information, see Myint-U [27].

Bibliography

1. Barnett, S., and C. Storey. *Matrix Methods in Stability Theory*. New York: Barnes & Noble, 1970.
2. Bentley, D., and K. Cooke. *Linear Algebra with Differential Equations*. New York: Holt, Rinehart and Winston, 1973.
3. Birkhoff, G., and G. Rota. *Ordinary Differential Equations*. Waltham, MA: Blaisdell, 1969.
4. Birkhoff, G., and S. MacLane. *A Survey of Modern Algebra*. New York: Macmillan, 1941.
5. Boyce, W., and R. Diprima. *Elementary Differential Equations and Boundary Value Problems*. New York: Wiley, 1969.
6. Brauer, F., and J. Nohel. *Ordinary Differential Equations, A First Course*. New York: Benjamin, 1967.
7. Coddington, E. *An Introduction to Ordinary Differential Equations*. New York: Prentice-Hall, 1961.
8. Coddington, E., and N. Levinson. *Theory of Ordinary Differential Equations*. New York: McGraw-Hill, 1955.
9. Cole, R. *Theory of Ordinary Differential Equations*. New York: Appleton-Century-Crofts, 1968.
10. Crowder, H. K., and S. W. McCuskey. *Topics in Higher Analysis*. New York: Macmillan, 1964.
11. Dwight, H. B. *Tables of Integrals and Other Mathematical Data*. New York: Macmillan, 1955.
12. Emde, F., and E. Jahnke. *Tables of Functions*. New York: Dover, 1945.
13. Gear, C. *Numerical Initial Value Problems in Ordinary Differential Equations* New York: Prentice-Hall, 1971.
14. Gillett, P. *Linear Mathematics*. Boston: Prindle, Weber, & Schmidt, 1970.
15. Hale, J. *Ordinary Differential Equations*. New York: Wiley-Interscience, 1969.
16. Hartman, P. *Ordinary Differential Equations*. New York: Wiley, 1964.
17. Henrici, P. *Discrete Variable Methods in Ordinary Differential Equations*. New York: Wiley, 1962.
18. Hurewicz, W. *Lectures on Ordinary Differential Equations*. Cambridge, MA: MIT Press, 1958.
19. Ince, E. *Ordinary Differential Equations*. New York: Dover, 1956.
20. Isaacson, E., and H. Keller. *Analysis of Numerical Methods*. New York: Wiley, 1966.
21. Keller, H. *Numerical Methods for Two Point Boundary Value Problems*. Waltham, MA: Blaisdell, 1968.

22. Kreider, D., R. Kuller, and D. Ostberg. *Elementary Differential Equations.* Reading, MA: Addison-Wesley, 1968.
23. Kreider, D., R. Kuller, D. Ostberg, and F. Perkins. *An Introduction to Linear Analysis.* Reading, MA: Addison-Wesley, 1966.
24. LaSalle, J., and S. Lefchetz. *Stability of Liapunov's Direct Method with Applications.* New York: Academic, 1961.
25. Lefchetz, S. *Differential Equations, Geometric Theory.* New York: Interscience, 1957.
26. Magnus, W., and F. Oberhettinger. *Formulas and Theorems for the Special Functions of Mathematical Physics.* New York: Chelsea, 1949.
27. Myint-U, T. Solution of the low-altitude satellite equations. *Annals of the New York Academy of Sciences*, vol. 172, 1971.
28. Myint-U, T. *Partial Differential Equations of Mathematical Physics.* New York: Elsevier, 1973.
29. Nemytskii, V., and V. Stepanov. *Qualitative Theory of Differential Equations.* Princeton, NJ: Princeton University Press, 1960.
30. Pennisi, L. *Elements of Ordinary Differential Equations.* New York: Holt, Rinehart & Winston, 1972.
31. Plaat, O. *Ordinary Differential Equations.* San Francisco: Holden-Day, 1971.
32. Pontryagin, L. *Ordinary Differential Equations.* Reading, MA: Addison-Wesley, 1962.
33. Rabenstein, A. *Introduction to Ordinary Differential Equations.* New York: Academic, 1966.
34. Ralston, A. *A First Course in Numerical Analysis.* New York: McGraw-Hill, 1965.
35. Reid, W. *Ordinary Differential Equations.* New York: Wiley, 1971.
36. Reiss, E., A. Callegari, and D. Ahluwalia. *Ordinary Differential Equations with Applications.* New York: Holt, Rinehart & Winston, 1976.
37. Ross, S. *Differential Equations.* Lexington, MA: Xerox, 1974.
38. Tenenbaum, M., and H. Pollard. *Ordinary Differential Equations.* New York: Harper & Row, 1963.
39. Watson, G. *Theory of Bessel Functions.* Cambridge: Cambridge University Press, 1966.
40. Widder, D. *The Laplace Transform.* Princeton, NJ: Princeton University Press, 1941.
41. Wilson, H. *Ordinary Differential Equations.* Reading, MA: Addison-Wesley, 1971.

Selected Solutions to Exercises

Chapter 1

1. (a) Second-order, linear, homogeneous with constant coefficients.
   (b) Third-order, nonlinear.
   (c) Fourth-order, linear, nonhomogeneous with constant coefficients.
   (d) Second-order, linear, homogeneous with variable coefficients.
   (e) Second-order, nonlinear.
   (f) Second-order, nonlinear.
   (g) Third-order, nonlinear.

2. (a) Initial-value problem.
   (b) Boundary-value problem.
   (c) Initial-value problem.
   (d) Boundary-value problem.

Chapter 2

1. Here $f(x,u) = u$, which is defined on the entire (x,u) plane D. Since $\phi'(x) = e^x = \phi(x)$, ϕ satisfies $u' = u$ in the interval $J: -\infty < x < \infty$. Also ϕ and ϕ' are continuous in J and $(x, \phi(x)) \in D$. Thus ϕ is a solution of $u' = u$.

4. $\phi(x) = 2 - e^{\sin x}$ for all $x \in R^1$;
   $\phi(x) = 2$.

5. $\phi(x) = \tan\left(x + \dfrac{\pi}{4}\right)$ for $x \in J = (-3\pi/4, \pi/4)$.

7. $\phi(x) = \dfrac{\alpha/\beta}{1 + \left(\dfrac{\alpha/\beta}{y_0} - 1\right)e^{-\alpha x}}.$

8. $\phi(x) = \pm(-x^2 \pm (x^4 + c^4)^{\frac{1}{2}})^{\frac{1}{2}}.$

10. $x = C \exp\left[- \int f(v)\, dv \right]$ where $f(v) = \dfrac{c + dv}{dv^2 + (c - b)v - a}$. Here $v = y/x$

and a, b, c, d in $f(v)$ are given constants.

$$r(\theta) = r(0)\exp\left[\int_0^\theta g(s)\, ds \right],$$

where

$$g(\theta) = \frac{c \cos^2\theta + (a + d)\sin\theta \cos\theta + b \sin^2\theta}{a \cos^2\theta + (b - c)\sin\theta \cos\theta - d \sin^2\theta}.$$

11. (a) $\phi(x) = \dfrac{x}{\ln|x| + c}$.

(b) $\phi(x)$ is given implicitly by $y \sin x - x \sin y = c$.

13. $\dfrac{y}{x} = c$, $\dfrac{x}{y} = c$, $\ln\dfrac{y}{x} = c$, $\arctan\dfrac{y}{x} = c$.

15. $\phi(x) = \dfrac{\sin x}{x} + \dfrac{c}{x}$, $\displaystyle\lim_{x \to 0} \phi(x) = \begin{cases} \pm\infty, & c \neq 0, \\ 1, & c = 0. \end{cases}$

17. $\phi_0 = \phi_1 = 0$; $\phi_2 = \dfrac{x^2}{2!}$; $\phi_3 = \dfrac{x^2}{2!} + \dfrac{x^3}{3!}$; $\phi_4 = \dfrac{x^2}{2!} + \dfrac{x^3}{3!} + \dfrac{x^4}{4!}$.

18. (b) $\phi(x) = \tan x$ for $|x| < \dfrac{\pi}{2}$.

Here $f(x, y) = 1 + y^2$ and $\dfrac{\partial f}{\partial y} = 2y$ are continuous for all (x, y).
Thus a unique solution exists on $R : |x - 0| \leqslant a, |y - 0| \leqslant b$. Here
$M = \max |f(x, y)| = 1 + b^2$ and $h = \min\left(a, \dfrac{b}{1 + b^2}\right)$. Consider
$g(b) = \dfrac{b}{1 + b^2}$; maximum value of $g(b)$ for $b > 0$ occurs at $b = 1$
and $g(1) = \tfrac{1}{2}$. If $a \geqslant \tfrac{1}{2}$, $b/(1 + b^2) \leqslant a$ for $b > 0$. Thus $h = b/(1 + b^2)$
$\leqslant \tfrac{1}{2}$. If $a < \tfrac{1}{2}$, then $h < \tfrac{1}{2}$. Hence $h \leqslant \tfrac{1}{2}$. For $a \geqslant \tfrac{1}{2}$, $b = 1$;
$h = \min\left(a, (b/(1 + b^2))\right) = \min(a, \tfrac{1}{2}) = \tfrac{1}{2}$.

20. (d) $\phi(x) = cx + c^2$ where c is an arbitrary constant; $\phi(x) = -\dfrac{x^2}{4}$ is the
singular solution.

21. (c) $\phi(x) = x + \dfrac{1}{c - x}$

Chapter 3

1. (a) $\phi(x) = c_1 e^x + c_2 e^{2x}$.
   (c) $\phi(x) = c_1 e^{-2x} + c_2 x e^{-2x}$.
   (e) $\phi(x) = c_1 e^{2x} \cos \sqrt{3}\, x + c_2 e^{2x} \sin \sqrt{3}\, x$.
   (g) $\phi(x) = c_1 \cos x + c_2 \sin x + c_3 x \cos x + c_4 x \sin x$.

3. Suppose that ϕ_1 and ϕ_2 are linearly dependent, that is

$$c_1 \phi_1 + c_2 \phi_2 = 0 \qquad \text{for all } x \in I.$$

   Then

$$c_1 \phi_1' + c_2 \phi_2' = 0 \qquad \text{for all } x \in I.$$

   Since c_1 and c_2 are not zero, the solution (c_1, c_2) exists and hence

$$W = \begin{vmatrix} \phi_1 & \phi_2 \\ \phi_1' & \phi_2' \end{vmatrix} = 0 \qquad \text{for all } x \in I.$$

   Suppose that $W = 0$. Then

$$\phi_1 \phi_2' - \phi_2 \phi_1' = 0.$$

   Thus

$$\frac{\phi_1'}{\phi_1} = \frac{\phi_2'}{\phi_2}.$$

   Integration yields

$$\ln \phi_1 = \ln \phi_2 + \ln c.$$

   Hence $\phi_1 = c \phi_2$ which implies linear dependence of ϕ_1 and ϕ_2.

5. $W = \begin{vmatrix} x^2 & x|x| \\ 2x & 2|x| \end{vmatrix} = 0 \qquad \forall x \in I.$

   This does not contradict the converse of Theorem 3.1.3 simply because ϕ_1 and ϕ_2 cannot be solutions of $L[y] = 0$.

6. (a) $\phi(x) = c_1 x^{\frac{1}{2}} + c_2 x^{-\frac{1}{2}}$.
   (b) $\phi(x) = c_1(x+2) + c_2(x+2)^{-3}$.

7. (a) $\phi(x) = c_1 \cos x + c_2 \sin x + x \cos x + \sin x \ln|\sec x|$.

    (c) $\phi(x) = c_1 \cos x + c_2 \sin x + |x - \sin x|$.

9. (b) $\phi_2(x) = -2 + x \ln\left|\dfrac{1+x}{1-x}\right|$.

10. (a) $\phi_p(x) = \frac{1}{2}e^x + x^2 - 2$.

    (c) $\phi_p(x) = \frac{1}{2}x^2 e^{2x}$.

13. Since $\phi_1(x) = \sin x$ and $\phi_2(x) = \sin x + \cos x$ are solutions of $L[y] = y'' + y = 0$ and $W \neq 0$ for all values of x, according to the Sturm separation theorem between every pair of successive zeros of ϕ_1 there is one zero of ϕ_2.

Chapter 4

1. (a) $\phi_1(x) = 1 + \displaystyle\sum_{k=1}^{\infty} \frac{(-1)^k x^{2k}}{(2k)(2k-2)\times\cdots\times 4\times 2}$, $-\infty < x < \infty$,

    $\phi_2(x) = x + \displaystyle\sum_{k=1}^{\infty} \frac{(-1)^k x^{2k+1}}{(2k+1)(2k-1)\times\cdots\times 5\times 3}$.

    (b) $\phi_1(x) = 1 + \displaystyle\sum_{k=1}^{\infty} \frac{(-1)^k x^{3k}}{3^k k! 2\times 5\times 8\times\cdots\times(3k-1)}$, $-\infty < x < \infty$,

    $\phi_2(x) = x + \displaystyle\sum_{k=1}^{\infty} \frac{(-1)^k x^{3k+1}}{3^k k! 4\times 7\times 10\times\cdots\times(3k+1)}$.

    (c) $\phi_1(x) = 1 + \displaystyle\sum_{k=1}^{\infty} \frac{3(-1)^k(k+1)x^{2k}}{2^{2k}(2k-1)(2k-3)}$, $|x| < 2$,

    $\phi_2(x) = x + \dfrac{5}{12}x^3$

    (d) $\phi_1(x) = 1 + \displaystyle\sum_{k=1}^{\infty} \frac{4(-1)^k x^{3k}}{3^k k!(3k-1)(3k-4)}$,

    $\phi_2(x) = x + \dfrac{1}{4}x^4$.

    (e) $\phi_1(x) = 1 + \displaystyle\sum_{k=1}^{\infty} \frac{1\times 4\times\cdots\times(3k-2)}{(3k)!}x^{3k}$, $-\infty < x < \infty$,

    $\phi_2(x) = x + \displaystyle\sum_{k=1}^{\infty} \frac{2\times 5\times\cdots\times(3k-1)}{(3k+1)!}x^{3k+1}$.

6. (a) $\phi_1(x) = \displaystyle\sum_{k=0}^{\infty} \frac{(-1)^k x^k}{(2k)!}$,

$\phi_2(x) = \displaystyle\sum_{k=0}^{\infty} \frac{(-1)^k x^k}{(2k+1)!}$.

(b) $\phi_1(x) = x^{\frac{1}{2}} \displaystyle\sum_{k=0}^{\infty} \frac{(-1)^k x^k}{k!}$,

$\phi_2(x) = \displaystyle\sum_{k=0}^{\infty} \frac{(-1)^k x^k}{\left(k-\frac{1}{2}\right)\left(k-\frac{3}{2}\right)\cdots\frac{1}{2}}$.

(c) $\phi_1(x) = x\left[1 + \displaystyle\sum_{k=1}^{\infty} \frac{(-1)^k x^k}{(2k+1)k(2k-1)(k-1)\cdots(5\cdot2)(3\cdot1)}\right]$,

$\phi_2(x) = x^{\frac{1}{2}}\left[1 + \displaystyle\sum_{k=1}^{\infty} \frac{(-1)^k x^k}{(2k)\left(k-\frac{1}{2}\right)(2k-2)\left(k-\frac{3}{2}\right)\cdots\left(4\cdot\frac{3}{2}\right)\left(2\cdot\frac{1}{2}\right)}\right]$.

(d) $\phi_1(x) = \displaystyle\sum_{k=0}^{\infty} \frac{x^k}{k!(k+1)!}$,

$\phi_2(x) = \phi_1(x)\ln x - x^{-1}\left(1 - x - \displaystyle\sum_{k=2}^{\infty} \frac{(H_{k-1}+H_k)}{(k-1)!k!}x^k\right)$,

where

$H_n = 1 + \dfrac{1}{2} + \dfrac{1}{3} + \cdots + \dfrac{1}{n}$.

(e) $\phi_1(x) = x^{-2} - 3x^{-1} + \frac{9}{2}$,

$\phi_2(x) = x + \displaystyle\sum_{k=4}^{\infty} \frac{2(-1)^{k-1}}{k!} 3^{k-2} x^{k-2}$.

(f) $\phi_1(x) = \displaystyle\sum_{k=0}^{\infty} \frac{(-1)^k x^k}{(k!)^2}$,

$\phi_2(x) = \phi_1(x)\ln x - 2\displaystyle\sum_{k=1}^{\infty} \frac{(-1)^k H_k x^k}{(k!)^2}$.

(g) $\phi_1(x) = x^{-1} + \displaystyle\sum_{k=1}^{\infty} \frac{2^k x^{k-1}}{(k!)^2}$,

$\phi_2(x) = \phi_1(x)\ln x - \displaystyle\sum_{k=1}^{\infty} \frac{2^{k+1} H_k x^{k-1}}{(k!)^2}$.

9. $\phi(x) = c_1 \dfrac{1}{(1-x)} + c_2 \dfrac{\ln x}{(1-x)}$.

10. $\phi_1(x) = -2 + 2x$,

$$\phi_2(x) = \phi_1(x)\ln x + x^{-1} + 1 - 5x + \sum_{k=3}^{\infty} \frac{2x^{k-1}}{(k-1)(k-2)}.$$

19. $\phi_1(x) = x^{-\frac{1}{2}} \displaystyle\sum_{k=0}^{\infty} \frac{(-1)^k x^{-2k}}{2^{2k+1}(2k+1)!} = x^{\frac{1}{2}} \sin(1/2x)$,

$$\phi_2(x) = x^{\frac{1}{2}} \sum_{k=0}^{\infty} \frac{(-1)^k x^{-2k}}{2^{2k}(2k)!} = x^{\frac{1}{2}} \cos(1/2x).$$

Chapter 5

1.   (a) $y_1 = c_1 e^t$,

  $y_2 = c_1 t e^t + c_2 e^t$.

  (b) $y_1 = -\dfrac{c_1}{3} e^{-t} + c_2 e^{2t}$,

  $y_2 = c_1 e^{-t}$.

2.   (b) $y_1 = c_1 e^{-t} + c_2 e^{4t}$,

  $y_2 = -c_1 e^{-t} + \frac{3}{2} c_2 e^{4t}$.

3. $\phi(t) = e^{-2t}(\cos 6t + \frac{1}{3}\sin 6t)$.

4.   (a)

$$Y' = F(t, Y) = \begin{pmatrix} y_1 + e^t y_2 \\ (\sin t)\, y_1 + t^2 y_2 \end{pmatrix}$$

Here F is continuous for $|t| < \infty, |Y| < \infty$. Moreover,

$$\frac{\partial F}{\partial y_1} = \begin{pmatrix} 1 \\ \sin t \end{pmatrix} \quad \text{and} \quad \frac{\partial F}{\partial y_2} = \begin{pmatrix} e^t \\ t^2 \end{pmatrix}$$

are continuous for all $|t| < \infty$. Thus a Lipschitz condition is satisfied and by Theorem 5.1.1 a unique solution passes through the point $(0, 1, 0)$.

6.   Here

$$\Phi_1 = \begin{pmatrix} \cos t \\ -\sin t \end{pmatrix} \quad \text{and} \quad \Phi_2 = \begin{pmatrix} \sin t \\ \cos t \end{pmatrix}.$$

Thus $\Phi'_1 = \begin{pmatrix} -\sin t \\ -\cos t \end{pmatrix}$. We see that

$$A\Phi_1 = \begin{pmatrix} 0 & 1 \\ -1 & 0 \end{pmatrix}\begin{pmatrix} \cos t \\ -\sin t \end{pmatrix} = \begin{pmatrix} -\sin t \\ -\cos t \end{pmatrix}$$

and hence $\Phi'_1 = A\Phi_1$ for all t. Similarly Φ_2 can be shown to be a solution. Thus Ψ is a solution matrix for the given system and since

$$\det \Psi(0) = \begin{vmatrix} 1 & 0 \\ 0 & 1 \end{vmatrix} = 1 \neq 0,$$

$\Psi(t)$ is a fundamental matrix.

11. (a) $\Psi(t) = \begin{pmatrix} e^{2t} & 0 \\ 0 & e^{4t} \end{pmatrix}$. (b) $\Psi(t) = e^{2t}\begin{pmatrix} 1 & t \\ 0 & 1 \end{pmatrix}$.

12. (a) $\Phi(t) = c_1 \begin{pmatrix} 7 \\ 1 \end{pmatrix} e^{5t} + c_2 \begin{pmatrix} 1 \\ 1 \end{pmatrix} e^{-t}$.

(b) $\Phi(t) = c_1 \begin{bmatrix} 1 \\ 0 \\ 1 \end{bmatrix} e^{-t} + c_2 \begin{bmatrix} 3 \\ 2 \\ 1 \end{bmatrix} e^t + c_3 \begin{bmatrix} 1 \\ 3 \\ 1 \end{bmatrix} e^{2t}$.

(c) $\Phi(t) = c_1 \begin{bmatrix} 0 \\ 1 \\ 0 \end{bmatrix} e^t + c_2 \begin{bmatrix} -1 \\ 0 \\ 1 \end{bmatrix} e^t + c_3 \begin{bmatrix} 1 \\ 0 \\ 1 \end{bmatrix} e^{3t}$.

(d) $\Phi(t) = c_1 e^{3t}\left[\begin{pmatrix} -1 \\ 1 \end{pmatrix}\cos t + \begin{pmatrix} 0 \\ -1 \end{pmatrix}\sin t \right]$

$\qquad + c_2 e^{3t}\left[\begin{pmatrix} 0 \\ -1 \end{pmatrix}\cos t - \begin{pmatrix} -1 \\ 1 \end{pmatrix}\sin t \right]$

(e) $\Phi(t) = c_1 e^{-t}\begin{pmatrix} \cos t \\ 2\cos t + \sin t \end{pmatrix} + c_2 e^{-t}\begin{pmatrix} \sin t \\ -\cos t + 2\sin t \end{pmatrix}$.

(f) $\Phi(t) = c_1 \begin{bmatrix} 1 \\ 1 \\ 3 \end{bmatrix} e^t + c_2 \begin{bmatrix} 1 \\ -1 \\ 0 \end{bmatrix} e^{2t} + c_3 \begin{bmatrix} 1 \\ 0 \\ 1 \end{bmatrix} e^{2t}$.

(g) $\Phi(t) = c_1 \begin{bmatrix} 1 \\ -2 \\ 1 \end{bmatrix} e^t + c_2 \left[\begin{bmatrix} 1 \\ -2 \\ 1 \end{bmatrix} te^t + \begin{bmatrix} -1 \\ 1 \\ 0 \end{bmatrix} e^t \right]$

$\qquad + c_3 \left[\begin{bmatrix} 1 \\ -2 \\ 1 \end{bmatrix}\frac{t^2 e^t}{2} + \begin{bmatrix} -1 \\ 1 \\ 0 \end{bmatrix} te^t + \begin{bmatrix} 1 \\ 0 \\ 0 \end{bmatrix} e^t \right]$.

Chapter 6

1. (a) $G(x,\xi)=\begin{cases} x, & x\leqslant\xi, \\ \xi, & x>\xi. \end{cases}$

2. (a) $\phi(x)=1-\cos x+\left(\dfrac{\cos 1-1}{\sin 1}\right)\sin x.$

3. (a) $\phi(x)=\displaystyle\int_0^x \xi f(\xi)d\xi+x\int_x^1 f(\xi)d\xi.$

4. (a) $\phi(x)=\dfrac{\sinh(1-x)}{\sinh 1}\displaystyle\int_0^x \sinh\xi f(\xi)d\xi+\dfrac{\sinh x}{\sinh 1}\int_x^1 \sinh(1-\xi)f(\xi)d\xi.$

    (b) $\phi(x)=\dfrac{\cosh(1-x)}{\sinh 1}\displaystyle\int_0^x \cosh\xi f(\xi)d\xi+\dfrac{\cosh x}{\sinh 1}\int_x^1 \cosh(1-\xi)f(\xi)d\xi.$

6. $G(x,\xi)=\begin{cases} -\ln\xi, & x\leqslant\xi, \\ -\ln x, & x>\xi. \end{cases}$

7. $G(x,\xi)=\begin{cases} \dfrac{1}{n}\left[\left(\dfrac{x}{\xi}\right)^n-(x\xi)^n\right], & x\leqslant\xi, \\[4mm] \dfrac{1}{n}\left[\left(\dfrac{\xi}{x}\right)^n-(x\xi)^n\right], & x>\xi. \end{cases}$

8. $G(x,\xi)=\begin{cases} \dfrac{1}{2h}\left(\dfrac{1+x}{1-x}\cdot\dfrac{1-\xi}{1+\xi}\right)^{h/2}, & x\leqslant\xi, \\[4mm] \dfrac{1}{2h}\left(\dfrac{1+\xi}{1-\xi}\cdot\dfrac{1-x}{1+x}\right)^{h/2}, & x>\xi. \end{cases}$

10. $G(x,\xi)=\begin{cases} \dfrac{x^2}{6}(\xi-1)^2(2x\xi+x-3\xi), & x\leqslant\xi, \\[4mm] \dfrac{\xi^2}{6}(x-1)^2(2x\xi+\xi-3x), & x>\xi. \end{cases}$

12. $G(x,\xi)=\begin{cases} -\frac{1}{2}\ln|1-x||1+\xi|+\ln 2-\frac{1}{2}, & x\leqslant\xi, \\[2mm] -\frac{1}{2}\ln|1+x||1-\xi|+\ln 2-\frac{1}{2}, & x>\xi. \end{cases}$

15. $G(\xi, x) = \begin{cases} \dfrac{1}{a}(2e^{2-2x} - 4e^{1-x})(e^{\xi} - e^{2\xi}), & \xi \leqslant x, \\ \dfrac{1}{a}\left[(2e^{2-2x} - 2e^2 - 1)e^{\xi-x} + (4e - 4e^{1-x} + e^{-x})e^{2\xi-x}\right], \\ & \xi > x, \end{cases}$

where $a = 1 - 4e + 2e^2$.

Chapter 7

1. (a) $\lambda_n = n^2$, $\phi_n(x) = \sin nx$ for $n = 1, 2, 3, \ldots$.

    (b) $\lambda_n = (2n-1)^2/4$, $\phi_n(x) = \sin\left(\dfrac{2n-1}{2}\right)\pi x$ for $n = 1, 2, 3, \ldots$.

    (c) $\lambda_n = n^2$, $\phi_n(x) = \cos nx$ for $n = 1, 2, 3, \ldots$.

2. (a) $\lambda_n = 0, n^2\pi^2$, $\phi_n(x) = 1, \sin n\pi x, \cos n\pi x$ for $n = 1, 2, 3, \ldots$.

    (b) $\lambda_n = 0, n^2$, $\phi_n(x) = 1, \sin nx, \cos nx$ for $n = 1, 2, 3, \ldots$.

    (c) $\lambda_n = 0, 4n^2$, $\phi_n(x) = 1, \sin 2nx, \cos 2nx$ for $n = 1, 2, 3, \ldots$.

3. (a) $\lambda_n = -\left(\frac{3}{4} + n^2\pi^2\right)$, $\phi_n(x) = e^{-x/2}\sin n\pi x$ for $n = 1, 2, 3, \ldots$.

5. (a) $\lambda_n = 1 + n^2\pi^2$, $\phi_n(x) = \dfrac{1}{x}\sin(n\pi \ln x)$ for $n = 1, 2, 3, \ldots$.

    (b) $\lambda_n = \dfrac{1}{4} + \left(\dfrac{n\pi}{\ln 3}\right)^2$, $\phi_n(x) = \dfrac{1}{(x+2)^{1/2}}\sin\left[\dfrac{n\pi}{\ln 3}\ln(x+2)\right]$

    for $n = 1, 2, 3, \ldots$.

    (c) $\lambda_n = \dfrac{1}{12}\left[1 + \left(\dfrac{2n\pi}{\ln 2}\right)^2\right]$, $\phi_n(x) = \dfrac{1}{(1+x)^{1/2}}\sin\left[\dfrac{n\pi}{\ln 2}\ln(1+x)\right]$

    for $n = 1, 2, 3, \ldots$.

6. (a) All real values of $\lambda > 0$, $\phi_n(x) = \sin(\sqrt{\lambda}\,\ln x)$.

    (b) All real values of $\lambda > 0$, $\phi_n(x) = \sin\sqrt{\lambda}\,x$.

8. $f(x) \sim \displaystyle\sum_{n=1}^{\infty} \dfrac{2}{\pi}\left[\dfrac{(-1)^n - 1}{n^2}\right]\cos nx$.

Chapter 8

1. (a) Unstable node.

    (b) Strictly stable spiral.

    (c) Stable center.

    (d) Strictly stable node.

    (e) Unstable saddle point.

    (f) Strictly stable spiral.

2. (a)   Unstable saddle point.
    (b)   Stable node.
    (c)   Unstable node.

3. $\dot{x} = y,$
    $\dot{y} = -\alpha x - \beta y, \ \alpha = k/m, \ \beta = c/m.$

    (a)   If $\sqrt{\beta^2 - 4\alpha} > 0$, the origin is an asymptotically stable node.

    (b)   If $\sqrt{\beta^2 - 4\alpha} < 0$, the origin is an asymptotically stable spiral.

    (c)   If $\beta^2 - 4\alpha = 0$, the origin is an asymptotically stable node.

    (d)   If $\beta = 0$, the origin is a stable center.

5. (a)   If $\mu > 2$, the critical point is an unstable node.
    (b)   If $-6 < \mu < 2$, the critical point is an asymptotically stable node.
    (c)   If $\mu < -6$, the critical point is a saddle.

8. Let $x_1(t) = x(t + c)$ and $y_1(t) = y(t + c)$. By the chain rule $\dot{x}_1 = \dot{x}(t + c)$, $\dot{y}_1 = \dot{y}(t + c)$. Thus

$$\dot{x}_1 = \dot{x}(t + c) = f(x(t + c), y(t + c)) = f(x_1, y_1),$$

$$\dot{y}_1 = \dot{y}(t + c) = g(x(t + c), y(t + c)) = g(x_1, y_1),$$

which implies that x_1 and y_1 are solutions on $t_1 - c < t < t_2 - c$.
    A solution of $\dot{x} = x, \dot{y} = tx$ is $x(t) = e^t, y(t) = te^t - e^t$. It can be seen that $\dot{x}(t + c) = e^{t+c} = x(t + c)$ but $\dot{y}(t + c) = (t + c)e^{t+c} \neq tx(t + c)$.

10. (a)   Asymptotically stable.
    (b)   Stable.
    (c)   Unstable.

11. When $f \geqslant 0$, the critical point is stable.
    When $f > 0$, the critical point is asymptotically stable.
    When $f < 0$, the critical point is unstable.

Chapter 9

4. (a) $\frac{1}{3}(\cos t - \cos 2t)$.
    (b) $\frac{1}{3}\sin t - \frac{1}{6}\sin 2t$.
    (c) $e^{2t} - e^t$.
    (d) $1 - e^{-t} - te^{-t}$.
    (e) $1 - e^{-t}$.
    (f) $t\cos 2t$.

5. (a) $\dfrac{1}{s^2}\tanh\dfrac{bs}{2}$. (d) $\dfrac{h}{bs^2}-\dfrac{he^{-bs}}{s(1-e^{-bs})}$.

 (b) $\dfrac{h}{s(1+e^{-bs})}$. (e) $\dfrac{he^{-bs}}{s(1-e^{-bs})}$.

 (c) $\dfrac{1}{(s^2+1)(1-e^{-\pi s})}$.

8. (b) $\phi(t)=-\dfrac{1}{3}+\dfrac{8}{15}e^{3t}+\dfrac{4}{5}e^{-2t}$.

 (d) $\phi(t)=3+2t-\dfrac{1}{2}e^t-2e^{2t}+\dfrac{1}{3}e^{3t}$.

9. (b) $\phi(t)=\dfrac{1}{8}(\sin t-\cos t)+\dfrac{e^{-2t}}{8}(\sin t+\cos t)$.

Chapter 10

1. (a) $y_2=1.24$ ($\phi(0.2)=1.2856$) for $h=0.1$.

2. $y_2=0.82$ ($\phi(0.2)=0.83746$) for $h=0.1$.

3. Here $f(x,y)=y$. By the Euler formula $y_{n+1}=y_n+hy_n$. Since $y_0=1$, we find $y_1=1+h$, $y_2=(1+h)\,y_1=(1+h)^2$ and by induction $y_n=(1+h)^n$. But $x=nh$ and we have $y_n=(1+h)^{x/n}$. Thus

$$\lim_{h\to0} y_n=\lim_{h\to0}\left[(1+h)^{1/h}\right]^x=e^x.$$

4. Consider the expression from the Euler formula $y_{n+1}-(y_n+hy_n)=y_{n+1}-(1+h)\,y_n$. Substituting the exact solution $\phi(x_n)=e^{nh}$, $\phi(x_{n+1})-(1+h)\phi(x_n)=e^{nh}(e^h-h-1)$. Thus $|\phi(x_{n+1})-(1+h)\phi(x_n)|\le kh^2$ for some constant k. Since $\lim_{h\to0}kh^2=0$, the Euler method is consistent.

6. $y_2=1.2489$ (Modified Euler)

 $y_2=1.2220$ (Euler)

8. Exact solution $\phi(x)=[(1-\alpha)x]^{1/1-\alpha}$ for $\alpha<1$. By the Euler method

$$y_{n+1}=y_n+hy_n'=y_n+hy_n^\alpha$$

Thus $y_1=y_0+hy_0^\alpha=0$ and consequently $y_n=0$. The Euler method fails.

14. (a) $y_1=1.4642$.

16. $x_2=1.25$, $y_2=0.2$.

Index